AS YOU WERE

*A Portable Library of American Prose and Poetry
Assembled for Members of the Armed Forces
and the Merchant Marine*

As You Were

A PORTABLE LIBRARY OF AMERICAN PROSE AND POETRY ASSEMBLED FOR MEMBERS OF THE ARMED FORCES AND THE MERCHANT MARINE

EDITED BY

Alexander Woollcott

NEW YORK: THE VIKING PRESS

1943

As You Were

Original Material Copyright 1943
by The Viking Press, Inc.

Published in March 1943

*Published on the same day in the Dominion of Canada
by The Macmillan Company of Canada Limited*
Second Printing before Publication

Printed and bound in U. S. A., by The Colonial Press Inc.

CONTENTS

AMERICAN FACT

CONTENTS

FOREWORD

YOU hold in your hands at this moment a variety of reading matter—just verse and prose, as the young man in *Crome Yellow* said when asked the nature of his literary work—prose and verse, here reprinted on thin paper in a pocket-size volume for the convenience of men who are mostly on the move and must travel light. Since many of them will read it overseas, its contents have been limited to American letters in the hope that one part or another will reach them as a fond, familiar voice from the land they've left behind them.

The editor takes full responsibility for all the more debatable choices made—why so much Frost and so little Longfellow, for example, or why, to mention only four of the more conspicuous absentees, such writers as Tom Paine, Herman Melville, Stephen Crane, and Edgar Lee Masters are, for the most various reasons, missing altogether. But he must avow his indebtedness to many neighbors whom he drafted as consultants. In particular his thanks are due to Stephen Vincent Benét, Mark Van Doren, Carl Carmer, Booth Tarkington, Willa Cather, J. T. Winterich, Thornton Wilder, Carl Sandburg, David McCord, E. B. White, and Felix Frankfurter.

The editor must next identify himself as a tottering noncombatant who, however, did serve in the ranks of what it is comforting to call not the Last War but the Next To The Last War. Like most old soldiers he is wont to talk prosily of that lesser and fast fading adventure and his cases in point are likely to be drawn from it. As now.

For whenever the talk turns to soldiers and books two episodes float back to me from the world of twenty-five years ago. One deals with those haze-hung months in the first half of 1919 when, as a member of the editorial council of the original *Stars and Stripes*, I had my sleeping-quarters in a small malodorous hotel on the Ile de la Cité where it touches the Pont Neuf and so came to know the twisting path to the boulevards from that ghost-thronged bridge as well as ever I knew any equivalent neighborhood in Kansas City, Philadelphia, or New York. True, the hotel had only one *salle-de-bain* but, as none of its other clients used water for any purpose, I even enjoyed the illusion of a private bath.

Indeed, the only fly in my ointment, the only cracker-crumb between my sheets, was the M.P. Just then the sole duty and pleasure of the M.P. was frustrating the A.W.O.L. Many times a day I must halt in my innocent tracks and produce from the depths of my blouse a document establishing that I had any right to be in Paris at all. There were unnerving stories of M.P.'s so testy that when a challenged soldier would show his pass, they would examine it critically, find it in order, tear it up and drag him to the hoosegow anyway.

Then came a day when I roamed all Paris without once being stopped. M.P.'s might glance at me with distaste but they all let me pass by unmolested. I meditated on this phenomenon. Why had I seemed less suspect? Wherein lay the difference? I could think of only one. By chance that day I was carrying a book. I determined to experiment. Thereafter I never ventured onto the highways unless armed with a prop volume. I do not recall that I ever looked inside this treasure but soon I would as lief have stepped out without my wrap-puttees. For not once in the remaining months of my servitude was I ever called upon to account for myself. To the

simple minds of the army's spoilsports it was unthinkable
that a bookish soldier could be on the loose. Wherefore
it is hereby recommended to all men in the ranks when
they go A.W.O.L. that they take this volume with them
and *display it prominently*.

The other memory recalls the only night I ever spent
on the British front. It was in midsummer of 1918 on the
eve of the great advance which was never in more than
twenty years to be retraced. I had traveled four-hundred
kilometers to reach my destination, had completed my
mission and, the sun having long since set, had thought
to turn in for the night then, and, what was more ingenuous of me, there. But room for casuals was not available. Tersely it was suggested that I get the hell out of
there. Plodding back in the general direction of Amiens,
I hardly noticed the boom of the big guns, the whine of
the shells overhead, the chatter of the archies. What I
did notice, what halted me in my tracks, was a sight
much more sensational. It was a thread of forbidden
light. Inside a brick farmhouse of which the family had
vanished and the top-floor had been blown away and of
which the long glassless windows were inadequately
curtained with gunnysack, some bold spirit had lighted
a candle.

That someone proved to be a courteous giant from the
Antipodes. Like most of his countrymen then in France,
this Australian was young and wide and handsome. Because of the disabling wounds he incurred at Gallipoli,
he had been entrusted with the cushy job of fetching the
mail. Now on his way forward with the latest batches of
mail from down under, he was turning in for the night.
He offered me a swig of the tea he was making and,
ensconced on a heap of rubble, he talked sagaciously and
tolerantly of many things—of the Americans and what
might be expected of them once they had gained a little

experience, of the weary British and why the Australians were worried about them, of the day already in sight when the guns would cease firing.

Then each of us cleared a place on the dirty floor which might serve as a bed. For his pillow, mine host took the mail-bag from Sydney and gave me the one from Melbourne. Then I saw him adjust the remains of his candle to a perch beside him, produce a book from somewhere as if by prestidigitation (I remember it was *The Sundering Flood* by William Morris) and start—a forgotten luxury—to read himself to sleep. In the blackness outside the artillery fire intensified and the blood-soaked earth of the Somme Valley trembled and twitched like a setter bitch, dreaming of the chase in her sleep. Beyond the blackness, the lamp-lit world watched and held its breath. Meanwhile my young friend from Australia had half a candle, a few moments to himself, and a book.

As I dozed off I found myself thinking of him as a lean and strong hand, cupping a candle flame in wind and darkness. The task of building well a new world after the war, I thought, might hopefully be left to the likes of him. I still think I was right about that. The likes of him could have managed it. But, to quote a better soldier than I ever was—I said a better not an older soldier. Did I say older?—there were not enough of them. That's all.

ALEXANDER WOOLLCOTT

Bomoseen, Vermont
January 1943.

American Fiction

THE DEVIL AND
DANIEL WEBSTER

BY STEPHEN VINCENT BENÉT

IT'S a story they tell in the border-country, where
Massachusetts joins Vermont and New Hampshire.

Yes, Dan'l Webster's dead—or, at least, they buried
him. But, every time there's a thunderstorm around
Marshfield, they say you can hear his rolling voice in the
hollows of the sky. And they say that if you go to his
grave and speak loud and clear, "Dan'l Webster—
Dan'l Webster!" the ground'll begin to shiver and the
trees begin to shake. And, after a while, you'll hear a
deep voice, saying, "Neighbour, how stands the Union?"
Then you better answer the Union stands as she stood,
rock-bottomed and copper-sheathed, one and indi-
visible, or he's liable to rear right out of the ground.
At least, that's what I was told, when I was a youngster.

You see, for a while he was the biggest man in the
country. He never got to be President but he was the
biggest man. There was thousands that trusted in him
right next to God Almighty—and they told stories about
him and all the things that belonged to him that were
like the stories of patriarchs and such. They said when
he stood up to speak stars and stripes came right out
in the sky—and once he spoke against a river and
made it sink into the ground. They said when he
walked the woods with his fishing-rod, Killall, the trout
would jump out of the streams right into his pockets,
for they knew it was no use putting up a fight against

3

him—and, when he argued a case, he could turn on the harps of the blessed and the shaking of the earth underground. That was the kind of man he was, and his big farm up at Marshfield was suitable to him. The chickens he raised were all white meat down through the drumsticks, the cows were tended like children and the big ram he called Goliath had horns with a curl like a morning-glory vine and could butt through an iron door. But Dan'l wasn't one of your gentlemen-farmers— he knew all the ways of the land and he'd be up by candlelight to see that the chores got done. A man with a mouth like a mastiff, a brow like a mountain and eyes like burning anthracite—that was Dan'l Webster in his prime. And the biggest case he argued never got written down in the books, for he argued it against the Devil, nip and tuck and no holds barred. And this is the way I used to hear it told.

There was a man named Jabez Stone, lived at Cross Corners, New Hampshire. He wasn't a bad man to start with, but he was an unlucky man. If he planted corn, he got borers, if he planted potatoes, he got blight. He had good enough land but it didn't prosper him—he had a decent wife and children, but the more children he had, the less there was to feed them. If stones cropped up in his neighbour's field, boulders boiled up in his—if he had a horse with the spavins, he'd trade it for one with the staggers and give something extra. There's some folks bound to be like that, apparently. But, one day, Jabez Stone got sick of the whole business.

He'd been ploughing that morning and he'd just broke the ploughshare on a rock that he could have sworn hadn't been there yesterday. And, as he stood looking at the ploughshare, the off horse began to cough—that ropy kind of cough that means sickness and horse-doctors. There were two children down with the measles, his wife was ailing, and he had a whitlow on his thumb. It was about the last straw for Jabez Stone.

"I vow," he said, and he looked around him kind of desperate, "I vow it's enough to make a man want to sell his soul to the Devil! And I would, too, for two cents!"

Then he felt a kind of queerness come over him, at having said what he'd said, though naturally, being New Hampshire, he wouldn't take it back. But, all the same, when it got to be evening and, as far as he could see no notice had been taken, he felt relieved in his mind, for he was a religious man. But notice is always taken, sooner or later, just like the Good Book says. And sure enough, next day, about suppertime, a soft-spoken, dark-dressed stranger drove up in a smart buggy and asked for Jabez Stone.

Well, Jabez told his family it was a lawyer, come to see him about a legacy. But *he* knew who it was. He didn't like the looks of the stranger, nor the way he smiled with his teeth. They were white teeth and plentiful—some say they were filed to a point, but I wouldn't vouch for that. And he didn't like it when the dog took one look at the stranger and ran away howling with his tail between his legs. But, having passed his word, more or less, he stuck to it, and they went out behind the barn and made their bargain. Jabez Stone had to prick his finger, to sign, and the stranger lent him a silver pin. The wound healed clean but it left a little white scar.

After that, all of a sudden, things began to pick up and prosper for Jabez Stone. His cows got fat and his horses sleek, his crops were the envy of the neighbour-hood and lightning might strike all over the valley but it wouldn't strike his barn. Pretty soon he was one of the prosperous people of the county—they asked him to stand for selectman and he stood for it—there began to be talk of running him for State Senate. All in all, you might say the Stone family was as happy and contented as cats in a dairy. And so they were, except for Jabez Stone.

He'd been contented enough, the first few years. It's a great thing when bad luck turns—it drives most other things out of your head. True, every now and then, especially in rainy weather, the little white scar on his finger would give him a twinge. And once a year, punctual as clockwork, the stranger with the smart buggy would come driving by. But the sixth year the stranger lighted, and, after that, his peace was over for Jabez Stone.

The stranger came up through the lower field, switching his boots with a cane—they were handsome black boots, but Jabez Stone never liked the look of them, particularly the toes. And, after he'd passed the time of day, he said, "Well, Mr. Stone, you're a hummer! It's a very pretty property you've got here, Mr. Stone."

"Well, some might favour it and others might not," said Jabez Stone, for he was a New Hampshireman.

"Oh—no need to decry your industry!" said the stranger, very easy, showing his teeth in a smile. "After all, we know what's been done—and it's been, according to contract and specifications. So when—ahem —the mortgage falls due, next year, you shouldn't have any regrets."

"Speaking of that mortgage, Mister," said Jabez Stone, and he looked around for help to the earth and the sky, "I'm beginning to have one or two doubts about it."

"Doubts?" said the stranger, not quite so pleasantly.

"Why, yes," said Jabez Stone. "This being the U.S.A. and me always having been a religious man." He cleared his throat and got bolder. "Yes sir," he said, "I'm beginning to have considerable doubts as to that mortgage holding in court."

"There's courts *and* courts," said the stranger, clicking his teeth. "Still—we might as well have a look at the original document," and he hauled out a big black pocket-book, full of papers. "Sherwin—Slater—Stevens —Stone," he muttered. "I, Jabez Stone—for a term of seven years—oh, it's quite in order, I think———"

But Jabez Stone wasn't listening, for he saw something else flutter out of the black pocket-book. It's something that looked like a moth but it wasn't a moth. And as Jabez Stone stared at it, it seemed to speak to him in a small sort of piping voice, terrible small and thin but terrible human. "Neighbour Stone!" it squeaked. "Neighbour Stone! Help me—for God's sake, help me!"

But, before Jabez Stone could stir hand or foot, the stranger whipped out a big bandanna handkerchief, caught the creature in it, just like a butterfly, and started tying up the ends of the bandanna.

"Sorry for the interruption," he said. "As I was saying———"

But Jabez Stone was shaking all over like a scared horse.

"That's Miser Stevens' voice!" he said, in a croak. "And you've got him in your handkerchief!"

The stranger looked a little embarrassed.

"Yes, I really should have transferred him to the collecting box," he said, with a simper, "but there were some rather unusual specimens there and I didn't want them crowded. Well, well, these little *contre-temps* will occur——"

"I don't know what you mean by contertan," said Jabez Stone, "but that was Miser Stevens' voice! And he ain't dead! You can't tell me he is! He was just as spry and mean as a woodchuck, Tuesday!"

"In the midst of life," said the stranger, kind of pious. "Listen!" Then a bell begun to toll in the valley and Jabez Stone listened, with the sweat running down his face. For he knew it was tolled for Miser Stevens and that he was dead.

"These long-standing accounts," said the stranger, with a sigh. "One really hates to close them. But business is business."

He still had the bandanna in his hand and Jabez Stone felt sick as he saw the cloth struggle and flutter.

"Are they all as small as that?" he asked hoarsely.

"Small?" said the stranger. "Oh, I see what you mean. Why, they vary." He measured Jabez Stone with his eyes and his teeth showed. "Don't worry, Mr. Stone," he said. "You'll go with a very good grade. I wouldn't trust *you* outside the collecting box. Now, a man like Dan'l Webster of course—well, we'd have to build a special box for him, and even at that, I imagine the wing-spread would astonish you. He'd certainly be a prize—I wish we could see our way clear to him! But, in your case, as I was saying——"

"Put that handkerchief away!" said Jabez Stone, and he begun to beg and pray. But the best he can get at the end is a three-years' extension, with conditions.

But till you make a bargain like that, you've got no idea of how fast four years can run. By the last months of those years, Jabez Stone's known all over the State and there's a talk of running him for Governor—and it's dust and ashes in his mouth. For every day, when he gets up, he thinks, "There's one more night gone," and every night when he lies down, he thinks of the black pocket-book and the soul of Miser Stevens and it makes him sick at heart. Till, finally, he can't bear it any longer, and, in the last days of the last year, he hitches up his horse and drives off to seek Dan'l Webster. For Dan'l was born in New Hampshire, only a few miles from Cross Corners, and it's well known that he has a particular soft spot for old neighbours.

It was early in the morning when he got to Marshfield, but Dan'l was up already, talking Latin to the farmhands and wrestling with the ram, Goliath, and trying out a new trotter and working up speeches to make against John C. Calhoun. But, when he heard a New Hampshireman had come to see him he dropped everything else he was doing, for that was Dan'l's way. He gave Jabez Stone a breakfast that five men couldn't eat, went into the living history of every man and woman in Cross Corners, and, finally, asked him how he could serve him.

Jabez Stone allowed that it was a mortgage-case.

"Well, I haven't pleaded a mortgage-case in a long time, and I don't generally plead now, except before the Supreme Court," said Dan'l. "But, if I can, I'll help you."

"Then I've got hope, for the first time in ten years," said Jabez Stone and told him the details.

Dan'l walked up and down as he listened, hands behind his back, now and then asking a question, now and then plunging his eyes at the floor, as if they'd bore through it like gimlets. When Jabez Stone had finished, he puffed out his cheeks and blew. Then he turned to Jabez Stone and a smile broke over his face, like the sunrise over Monadnock.

"You've certainly given yourself the Devil's own road

to hoe, Neighbour Stone," he said. "But I'll take your case."

"You'll take it?" said Jabez Stone, hardly daring to believe.

"Yes," said Dan'l Webster. "I've got about seventy-five other things to do and the Missouri Compromise to straighten out—but I'll take your case. For if two New Hampshiremen ain't a match for the Devil, we might as well give the country back to the Indians."

Then he shook Jabez Stone by the hand and said, "Did you come down here in a hurry?"

"Well, I admit I made time," said Jabez Stone.

"You'll go back faster," said Dan'l Webster and he told 'em to hitch up Constitution and Constellation to the carriage. They were matched greys with one white forefoot, and they stepped like greased lightning.

Well, I won't describe how excited and pleased the whole Stone family was to have the great Dan'l Webster for a guest, when they finally got there. Jabez Stone had lost his hat on the way, blown off when they overtook a wind, but he didn't take much account of that. But, after supper, he sent the family off to bed, for he had most particular business with Mr. Webster. Mrs. Stone wanted them to sit in the front-parlour—but Dan'l Webster knew front-parlours and said he preferred the kitchen. So it was there they sat, waiting for the stranger, with a jug on the table between them and a bright fire on the hearth—the stranger being scheduled to show up on the stroke of midnight, according to specification and whereas and therefore.

Well, most men wouldn't have asked for better company than Dan'l Webster and a jug. But with every tick of the clock Jabez Stone got sadder and sadder. His eyes roved round the room, and, though he sampled the jug, you could see he couldn't taste it. Finally, on the stroke of eleven-thirty, he reached over and grabbed Dan'l Webster by the arm.

"Mr. Webster, Mr. Webster!" he said, and his voice was shaking with fear and a desperate courage. "For God's sake, Mr. Webster, harness your horses and get away from this place while you can!"

"You've brought me a long way, neighbour, to tell me you don't like my company," said Dan'l Webster, quite peaceable, pulling at the jug.

"Miserable wretch that I am!" groaned Jabez Stone. "I've brought you a devilish way—and now I see my folly. Let him take me if he wills—I don't hanker after it, I must say, but I can stand it. But you're the Union's stay and New Hampshire's pride! He mustn't get you, Mr. Webster! He mustn't get you!"

Dan'l Webster looked at the distracted man, all grey and shaking in the firelight, and laid a hand on his shoulder.

"I'm obliged to you, Neighbour Stone," he said gently. "It's kindly thought of. But there's a jug on the table and a case in hand. And I never left a jug or a case half-finished in my life."

And, just at that moment, there was a sharp rap on the door.

"Ah," said Dan'l Webster, very coolly, "I thought your clock was a trifle slow, Neighbour Stone." He stepped to the door and opened it. "Come in!" he said.

The stranger came in—very dark and tall he looked in the firelight. He was carrying a box under his arm— a black, japanned box with little air-holes in the lid. At the sight of the box Jabez Stone gave a low cry and shrank into a corner of the room.

"Mr. Webster, I presume," said the stranger, very polite, but with his eyes glowing like a fox's deep in the woods.

"Attorney of record for Jabez Stone," said Dan'l Webster, but his eyes were glowing, too. "Might I ask your name?"

"I've gone by a good many," said the stranger, carelessly. "Perhaps Scratch will do for the evening. I'm often called that in these regions."

Then he sat down at the table and poured himself a drink from the jug. The liquor was cold in the jug, but it came steaming into the glass.

"And now," said the stranger, smiling and showing his teeth, "I shall call upon you, as a law-abiding citizen, to assist me in taking possession of my property."

Well, with that the argument began—and it went hot and heavy. At first Jabez Stone had a flicker of hope —but when he saw Dan'l Webster being forced back at point after point he just sat scrunched in his corner with his eyes on that japanned box. For there wasn't any doubt as to the deed or the signature—that was the worst of it. Dan'l Webster twisted and turned and thumped his fist on the table—but he couldn't get away from that. He offered to compromise the case— the stranger wouldn't hear of it. He pointed out the property had increased in value and State Senators ought to be worth more—the stranger stuck to the letter of the law. He was a great lawyer, Dan'l Webster—but we know who's the King of Lawyers, as the Good Book tells us—and it seemed as if, for the first time, Dan'l Webster had met his match.

Finally, the stranger yawned a little. "Your spirited efforts on behalf of your client do you credit, Mr. Webster," he said. "But if you have no more arguments to adduce—I'm rather pressed for time," and Jabez Stone shuddered.

Dan'l Webster's brow looked dark as a thundercloud.

"Pressed or not, you shall not have this man!" he thundered. "Mr. Stone is an American citizen—and no American citizen may be forced into the service of a foreign prince! We fought England for that in '12 and we'll fight all Hell for it again!"

"Foreign?" said the stranger. "And who calls me a foreigner?"

"Well I never yet heard of the Dev—of your claiming American citizenship," said Dan'l Webster, with surprise.

"And who with better right?" said the stranger, with one of his terrible smiles. "When the first wrong was done to the first Indian—I was there. When the first slaver put out for the Congo—I stood on her deck. Am I not in your books and stories and beliefs, from the first settlements on? Am I not spoken of still, in every church in New England? 'Tis true the North claims me for a Southerner and the South for a Northerner—but I am neither. I am merely an honest American like yourself—and of the best descent— for, to tell the truth, Mr. Webster, though I don't like to boast of it, my name is older in this country than yours."

"Aha!" said Dan'l Webster, with the veins standing out in his forehead. "Then I stand on the Constitution! I demand a trial for my client!"

"The case is hardly one for an ordinary court," said the stranger, his eyes flickering, "and, indeed, the lateness of the hour——"

"Let it be any court you choose, so it is an American judge and an American jury!" said Dan'l Webster in his pride. "Let it be the quick or the dead—I'll abide the issue!"

"You have said it," said the stranger and pointed his finger at the door. And with that, and all of a sudden, there was a rushing of wind outside and a noise of footsteps. They came clear and distinct, through the night. And yet, they were not like the footsteps of living men.

"In God's name, who comes by so late?" cried Jabez Stone, in an agony of fear.

"The jury Mr. Webster demands," said the stranger, sipping at his boiling glass. "You must pardon the rough appearance of one or two—they will have come a long way."

And, with that, the fire burned blue and the door blew open and twelve men entered, one by one.

If Jabez Stone had been sick with terror before, he was blind with terror now. For there was Walter Butler, the loyalist, who spread fire and horror through the Mohawk Valley in the times of the Revolution —and there was Simon Girty, the renegade, who saw white men burned at the stake and whooped with the Indians to see them. His eyes were green, like a catamount's, and the stains on his huntingshirt did not come from the blood of the deer. King Philip was there, wild and proud as he had been in life, with the great gash in his head that gave him his death-wound, and cruel Governor Dale who broke men on the wheel. There was Morton of Merry Mount, who so vexed the Plymouth Colony, with his flushed, loose, handsome face and his hate of the godly—there was Teach, the bloody pirate, with his black beard curling on his breast. The Reverend John Smeet, with his strangler's hands and his Geneva gown, walked as daintily as he had to the gallows. The red print of the rope was still around his neck but he carried a perfumed handkerchief in one hand. One and all, they came into the room with the fires of hell still upon them, and the stranger named their names and their deeds as they came, till the tale of twelve was told. Yet the stranger had told the truth—they had all played a part in America.

"Are you satisfied with the jury, Mr. Webster?" said the stranger, mockingly, when they had taken their places.

The sweat stood upon Dan'l Webster's brow but his voice was clear.

"Quite satisfied," he said. "Though I miss General Arnold from the company."

"General Arnold is engaged upon other business," said the stranger, with a glower. "Ah, you asked for a justice, I believe."

He pointed his finger once more, and a tall man, soberly clad in Puritan garb, with the burning gaze of the fanatic, stalked into the room and took his judge's place.

"Justice Hathorne is a jurist of experience," said the stranger. "He presided at certain witch-trials, once held in Salem. There were others who repented of the business later, but not he."

"Repent of such notable wonders and undertakings?" said the stern old justice. "Nay, hang them—hang them all!" and he muttered to himself in a way that struck ice into the soul of Jabez Stone.

Then the trial began, and, as you must expect, it didn't look anyways good for the defence. And Jabez Stone didn't make much of a witness in his own behalf. He took one look at Simon Girty aand screeched, and they had to put him back in his corner, in a kind of swoon.

It didn't halt the trial, though—the trial went on, as trials do. Dan'l Webster had faced some hard juries and hanging judges in his time—but this was the hardest he'd ever faced, and he knew it. They sat there, with a kind of glitter in their eyes, and the stranger's smooth voice went on and on. Every time he'd raise an objection, it'd be, "Objection sustained," but whenever Dan'l objected, it'd be "Objection denied." Well, you couldn't expect fair play from a fellow like this Mr. Scratch.

It got to Dan'l in the end, and he began to heat, like iron in the forge. When he got up to speak, he was going to flay that stranger with every trick known to the law, and the judge and jury, too. He didn't care if it was contempt of court or what would happen to him for it. He didn't care any more what happened to Jabez Stone. He just got madder and madder, thinking of what he'd say. And yet, curiously enough, the more he thought about it, the less he was able to arrange his speech in his mind.

Till, finally, it was time for him to get up on his feet, and he did so—all ready to bust out with lightnings and denunciations. But before he started he looked over the judge and jury for a moment, such being his custom. And he noticed the glitter in their eyes was twice as strong as before, and they all leaned forward. Like hounds just before they get the fox, they looked —and the blue mist of evil in the room thickened as he watched them. Then he saw what he'd been about to do—and he wiped his forehead, as a man might who's just escaped falling into a pit in the dark.

For it was him they'd come for—not only Jabez Stone. He read it in the glitter of their eyes and in the way the stranger hid his mouth with one hand. And, if he fought them with their own weapons, he'd fall into their power—he knew that, though he couldn't have told you how. It was his own anger and horror that burned in their eyes—and he'd have to wipe that out or the case was lost. He stood there for a moment, his black eyes burning like anthracite. And then he began to speak. He started off in a low voice, though you could hear every word. They say he could call on the harps of the blessed when he chose. And this was just as simple and easy as a man could talk. But he didn't start out by condemning or reviling. He was talking about the things that make a country a country, and a man a man.

And he begun with the simple things that everybody's known and felt—the freshness of a fine morning, when you're young and the taste of food when you're hungry and the new day that's every day when you're a child. He took them up and he turned them in his hands. They were good things for any man. But, without freedom, they sickened. And when he talked of those enslaved, and the sorrows of slavery, his voice got like a big bell. He talked of the early days of America and the men who had made those days. It wasn't a spread-eagle speech but he made you see it. He admitted all the wrong that had ever been done. But he showed how, out of the wrong and the right, the suffering and the starvations, something new had come. And everybody had played a part in it, even the traitors.

Then he turned to Jabez Stone and showed him as he was—an ordinanry man who'd had hard luck and wanted to change it. And, because he'd wanted to change it, now he was going to be punished for all eternity. And yet there was good in Jabez Stone—and he showed that good. He was hard and mean, in some ways—but he was a man. There was sadness in being a man but it was a proud thing, too. And he showed what the pride of it was till you couldn't help feeling it. Yes, even in hell, if a man was a man, you'd know it. And he wasn't pleading for any one person any more—though his voice rang like an organ. He was telling the story and the failures and the endless journey of mankind. They got tricked and trapped and bamboozled, but it was a great journey. And no demon that was ever foaled could know the inwardness of it—it took a man to do that.

The fire began to die on the hearth and the wind before morning to blow. The light was getting grey in the room when Dan'l Webster finished. And his words came back at the end to New Hampshire ground—and the one spot of land that each man loves and clings to. He painted a picture of that—and, to each one of that jury he spoke of things long-forgotten. For his voice could search the heart, and that was his gift and his strength. And to one his voice was like the forest and its secrecy, and to another like the sea and the storms of the sea; and one heard the cry of his lost nation in it, and another saw a little harmless scene he hadn't remembered for years. But each saw something. And, when Dan'l Webster finished, he didn't know whether or not he'd saved Jabez Stone. But he knew he'd done a miracle. For the glitter was gone from the eyes of judge and jury, and, for the moment, they were men again, and knew they were men.

"The defence rests," said Dan'l Webster, and stood there like a mountain. His ears were still ringing with his speech and he didn't hear anything else till he heard Judge Hathorne say, "The jury will retire to consider its verdict."

Walter Butler rose in his place and his face had a dark gay pride on it.

"The jury has considered its verdict," he said, and looked the stranger full in the eye. "We find for the defendant, Jabez Stone."

With that the smile left the stranger's face, but Walter Butler did not flinch.

"Perhaps 'tis not strictly in accordance with the evidence," he said. "But even the damned may salute the eloquence of Mr. Webster."

With that, the long crow of a rooster split the grey morning sky, and judge and jury were gone from the room like a puff of smoke and as if they had never been there. The stranger turned to Dan'l Webster, smiling wryly.

"Major Butler was always a bold man," he said. "I had not thought him quite so bold. Nevertheless—my congratulations, as between two gentlemen."

"I'll have that paper first, if you please," said Dan'l Webster and he took it and tore it into four pieces. It was queerly warm to the touch. "And now," he said, "I'll have you!" and his hand came down like a bear-trap on the stranger's arm. For he knew that once you bested anybody like Mr. Scratch in fair fight, his power on you was gone. And he could see that Mr. Scratch knew it, too.

The stranger twisted and wriggled but he couldn't get out of that grip. "Come, come, Mr. Webster," he said, smiling palely. "This sort of thing is ridic—ouch!—is ridiculous. If you're worried about the costs of the case —naturally, I'll be glad to pay——"

"And so you shall!" said Dan'l Webster, shaking him till his teeth rattled. "For you'll sit right down at that table and draw up a document, promising never to bother Jabez Stone nor his heirs or assigns nor any other Newhampshireman till Doomsday! For any Hades we want to raise in this State, we can raise ourselves, without assistance from strangers."

"Ouch!" said the stranger. "Ouch! Well, they never did run very big to the barrel but—ouch! I agree!"

So he sat down and drew up the document. But

Dan'l Webster kept his hand on his coat-collar all the time.

"And now—may I go?" said the stranger, quite humble, when Dan'l's seen the document's in proper and legal form.

"Go?" said Dan'l, giving him another shake. "I'm still trying to figure out what I'll do with you. For you've settled the costs of the case, but you haven't settled with me. I think I'll take you back to Marshfield," he said, kind of reflective. "I've got a ram there named Goliath that can butt through an iron door. I'd kind of like to turn you loose in his field and see what he'd do."

Well, with that the stranger began to beg and to plead. And he begged and he pled so humble that finally Dan'l, who was naturally kind-hearted, agreed to let him go. The stranger seemed terrible grateful for that and said, just to show they were friends, he'd tell Dan'l's fortune, before leaving. So Dan'l agreed to that, though he didn't take much stock in fortune-tellers ordinarily. But, naturally, the stranger was a little different.

Well, he pried and peered at the lines in Dan'l's hands. And he told him one thing and another that was quite remarkable. But they were all in the past.

"Yes, all that's true, and it happened," said Dan'l Webster. "But what's to come in the future?"

The stranger grinned, kind of happily, and shook his head.

"The future's not as you think it," he said. "It's dark. You have a great ambition, Mr. Webster."

"I have," said Dan'l, firmly, for everybody knew he wanted to be President.

"It seems almost within your grasp," said the stranger. "But you will not attain it. Lesser men will be made President and you will be passed over."

"And, if I am, I'll still be Daniel Webster," said Dan'l. "Say on."

"You have two strong sons," said the stranger, shaking his head. "You look to found a line. But each will die in war and neither reach greatness."

"Live or die, they are still my sons," said Dan'l Webster. "Say on."

"You have made great speeches," said the stranger. "You will make more."

"Ah!" said Dan'l Webster.

"But the last great speech you make will turn many of your own against you," said the stranger. "They will call you Ichabod—they will call you by other names. Even in New England some will say you have turned your coat and sold your country, and their voices will be loud against you till you die."

"So it is an honest speech, it does not matter what men say," said Dan'l Webster. Then he looked at the stranger and their glances locked.

"One question," he said. "I have fought for the Union all my life. Will I see that fight won, against those who would tear it apart?"

"Not while you live," said the stranger, grimly. "But it will be won. And, after you are dead, there are thousands who will fight for your cause, because of words that you spoke."

"Why, then, you long-barrelled, slab-sided, lantern-jawed, fortune-telling note-shaver!" said Dan'l Webster with a great roar of laughter, "be off with you to your own place before I put my mark on you! For, by the Thirteen Original Colonies, I'd go to the Pit itself to save the Union!"

And with that he drew back his foot for a kick that

would have stunned a horse. It was only the tip of his shoe that caught the stranger, but he went flying out of the door with his collecting-box under his arm.

"And now," said Dan'l Webster, seeing Jabez Stone beginning to rouse from his swoon, "let's see what's left in the jug, for it's dry work talking all night. I hope there's pie for breakfast, Neighbour Stone."

But they say that whenever the Devil comes near Marshfield, even now, he gives it a wide berth. And he hasn't been seen in the State of New Hampshire from that day to this. I'm not talking about Massachusetts or Vermont.

TOM WHIPPLE

BY WALTER D. EDMONDS

Here the author of Drums Along the Mohawk *retells an American legend first recorded in 1840 by L. Maria Child. In the first half of the nineteenth century, Mrs. Child flooded this country with her literary works and alienated conservatives by her intransigence as an abolitionist.*

ON a late October morning in 1837, just after sunrise, a woman and a grown boy, approaching the Cortlandt Street wharf, asked a deck hand if that was the steamboat for Albany. When he said it was, the boy turned to the woman.

"See, ma. You didn't miss it anyhow."

Her voice was timid. "I was only feared the Amboy boat had made us late. I'd be feared to stay all day in a big city like this one. Washington City was big enough for me." She cast an anxious glance over her shoulder. New York was waking up, and the frosty streets echoed with the clatter of drays and water carts. "Hadn't we ought to get on to the boat, Tom?"

"Might as well."

Beside her small bent figure, he looked tall. He was a big boy, anyway, with the flesh on him not yet grown up to his bones. He was carrying a small satchel and a bundle rolled up in a cotton print, and his hands hung well below the cuffs of his shabby coat, showing the wrist joints.

Choosing a corner behind the stove in the main saloon, they stowed the satchel under the seat, and the woman sat down. "This here's real nice," she said, looking up

at her son. "I think it's prettier than the other boat, don't
you, Tom?"

"Yes, ma."

He was looking out of the window that faced south.
He could see the bay beyond the river's mouth, the
white gulls against the sky and a ship sailing past the
Castle Garden.

She watched his face for a moment, thinking, perhaps,
that it favored her own more than his father's.

Then he turned to her and fixed his eyes on a nail
in the wall about two feet over her shawled head. "You
ought to get home all right," he said.

"We ought to," she said sharply, as if she had been
seeing into his mind for some time. "You don't mean—"

He nodded and said, "Yep."

She said then, angrily, "You know I'm feared of traveling alone. It ain't right of you to leave me here, Tom.
This way. In this big boat." She saw that she was
getting nowhere. "Ain't it enough for you to go see
Washington City? Didn't we traipse all the way over to
that Mount Vernon? And we rode on the cars. Ain't
many boys done that much. Not even Supervisor Utley
has rode on railroad cars. Besides, how'm I going to
run the place?"

He was still looking over her head. His face was
blank, as only a seventeen-year-old boy's can be, de-
fensive and stubborn. She took the end of her shawl to
put it to her eyes. "When pa moved us from New Haven
way out into York State, he promised I was to have a
home permanent in Westernville. And then he died,
and I calculated you would grow up there and take
care of me. Remember how you promised pa? What will
I say to the Utleys?"

"Tell them I aim to see something of the world,"
Tom said. "I aim to look me around a spell. I'll come

home, maybe in the spring. You'll be all right. You got your widow pension off the government, didn't you? You can hire help now."

She sniffed two or three times. "Oh, Tom," she said, "where'll you go to?"

"I don't know," he said, shuffling his feet. "Maybe Europe. Maybe I'll go to China."

"But, oh, Tom, you ain't got money. You ain't never been nowhere."

"That's it. I ain't been nowhere," he said.

Passengers were coming onto the boat, their feet crackling sharply on the deck outside. She saw that his face was set, and she looked at the freckles as if she wanted to count them over before he left her. His father had been just as stubborn; you couldn't turn him; wasn't anything more stubborn, she thought with a little twinge of pain and pride, than a Whipple man when he got dead set.

He cast a look around and saw that they were partly screened by the stove. He bent down awkwardly to kiss her.

"Good-by, ma," he said. "See you come spring, I guess."

The warning bell began to toll as he stepped off the boat.

"Well, bub," said the man with the hedge of black chin whiskers. "What do you want?"

"You're hiring help, ain't you?" asked Tom Whipple.

The man shoved the stiff-visored cap back on his head and put his feet on the box he had been writing on. He had a square face, the skin like red leather on his cheeks. His eyes were piercing, gray, and hard.

"Yep," he said. "What can you do? Milk perty good, hey? Pitch hay? Say, maybe you can make butter too?"

"I could," said Tom. "I ain't done much, but my ma makes dandy butter. We sell ourn to Supervisor Utley."

"Yew deaow, hey?" The mate got a big laugh from the men in the three-cent-gin shop where he was signing on the crew. "Now that's real handy of yeaow."

Tom Whipple stared at him. He said, "I calculate you must come from Massachusetts State."

This time he got the laugh, and the mate's eyes narrowed. But though he let it go, anybody could see he wasn't going to let Tom Whipple out of his hands after that.

His voice was even and cold. "Ever been to sea?" he asked.

"No," said Tom.

The mate turned to the saloonkeeper for sympathy. "Jeff, did you ever see a crummier lot of ditch lice?" He wheeled round again on Tom. "This is a ship, not a farm. You'll get eleven dollars a month, and you don't milk cows. But we make a ship sail, see?"

"Yes," said Tom. "That's what I want. I want to travel."

"You'll travel all right aboard the *Flora Bascom*." The mate smiled thinly. "Name?"

"Tom Whipple."

The mate's pen squeaked.

"All right," he said. "Next man."

"Just a minute," Tom said. "Where's the *Flora Bascom* sailing to?"

"It's none of your business," said the mate. He rose behind the box. "My name is Mr. Bullett," he said evenly. "I don't want remarks from you. I don't want questions. But when you speak, I'm 'Mister.' Understand?"

"All right," Tom said good-naturedly.

He didn't know what happened. The mate did not

move from behind his box, but his fist hit Tom between the eyes. The next he knew, he was lying on the floor and Mr. Bullett was saying, "Mister!" and breathing gently on his knuckles. "Mr. Freel," he said, "take him aboard and see if you can pick some of the straws out of his ears."

A thick-shouldered man yanked Tom to his feet and shoved him toward the door. "Come along, hayfoot," he said. He smelled of tar and plug tobacco and gin and a peculiar kind of hair grease. Half a dozen of the other new hands came after them, but their sycophants' laughter stopped as they emerged into the rumbling clatter of South Street.

"The mate's a bully, ain't he?" one asked.

"Not too bad, if you look sharp and jump when he spits," replied the second mate. "Besides, he's found himself a toy." He nodded at Tom, who was giddily trying to avoid a cart horse.

Tom spent all that day trying to do what he was told, along with the other men. The idea seemed not so much to get work done as to keep the hands busy, and there were moments when Mr. Freel scratched the bald spot on his head and looked hopefully toward Mr. Bullett.

At noon and at four the men were allowed ashore for an hour, but Tom was kept on board, for Mr. Freel had an idea he might clear out. He told Tom that somebody had to keep watch on the ship. Tom didn't know his rights, of course. Nobody told him that the one-armed old fellow smoking a clap pipe amidships was the shipkeeper, hired according to law. He was glad enough to stay on board and take the hour admiring the vessel. Mr. Freel brought him some scraps of food from the captain's table. Mr. Freel, it appeared, did not eat in the cabin, but, like other second mates, lived a kind of ghostly existence halfway between the forecastle and the cabin. And because Tom had proved handy with the ropes, he acted friendly.

One of the first things he asked was whether Tom had any money.

Tom said no, but he expected to have plenty when they docked across the ocean. Eleven dollars a month was good pay for an apprentice, he thought. Mr. Freel, whittling a plug into a horny palm, grunted.

"You'll need clothes," he said. "Sea boots and a pea jacket. You'll have to buy them from the slop chest. And you'll pay the master a hundred and fifty per cent profit on the transaction," he said.

Tom thought about it for a while before he said, "That don't seem honest."

"Maybe not," Mr. Freel said shortly. "But it's regular. He keeps good stuff in the slop, which is more than some do. You won't have such a hell of a big fortune, though, when you reach St. Petersburg."

Tom cleaned up his beans and said, "Where's that, Mr. Freel?"

"Russia. And a damned cold place, they say."

"Ain't you never been there?"

"No. And I ain't got much desire to go."

Tom lay on his back and looked up into the rigging. The sun and the wind put a kind of shine on the spars that was foreign to the hull.

"I'm glad we're going to Russia," he said. "I've had a fancy to see that place. Maybe I'll get to see the Emperor. Have you ever seen an emperor, Mr. Freel?"

"No," said Mr. Freel. "Captain Stath is emperor enough for me. Him and Mr. Bullett. What do you want to see the Emperor for, anyway?" he asked.

"Oh," said Tom, "I'd kind of like to talk to him. When you want to find out about something, Supervisor Utley says you want to ask the top man, as long as you ain't buying."

Tom Whipple had the bunk in the peak of the fore-castle, where the air still smelled of the Dago Portuguese who had occupied it on the preceding voyage. When the crew laid aft to be chosen into watches, he was taken by Mr. Bullett. The choosing was done under the eye of Captain Stath, a clean-shaven man with a calculating face. He was short with the first mate, and he did not speak to the second except to give orders, but he took the ship down the river in fine style. By evening the brig was a lonely box on the waves with eighteen men and a spotted cat, and America was a place on which the sun had set.

He was sick, and the cold bit as the sun went under, and Mr. Bullett, who had been driving him since the *Flora Bascom* dropped Castle Garden, ordered him aloft with a ball of marline for the boatswain.

"Stay up there till he tells you to bring it down. Maybe the wind will blow the hayseed out."

Tom took the ball in his right hand and worked him-self onto the shrouds. He could hear the hiss of the water under him, and the cross ropes pushed against his chest. But he went up, and the only time he looked down he could see Mr. Bullett and Mr. Freel both look-ing up at him, and Captain Stath coming out of the cabin. Mr. Freel looked anxious, the captain showed nothing on his face at all, but Mr. Bullett was smiling his thin smile.

"Damn him," Tom said to himself. "I'm just as good as he is off this ship."

He didn't stop again. He felt the back wind off the sails against his face; the curve of them made dingy feather beds to lure a man to let go; but he went up.

He saw, after a while, the noncommittal face of the boatswain leaning over the yard. The boatswain's feet were like glue, and his hands were careless, and he laid a long line of tobacco spit level on the wind.

"I've seen a snail go up a bush!" he shouted. "But he got there, too, bub!"

It wasn't praise, exactly, but it made Tom feel easier. He found the yard a comfortable pressure on his belly. He let it carry his weight, gingerly, then with more confidence. Then he looked down and saw the hull slitting the water like a needle that a bug might straddle.

"It's bigger than it looks!" shouted the boatswain. "But don't look at it too long, bub! You'll see plenty of it when you're down!"

So Tom looked out while the boatswain worked. He saw the night on the Atlantic; the great heaving mass of it was leveled from that height, and he felt himself swoop over it, a little like the motion of a gull. But a gull didn't fly in the squeak and crash and booming of rigging. He had feathers to silence the wind.

Out there was Russia, he thought, and back of him was Westernville. He could imagine his mother, when she got home, telling Mrs. Utley and the supervisor what had become of him. She would say he was on a ship; maybe for Europe, maybe for China. He could imagine her crying and saying, "He didn't have any money. He didn't want any. You know how Tom is. Always going round with his pocket full of nails and things he picks up, thinking he is as good as the richest man alive." She would think of him asleep in bed, possibly. She would never imagine him up alone in the wind with the yard against his belly and his feet balanced on a spider thread. And the supervisor would clear his throat and say, "Pshaw, Mrs. Whipple," and ask where his supper was.

Thinking of supper at the Utley's made Tom hungry. For the first time since the brig had met the Atlantic swell, he felt his stomach take a rational shape. "By holy," he said to himself, "I'm all right."

Then the marline ball was slapped against his palm, and the boatswain said, "Get down, bub. And take it easy. Any man can climb."

He went down easy, and when he hit the deck, the roll met his feet squarely. He could smell pork in the galley vent. Mr. Bullett came stamping aft along the deck. His eyes had not changed, and he was still smiling thinly. But all he said was, "Take the marline back to Mr. Freel."

After a week or so, Tom was getting along well enough with the officers. But the fact that he was planning to see the Emperor was too much for Mr. Freel to keep to himself, and, once the foremast hands got wind of it, they talked about it all the way to Russia.

It didn't bother Tom a great deal, though. He didn't know, himself, how he was going to get to talk with him. He didn't even know what his name was, and nobody in the forecastle was able to tell him. They were a pretty mixed crew. Tom was the only genuine American citizen in the forecastle, except a man from New Orleans; and he wasn't hardly what Tom thought of as a Yankee. He saw they didn't mean harm; they had to have something to occupy their minds; but he thought they plain didn't understand how a man could get along. He wasn't worried, except about finding out the Emperor's name.

The bos'n told him that Russian names didn't count. You couldn't pronounce them anyway. And the carpenter said they didn't have last names in Russia at all; the names all ended in "sky," which meant "son of." The cook said, why didn't he ask the old man? So Tom said maybe he would.

But he didn't make up his mind to it till the *Flora Bascom* had worked her way across the Baltic Sea and was heading in for the gulf. At the wheel was the dimwitted Swede, but he could steer a ship like a dreaming archangel. It was Tom's turn at polishing the brass work, and he was rubbing up the binnacle when Captain Stath came up for his morning constitutional.

All the time Tom worked he could hear the smart crack of the captain's heels on the frosty deck, measuring out his exact rectangle. It was easy to tell that the captain was feeling brisk. So Tom gave the shining brass a last flourish of the rag and caught the captain on his twenty-third quarter turn.

He touched his forelock smartly with the knuckle of the hand holding the brass polish and said, "Excuse me, captain. Could you tell me the name of the Emperor of Russia?"

The captain wheeled like a speared sturgeon and roared, "What?" in a t'gallant bellow that brought the entire crew up standing.

Tom saw that he had put his foot in it, but he had to get out the question now, so he asked it again.

The captain's voice cut like the ice spray as he shouted for Mr. Bullett. The rest of the crew all grinned, for they had been waiting this minute; only the Swede didn't change face, but he wiggled his ears for a moment, as if he felt a shift coming in the wind. The sight of them didn't help the captain. By the time Mr. Bullett came up, he was in a state of frenzy.

"Do you know what's happened, mister?" he demanded, leveling his voice.

"No, sir," said Mr. Bullett.

"I've been interrupted on my own deck by one of the watch. Your watch, Mr. Bullett. And do you know what he wanted to know? He wanted to know the name of the Emperor of Russia, Mr. Bullett! . . . Are you going to stand there like a blasted gaping marble image, Mr. Bullett? Ain't you going to do something?"

Mr. Bullett did. He hailed Tom down amidships and had a couple of seamen hold him over a barrel, and he put a rope's end on his bare back twenty times.

When he was through, they rolled Tom over on his back and emptied buckets of sea water over him and told him to put his shirt on and get to work. Tom felt sore, inside as well as out; the captain had taken up his walk at the exact point at which he had left off, and the only times he watched the flogging was during the short space when he was coming forward and crossing to starboard. The crew thought it was a prodigious joke, discussing it in the forecastle when the watch was off. It was the carpenter's opinion that none of the officers knew the Emperor's name.

Somehow the word of that got aft, and the rest of the voyage became pretty brisk for all of them, and Tom wasn't sorry to jump the brig as soon as she berthed in Kronstadt.

But when he reached St. Petersburg, he got to feeling better. He couldn't talk to anybody. They all looked foreign and many of them had a queer fat smell that made him think of a sheep's carcass hanging in the cool room. He was immensely excited by what he saw, and spent days walking the streets. New York, he thought, or even Washington City, wasn't in it, for strange sights. He saw all sorts of different-appearing people, and they didn't all talk one language either; even a stranger could tell that. He could tell it was a big country, and the urge to find out about it got more and more intense, and he felt surer than ever that the only way to do that was to have a talk with the man at the top, the Emperor.

He tried two or three times at the palace, and he kept watch on the gates, until he began to realize that to get next to the Emperor he would have to have letters or something of that sort.

He didn't know how to get hold of letters, and he had been there two weeks and his money was about gone. He was feeling a bit low that afternoon, standing outside a pub, when he saw a sailor ambling down the street and looking as footloose as himself.

He hadn't dared go back to the port in all this time, for fear of being picked up by Mr. Bullett. So, seeing that this sailor was a stranger, he hailed him, and they shook hands like two white men in a foreign country; fingering the few coins left in his pockets, he asked the sailor in for a drink. "It's just a pot likker," he said. "But it warms a person."

The sailor turned out to be off a British ship, and he was sympathetic. He had Tom's drink, and then he bought Tom one, and they got so friendly that Tom told him how he had been trying to get to see the Emperor, but didn't know how to go about it.

The sailor said it appeared to him like a difficult problem. "Can't your minister help you out?" he asked.

Tom said, "My minister?" and the sailor said, "Yes. The minister of the United States."

Tom said he hadn't been to see him. He hadn't thought of it; as a matter of fact, it had not even occurred to him that there could be such a job. It made him feel that the United States was a pretty fine country to send a minister all the way to St. Petersburg. He felt considerably better immediately; it was the next best thing to seeing a picture of Old Hickory himself on the wall. Well, said the sailor, why didn't Tom go to see him? Taking care of the interests of American citizens in Russia was what the American minister was paid to do. "And he's got to look after you same as the British minister has to look after me," he said. "That's what they collect the taxes off us for." Tom said he would go. The sailor offered to lend him the money to hire a sled with, but Tom declined. He didn't care to be beholden to a man he didn't know well, and a foreigner at that. So he said good-by and started off for the American embassy. He had a good idea of the direction because there turned out to be a Frenchman in the pub who said he knew.

Well, the minister lived in a mighty fine big house with the American flag flying over it, and when he saw it, Tom Whipple felt good. While he was looking at it, a man came walking from the other direction, and he was dressed in a good American coat; you could tell it a mile. He had a sealskin cap on his head, with the flaps up, pretty near exactly like the one Supervisor Utley wore when he got into the cutter behind the bays and drove down to a Sunday dinner in Rome. But even without those garments, Tom could have told he was an American by the way he walked. He was coming right along, and you could see he meant business. So Tom stepped across the roadway, dodging a couple of droshkies with their jingling bells, and touched his hat to the American, and asked whether the American minister was to home.

The man looked Tom up and down from his worn

felt hat and pea jacket to the old pants and the sea
boots. He looked at Tom's freckled face and his young
turkey neck and his rawboned wrists, and he gave him
a smile.

"No," he said, "the minister's not home yet, but he
will be in two shakes. Come in and let me see what I
can do for you." He took off his hat, so Tom took his
off and they went in the outer door.

"My name's Dallas," said the man. "I'm the minister."

"Whipple," said Tom. "I'm pleased to meet you."

Well, when they came to the inner door, the minister
steel to one side to let Tom in first, and then a couple
of Russian-dressed servants came up, and one took the
minister's hat and coat and one took Tom's hat and his
pea jacket. They went upstairs together to where the
minister had a kind of office. There was coal burning in
a tiled stove, there were books on the walls, and there
was a table, something like a dresser, laid out with
about every kind of bottle there was.

Mr. Dallas pointed to it and asked whether Tom
would have anything to drink. But Tom declined.
"There ain't nothing I'd like now except a glass of
fresh buttermilk," he said. "I ain't been able to find
none anywhere, Mr. Dallas. I can't figure out no Russian
for it either."

Mr. Dallas smiled. He said he hadn't thought of
buttermilk himself, but if there was anything that would
taste good to him at that moment, buttermilk was what
it would be. So he pulled a velvet rope hanging on the
wall, and a servant came and went, and pretty soon he
came in with two big glasses on a gold tray. Mr. Dallas
took one and Tom the other; Mr. Dallas raised his and
said, "Your very good health, Mr. Whipple." So Tom
raised his and returned the compliment, and they took
chairs and drank the buttermilk. Tom thought it wasn't

near so good as what came out of his mother's churning, but he didn't like to say so. And after being so long without it, he had to admit is tasted pleasant.

The minister talked plain to him. He asked how the U. S. A. was getting along, and Tom said that money was awful tight. He told how he and his mother had been to Washington to get her pension, and how he had seen the President go by down the avenue. He said he had gone over to Mount Vernon. And then he told about putting his mother on the Albany steamboat and how he had signed on the *Flora Bascom*. He hadn't known she was coming to Russia when he did it, but he was mighty glad when he learned, for he had heard about the Russians licking Napoleon Bonaparte, so he knew it was a great country, and he had made up his mind to see the Emperor. That, as a matter of fact, was what he had called on Mr. Dallas about. He would like to get a letter from Mr. Dallas, saying who he was and that he would like a little conversation with the Emperor.

Mr. Dallas looked at him for a moment before he said, picking his words, "You know, Whipple, the Emperor's a pretty hard man to get to see." Then he tried to explain how it was in an empire as compared to a democratic country. Tom thought it over, but he shook his head. He said he couldn't see it that way. He could see it might apply to a Russian farmer, in a manner of speaking, but he was a United States citizen. Martin Van Buren, now, he could see the Emperor, couldn't he? Mr. Dallas nodded his head; that was true. Then why couldn't Tom Whipple?

Well, they sawed away at it for a spell, and Mr. Dallas was as friendly a man as you could ask to argue with. But Tom got the best of him at every turn, and finally he agreed to write a letter to the imperial court chamberlain for Tom. But he said there was one thing:

It was the custom, when you went to call on an Emperor, to take him a present. Tom hadn't thought of that, but he could see how it would be; and he stuck his hand in his pants pocket to fiddle the junk he carried, the way he always did when he was puzzled, and his fingers closed on an object he'd hardly thought of since leaving Washington City. Holding it, he thought how lucky it was he hadn't dropped it anywhere, like up on the topsail yards of the *Flora Bascom* driving off Finisterre. "All right," he said. "Tell him I got a present I'd mighty like to give the Emperor, and that I figure the Emperor is going to be mighty pleased to have."

Mr. Dallas looked at Tom's face, and he wrote the message down without asking what the present was. Then he sealed the letter inside and out, prettifying it like anything, to Tom's way of thinking. He gave it to Tom, telling him to come around in the morning and he would send a man with him to be sure he got in to see the chamberlain. Then he asked Tom if he would have supper. He had to go out himself, he explained; his family was going with him, but he couldn't offer to take Tom, as it was a formal court dinner. However, if Tom didn't mind eating alone, he could have dinner here.

So Tom ate alone in the dining room, with five men to wait on him, not one of whom could talk good English; and after dinner, to save money, he found himself a stable and slept in the hay.

It meant a good deal of picking and dusting to get clear of the hay in the morning, but he turned up at the minister's house on time and was sent off with a clerk. Mr. Dallas came down to shake hands with him and said for him to come back when he was ready; he would see that Tom got a berth on a ship to go home. Tom thanked him and said he would.

He could tell that Mr. Dallas didn't expect he would

get to see the Emperor at all, but he didn't hold it against him. Mr. Dallas had been as neighborly as any man could be.

The clerk was a dapper man. Tom could tell at first glance that he wasn't the quality of man Mr. Dallas was. As soon as they got round the corner, he asked Tom whether he had the minister's letter. Tom slapped his coat pocket to show he did, and the clerk said, "Well, come on, then."

It amused Tom some to see how walking alongside of him made the clerk uneasy. He kept pressing forward as if he was trying to leave Tom behind, but he couldn't walk worth a duck. It didn't bother Tom. He could imagine how the clerk would look setting out to pitch hay.

But the clerk knew where to go and whom to speak to. Inside the palace he kept whispering to Tom not to make such a hooraw with his boots; but you can't help making some noise with sea boots on a tile floor, so Tom went the quietest he could without tiptoeing, and let it go at that. He knew people were looking at him; they in their Russian costumes and he in his pea jacket made kind of a mixture, he could see. But it didn't bother him. They liked to wear that kind of clothes, and he liked his own. When they got to the chamberlain's room, the clerk gave his message to a flunky, and pretty soon this man came out and told them to go in through the inner door.

Tom had supposed that the clerk would go in with him to see the chamberlain, but the clerk was through. He said, "In there," to Tom, as if he was driving a pig to a sticker, and turned on his heel. Tom let him go. He didn't feel that the clerk would have been much help anyhow.

In the chamberlain's office there was a handsome, bearded, elderly man sitting at a desk. He got up and bowed, when Tom entered, and Tom handed him Mr. Dallas' letter, and the chamberlain said he was honored, in very unsteady English, but understandable. He read the letter, and then he looked at Tom for a spell.

He said, "You know the Emperor is a very busy man, Mr. Whipple."

"I calculate he must be, running a country this size, and without no congress either, so far as I know," said Tom.

The chamberlain bowed. "For instance, today he has five audiences in the morning; then an hour of state papers to sign and the imperial policies to consider. Then he has to go to a military review. Then he eats with the Empress. Then this afternoon he receives a delegation of Cossacks, and must inspect the Palace Guard and decorate a grand duke, and in the evening he has to appear at the opera. You see, he is busy."

"I expected he would be," Tom said. "But I don't aim to take a lot of his time."

"Well," said the chamberlain, "using my influence, I might be able to arrange an audience with him next April."

But that didn't suit Tom's book at all. "It's this way," he said: "I ain't got the money to stay here that long. In fact, if I don't see the Emperor in the next day or two, I'll have to just take ship without seeing him at all. I'd hate to do that. You tell him, seeing he's so all-fired busy, I won't take any of his time. I'll just give him my present and wish him luck and clear out."

"Well," said the chamberlain, "I will see. But perhaps you would give me the present to present it for you."

"I wouldn't," said Tom. He wanted to be polite, though, so he added, "I got this present in America, mister, and I'd like to give it to the Emperor with my own hand."

Well, the chamberlain hadn't ever come up against a genuine Yankee, and he couldn't make him out. He looked baffled, biting the inside whiskers of his mustache as if he'd like to turn Tom over to a squad of Cossacks, maybe; but there was Mr. Dallas' letter in his hand, so he couldn't do that. And after a couple of minutes of thinking, he made up his mind.

"I'll take your letter in to the Emperor now," he said.

"That's fine," said Tom. "Just put it up to him. It's a fair proposition."

Well, in about ten minutes, back came the chamberlain, and along with him was a fine tall man. From the way he walked, Tom saw he was a man who didn't have to fiddle with this and that, but marked his first chip and axed right to the line. He was a good deal bigger than the chamberlain and he had a bold sharp eye. He wasn't dressed so fancy, but he didn't have to be dressed fancy to tell a person he was somebody. There wasn't any doubt he was the Emperor. And then Tom realized he didn't know the man's name.

He hesitated a moment, and then he decided, even though he was younger, the thing was up to him, so as not to embarrass the man. So he took three steps forward and held out his hand.

"My name's Tom Whipple," he said. "I'm from the U. S. A. I ain't been in your country long, but it seems like a fine country, and before I left I wanted to give you a present."

The Emperor looked at him a minute. His eyes went

all over Tom in a glance and then rested on his face. Then he smiled and held out his own hand and they shook.

"Hello, Tom," he said. "My name's Nicholas. I'm glad to welcome you. I wish you'd come to see me sooner."

"Well," said Tom, "you're a mighty hard man to get to see, Emperor. I tried half a dozen times."

"That's the trouble with being an emperor," said Nicholas. "They run in all the people you don't want to talk to, and they keep out the people you do."

He had an easy way with him; he seemed neighborly.

He said, "Now you've got here, though, we'll have a talk. You come with me, Tom."

But the chamberlain interrupted in Russian, and from the way the Emperor talked back, it sounded like swearing. The chamberlain stepped back, and the two of them walked out on him. As soon as they were outside, Nicholas laughed and put his hand on Tom's shoulder.

"I told him to throw out everybody," he said, "and he don't like it much. But he's got to do it. That's one of the good things about being an emperor, even if there aren't many."

Well, he took Tom to another room, as big as a convention hall, to Tom's eyes, which, he said, was his own snug place where they wouldn't be disturbed, and the first thing he did was ask to see his present.

Tom was glad he had thought of it then. He pulled his hand out of his pocket, and then he opened it and he showed the Emperor an acorn resting in the palm of his hand.

The Emperor looked at it, and then he took it and said, "Thanks," in a friendly way, but Tom could see he was a mite puzzled. It made him grin.

"Shucks," he said. "I wouldn't bring you no ordinary

acorn, Emperor. I picked that up in Mount Vernon. That was the place George Washington lived and died at. This nut's right off one of his own personal trees." Then he felt a little bashful, so he added, "I thought you'd appreciate it, being as it comes from the home of the greatest man of the U. S. A., greater even than Old Hickory."

"I do, Tom," said the Emperor. "I've studied the history of your country, and I admire General Washington more than about any man I know of."

"Well, you ought to," said Tom. "And over there we admire you folks too. The way you licked Napoleon Bonaparte. I calculate that took some doing too."

"I value this acorn a lot, Tom," said the Emperor, "and I'll tell you what I plan to do. We'll have a good talk till the day warms up some, and then we'll go out and plant this acorn. I'll have them thaw out a piece in my own palace garden, and you and I'll plant this acorn there together. An American and a Russian."

"That sounds just proper to me," Tom agreed.

"And then we'll have lunch with my wife and family," said the Emperor, just as Supervisor Utley might have said it. "But now you sit down."

Well, the Emperor put Tom right through the business. He wanted to know all about America. He was most interested in the railroads and the schools and the steamboats, and Tom was proud that he had been through grammar school and had ridden on the railroad cars. He was able to tell the Emperor a lot he didn't know.

Then they talked about tight money, and the Emperor told him about a famine he had had, and it seemed in Russia you didn't have a money panic at all, you had a famine—which was simpler, in a way, but Tom thought it amounted to much the same thing for the people who were hard up to start with.

They kept at it till noon, and Tom gave the Emperor some of Supervisor Utley's ideas about banking, which interested the Emperor a whole lot. Then they went out and planted the acorn. There was a squad of Cossacks standing round, but they kept out of the way.

The Emperor wondered whether the acorn would grow, and Tom didn't see why not. It was a sound nut from a sound tree, he said.

So then they took a turn round the palace grounds, and a couple of big, spotted, silk-haired dogs, kind of like greyhounds, joined up with the Cossacks. They looked at some horses, which, Tom could see, were dandies, and he asked where the Emperor kept his cows. He was mighty keen to see a Russian milch cow, he said, but the Emperor told him he would have to go out of the city, and he said he would send him out tomorrow. He couldn't go himself, because an Emperor might kick over the thills once in a while, but he had to keep on the road, too, by and large, to get along, just like an ordinary man.

Well, they had their food in another apartment of the palace, and the Empress turned out to be obliging. She talked English better than the Emperor did, and she wanted to know all about housekeeping in the U. S. A. Tom told her all he knew, which wasn't so much, since his mother took care of that end of their lives. But he told her how they made butter, and maple sugar, and mincemeat, and corn bread, and she called a servant and had it all written down, just as he said it. Then she said she guessed she was right in thinking that there weren't any servants in America. And Tom had to laugh at her, and said she must have been reading Mrs. Trollope's book. He hadn't read Mrs. Trollope's book himself, but he had heard Supervisor Utley talk about it enough to know the kind of nonsense that was in it.

The Empress admitted she had, so Tom told her that while poor folks did their own work—and weren't ashamed to, either—rich people in the U. S. A. were just like other folks, and had servants, and plenty of them. But the Empress said you didn't call them servants, but help, and Tom said that was so, but it always seemed to him like a good idea. The Emperor seemed pleased by the conversation, and he made one of his daughters go out for some crocheting or some kind of fancywork she had been doing, and Tom admired it. The Emperor's girls were fine girls, modest and well-mannered, but shy of him. When he praised the fancywork, the girl that had made it colored all up and made him a curtsy, and then asked him if he would take it back to his mother as a present from her.

That made Tom blush, but he said he would. He hadn't felt so much at home since he left Westernville, and he made up his mind he would have to show the crocheting to Mr. Dallas.

Well, they talked all through the afternoon, and the Emperor called in some Russian dancers to show Tom how they danced in Russia, and he tried to show them a square dance, but only the girl who had given him the fancywork and the Emperor himself seemed to catch on. The rest weren't handy at it at all. But he put that down to their being bashful and foreign, and it didn't bother him.

Then the Emperor said he would have to get back to work, but he asked Tom where he was staying, so he could send round a sleigh for him in the morning to go see the cows. Tom told him he was getting hard up, so he was sleeping in barns, but would meet the sleigh at the palace door. The Emperor wanted him to stay at the palace, but Tom wouldn't. He said he could take care of himself, and wouldn't put anybody out, so the Emperor shook hands with him and said to see him after he had looked at the cows.

Tom looked at them next day. He went out in a sleigh with three horses, and a fine fur robe over him, and a squad of Cossacks ahead and another behind.

He saw the Emperor the next day and told him he had a nice barn, and that he had milked a couple and thought they were a fair-to-middling good breed, and there was one of the springers he downright fancied. The Emperor said he was glad of Tom's opinion; he had never been able to judge a cow himself.

Then he asked Tom whether there was anything else he wanted to see, and though Tom didn't like to ask so much, he finally admitted he would like to look at Moscow, where Napoleon was licked. So the Emperor sent him to Moscow, and this time Tom traveled with all the luxuries and stayed in the palaces and the best hotels, and the officer who went with him took him to the theater and gave him a champagne supper every night.

Tom found it hard to keep going, not being used to so much high life, and he had to admire the Russians for the way they could keep it up. But he enjoyed it, too, and he had to tell the Emperor he was sorry to think of leaving for home. "But I got to get back and get to work," he said. "Ma's expecting me." And he pointed out that even an ordinary man had to work, like an Emperor.

The Emperor said he was sorry to see him go. But if Tom had to get back he would have to go down into

Europe to Germany, for the gulf was frozen over and no ships leaving. To Tom that seemed like putting the Emperor to a lot of trouble, but he told Tom to think nothing of it. If a man had to get to work, he had to. So they shook hands, and Tom said good-by to the Empress and her girls, and he called on Mr. Dallas, who was surprised and interested to hear his story. Then the Emperor's Cossacks took Tom out of Russia.

When he got to Westernville in the spring, though, he was mighty glad to be home. He had kept thinking of maple sirup and buckwheat cakes all the way across the Atlantic; and sure enough, his mother had them for him when he sat down to supper.

After supper they went up to the Utleys', and there he told them all about the trip. The women could hardly credit the wonders Tom had seen, till he pulled out the fancywork the Emperor's girl had sent to Mrs. Whipple. Then he showed them a big watch and chain with a ruby stone hanging to it that the Emperor had given him in return for the acorn. It struck its own hours and half hours, and was made of gold.

But even then it seemed like a fairy story to Mrs. Whipple—the great people treating her Tom like a prince—and she remarked on it so often that Supervisor Utley was obliged to say, "Pshaw, Mrs. Whipple. Any American lad, like Tom here, can get along anywhere on earth."

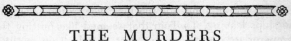

THE MURDERS
IN THE RUE MORGUE

BY EDGAR ALLAN POE

*This piece of fiction was written by an alumnus of the University of
Virginia who, after soldiering for three years and then flunking out of
West Point, abandoned the military art and took to the trade of writing. Originally published in Philadelphia in the April 1841 issue of
Graham's Gentlemen's Magazine (of which the author as editor
could judiciously accept his own contributions), "The Murders in the
Rue Morgue" was the world's first detective-story. After two or three
more demonstrations of great brilliance—among them "The Purloined
Letter" and "The Mystery of Marie Roget"—Poe himself lost interest in the form, but he soon had imitators in Paris and in London and
a generation later a needy young English medico took the hint and
Sherlock Holmes was the result. After him, the deluge.*

THE mental features discoursed of as the analytical,
are, in themselves, but little susceptible of analysis.
We appreciate them only in their effects. We know of
them, among other things, that they are always to their
possessor, when inordinately possessed, a source of the
liveliest enjoyment. As the strong man exults in his
physical ability, delighting in such exercises as call his
muscles into action, so glories the analyst in that moral
activity which *disentagles*. He derives pleasure from
even the most trivial occupations bringing his talents
into play. He is fond of enigmas, of conundrums, of
hieroglyphics; exhibiting in his solutions of each a degree of *acumen* which appears to the ordinary apprehension preternatural. His results, brought about by the
very soul and essence of method, have, in truth, the

whole air of intuition. The faculty of re-solution is possibly much invigorated by mathematical study, and especially by that highest branch of it which, unjustly, and merely on account of its retrograde operations, has been called, as if *par excellence,* analysis. Yet to calculate is not in itself to analyze. A chess-player, for example, does the one without effort at the other. It follows that the game of chess, in its effects upon mental character, is greatly misunderstood. I am not now writing a treatise, but simply prefacing a somewhat peculiar narrative by observations very much at random; I will, therefore, take occasion to assert that the higher powers of the reflective intellect are more decidedly and more usefully tasked by the unostentatious game of draughts than by all the elaborate frivolity of chess. In this latter, where the pieces have different and *bizarre* motions, with various and variable values, what is only complex is mistaken (a not unusual error) for what is profound. The *attention* is here called powerfully into play. If it flag for an instant, an oversight is committed, resulting in injury or defeat. The possible moves being not only manifold but involute, the chances of such oversights are multiplied; and in nine cases out of ten it is the more concentrative rather than the more acute player who conquers. In draughts, on the contrary, where the moves are *unique* and have but little variation, the probabilities of inadvertence are diminished, and the mere attention being left comparatively unemployed, what advantages are obtained by either party are obtained by superior *acumen.* To be less abstract— Let us suppose a game of draughts where the pieces are reduced to four kings, and where, of course, no oversight is to be expected. It is obvious that here the victory can be decided (the players being at all equal) only by some *recherché* movement, the result of some strong exertion of the intellect. Deprived of ordinary resources, the analyst throws himself into the spirit of his opponent, identifies himself therewith, and not unfrequently sees thus, at a glance, the sole methods (sometimes indeed absurdly simple ones) by which he may seduce into error or hurry into miscalculation.

Whist has long been noted for its influence upon what is termed the calculating power; and men of the highest order of intellect have been known to take an apparently unaccountable delight in it, while eschewing chess as frivolous. Beyond doubt there is nothing of a similar nature so greatly tasking the faculty of analysis. The best chess-player in Christendom *may* be little more than the best player of chess; but proficiency in whist implies capacity for success in all these more important undertakings where mind struggles with mind. When I say proficiency, I mean that perfection in the game which includes a comprehension of *all* the sources whence legitimate advantage may be derived. These are not only manifold but multiform, and lie frequently among recesses of thought altogether inaccessible to the ordinary understanding. To observe attentively is to remember distinctly; and, so far, the concentrative chess-player will do very well at whist; while the rules of Hoyle (themselves based upon the mere mechanism of the game) and sufficiently and generally comprehensible. Thus to have a retentive memory, and to proceed by "the book," are points commonly regarded as the sum total of good playing. But it is in matters beyond the limits of mere rule that the skill of the analyst is evinced. He makes, in silence, a host of observations and inferences. So, perhaps, do his companions; and the difference in the extent of the information obtained, lies not so much in the validity of the inference as in the quality of the observation. The necessary knowledge is that of *what* to observe. Our player confines himself not at all; nor, because the game is the object, does he reject deductions from things external to the game. He examines the countenance of his partner, comparing it carefully with that of each of his opponents. He considers the mode of assorting the cards in each hand; often counting trump by trump, and honor by honor, through the glances bestowed by their holders upon each. He notes every variation of face as the play progresses, gathering a fund of thought from the differences in the expression of certainty, of surprise, of triumph, or chagrin. From the manner of gathering up a trick he judges whether the person taking it can make another in the suit. He recognizes what is played through feint, by the air with which it is thrown upon the table. A casual or inadvertent word; the accidental dropping or turning of a card, with the accompanying anxiety or carelessness in regard to its concealment; the counting of the tricks, with the order of their arrangement; embarrassment, hesitation, eagerness or trepidation—all afford, to his apparently intuitive perception, indications of the true state of affairs. The first two or three rounds having been played, he is in full possession of the contents of each hand, and thenceforward puts down his cards with as absolute a precision of purpose as if the rest of the party had turned outward the faces of their own.

The analytical power should not be confounded with simple ingenuity; for while the analyst is necessarily ingenious, the ingenious man is often remarkably incapable of analysis. The consecutive or combining power, by which ingenuity is usually manifested, and to which the phrenologists (I believe erroneously) have assigned a separate organ, supposing it a primitive faculty, has been so frequently seen in those whose intellect bordered otherwise upon idiocy, as to have attracted general observation among writers on morals. Between ingenuity and the analytic ability there exists a difference far greater, indeed, than that between the fancy and the imagination, but of a character very strictly analogous. It will be found, in fact, that the ingenious are always fanciful, and the *truly* imaginative never otherwise than analytic.

The narrative which follows will appear to the reader somewhat in the light of a commentary upon the propositions just advanced.

Residing in Paris during the spring and part of the summer of 18—, I there became acquainted with a Monsieur C. Auguste Dupin. This young gentleman was of an excellent—indeed of an illustrious family, but, by a variety of untoward events, had been reduced to such poverty that the energy of his character succumbed beneath it, and he ceased to bestir himself in the world, or to care for the retrieval of his fortunes. By courtesy of his creditors, there still remained in his possession a small remnant of his patrimony; and, upon the income arising from this, he managed, by means of a rigorous economy, to procure the necessaries of life, without troubling himself about its superfluities. Books, indeed, were his sole luxuries, and in Paris these are easily obtained.

Our first meeting was at an obscure library in the Rue Montmartre, where the accident of our both being in search of the same very rare and very remarkable volume, brought us into closer communion. We saw each other again and again. I was deeply interested in the little family history which he detailed to me with all that candor which a Frenchman indulges whenever mere self is the theme. I was astonished, too, at the vast extent of his reading; and, above all, I felt my soul enkindled within me by the wild fervor, and the vivid freshness of his imagination. Seeking in Paris the objects I then sought, I felt that the society of such a man would be to me a treasure beyond price; and this feeling I frankly confided to him. It was at length arranged that we should live together during my stay in the city; and as my worldly circumstances were somewhat less embarrassed than his own, I was permitted to be at the expense of renting, and furnishing in a style which suited the rather fantastic gloom of our common temper, a time-eaten and grotesque mansion, long deserted through superstitions into which we did not inquire, and tottering to its fall in a retired and desolate portion of the Faubourg St. Germain.

Had the routine of our life at this place been known to the world, we should have been regarded as madmen —although, perhaps, as madmen of a harmless nature. Our seclusion was perfect. We admitted no visitors. Indeed the locality of our retirement had been carefully kept a secret from my own former associates; and it had been many years since Dupin had ceased to know or be known in Paris. We existed within ourselves alone.

It was a freak of fancy in my friend (for what else shall I call it?) to be enamored of the Night for her own sake; and into this *bizarrerie*, as into all his others, I quietly fell; giving myself up to his wild whims with a perfect *abandon*. The sable divinity would not herself dwell with us always; but we could counterfeit her presence. At the first dawn of the morning we closed all the massy shutters of our old building; lighted a couple of tapers which, strongly perfumed, threw out only the ghastliest and feeblest of rays. By the aid of these we then busied our souls in dreams—reading, writing, or conversing, until warned by the clock of the advent of the true Darkness. Then we sallied forth into the streets, arm and arm, continuing the topics of the day, or roaming far and wide until a late hour, seeking, amid the wild lights and shadows of the populous city, that infinity of mental excitement which quiet observation can afford.

At such times I could not help remarking and admiring (although from his rich ideality I had been prepared to expect it) a peculiar analytic ability in Dupin. He seemed, too, to take an eager delight in this exercise—if not exactly in its display—and did not hesitate to confess the pleasure thus derived. He boasted to me, with a low chuckling laugh, that most men, in respect to himself, wore windows in their bosoms, and was wont to follow up such assertions by direct and very startling proofs of his intimate knowledge of my own. His manner at these moments was frigid and abstract; his eyes were vacant in expression; while his voice, usually a rich tenor, rose into a treble which would have sounded petulantly but for the deliberateness and entire distinctness of the enunciation. Observing him in these moods, I often dwelt meditatively upon the old philosophy of the Bi-Part Soul, and amused myself with the fancy of a double Dupin—the creative and the resolvent.

Let it not be supposed, from what I have just said, that I am detailing any mystery, or penning any romance. What I have described in the Frenchman was merely the result of an excited, or perhaps of a diseased, intelligence. But of the character of his remarks at the periods in question an example will best convey the idea.

We were strolling one night down a long dirty street, in the vicinity of the Palais Royal. Being both, apparently, occupied with thought, neither of us had spoken a syllable for fifteen minutes at least. All at once Dupin broke forth with these words:

"He is a very little fellow, that's true, and would do better for the *Théâtre des Variétés.*"

"There can be no doubt of that," I replied unwittingly, and not at first observing (so much had I been absorbed in reflection) the extraordinary manner in which the speaker had chimed in with my meditations. In an instant afterwards I recollected myself, and my astonishment was profound.

"Dupin," said I, gravely, "this is beyond my comprehension. I do not hesitate to say that I am amazed, and can scarcely credit my senses. How was it possible you should know I was thinking of ————?" Here I paused, to ascertain beyond a doubt whether he really knew of whom I thought.

———— "of Chantilly," said he, "why do you pause? You were remarking to yourself that his diminutive figure unfitted him for tragedy."

This was precisely what had formed the subject of my reflections. Chantilly was a *quondam* cobbler of the Rue St. Denis, who, becoming stage-mad, had attempted the *rôle* of Xerxes, in Crébillon's tragedy so called, and been notoriously Pasquinaded for his pains.

"Tell me, for Heaven's sake," I exclaimed, "the method—if method there is—by which you have been enabled to fathom my soul in this matter." In fact I was even more startled than I would have been willing to express.

"It was the fruiterer," replied my friend, "who brought you to the conclusion that the mender of soles was not of sufficient height for Xerxes *et id genus omne.*"

"The fruiterer!—you astonish me—I know no fruiterer whomsoever."

"The man who ran up against you as we entered the street—it may have been fifteen minutes ago."

I now remembered that, in fact, a fruiterer, carrying upon his head a large basket of apples, had nearly thrown me down, by accident, as we passed from the Rue C—— into the thoroughfare where we stood; but what this had to do with Chantilly I could not possibly understand.

There was not a particle of *charlatanerie* about Dupin. "I will explain," he said, "and that you may comprehend all clearly, we will first retrace the course of your meditations, from the moment in which I spoke to you until that of the *rencontre* with the fruiterer in question. The larger links of the chain run thus— Chantilly, Orion, Dr. Nichols, Epicurus, Stereotomy, the street stones, the fruiterer."

There are few persons who have not, at some period of their lives, amused themselves in retracing the steps by which particular conclusions of their own minds have been attained. The occupation is often full of interest; and he who attempts it for the first time is astonished by the apparently illimitable distance and incoherence between the starting-point and the goal. What, then, must have been my amazement when I heard the Frenchman speak what he had just spoken, and when I could not help acknowledging that he had spoken the truth. He continued:

"We had been talking of horses, if I remember aright, just before leaving the Rue C——. This was the last subject we discussed. As we crossed into this street, a fruiterer, with a large basket upon his head, brushing quickly past us, thrust you upon a pile of paving-stones collected at a spot where the causeway is undergoing repair. You stepped upon one of the loose fragments, slipped, slightly strained your ankle, appeared vexed or sulky, muttered a few words, turned to look at the pile, and then proceeded in silence. I was not particularly attentive to what you did; but observation has become with me, of late, a species of necessity.

"You kept your eyes upon the ground—glancing, with a petulant expression, at the holes and ruts in the pavement (so that I saw you were still thinking of the stones), until we reached the little alley called Lamartine, which has been paved, by way of experiment, with the overlapping and riveted blocks. Here your countenance brightened up, and, perceiving your lips move, I could not doubt that you murmured the word 'stereotomy,' a term very affectedly applied to this species of pavement. I knew that you could not say to yourself 'stereotomy' without being brought to think of atomies, and thus of the theories of Epicurus; and since, when we discussed this subject not very long ago, I mentioned to you how singularly, yet with how little notice, the vague guesses of that noble Greek had met with confirmation in the late nebular cosmogony, I felt that you could not avoid casting your eyes upwards to the great *nebula* in Orion, and I certainly expected that you would do so. You did look up; and I was now assured that I had correctly followed your steps. But in that bitter *tirade* upon Chantilly, which appeared in yesterday's '*Musée*,' the satirist, making some disgraceful allusions to the cobbler's change of name upon assuming the buskin, quoted a Latin line about which we have often conversed. I mean the line

Perdidit antiquum litera prima sonum

I had told you that this was in reference to Orion, formerly written Urion; and, from certain pungencies connected with this explanation, I was aware that you could not have forgotten it. It was clear, therefore, that you would not fail to combine the two ideas of Orion and Chantilly. That you did combine them I saw by the character of the smile which passed over your lips. You thought of the poor cobbler's immolation. So far, you had been stooping in your gait; but now I saw you draw yourself up to your full height. I was then sure that you reflected upon the diminutive figure of Chantilly. At this point I interrupted your meditations to remark that as, in fact, he *was* a very little fellow—that Chantilly—he would do better at the *Théâtre des Variétés*."

Not long after this, we were looking over an evening edition of the "Gazette des Tribunaux," when the following paragraphs arrested our attention.

"EXTRAORDINARY MURDERS.—This morning, about three o'clock, the inhabitants of the Quartier St. Roch were aroused from sleep by a succession of terrific shrieks, issuing, apparently, from the fourth story of a house in the Rue Morgue, known to be in the sole occupancy of one Madame L'Espanaye, and her daughter, Mademoiselle Camille L'Espanaye. After some delay, occasioned by a fruitless attempt to procure admission in the usual manner, the gateway was broken in with a crowbar, and eight or ten of the neighbors entered, accompanied by two *gendarmes*. By this time the cries had ceased; but, as the party rushed up the first flight of stairs, two or more rough voices, in angry contention, were distinguished, and seemed to proceed from the upper part of the house. As the second landing was reached, these sounds, also, had ceased, and everything remained perfectly quiet. The party spread themselves, and hurried from room to room. Upon arriving at a large back chamber in the fourth story (the door of which, being found locked, with the key inside, was forced open), a spectacle presented itself which struck every one present not less with horror than with astonishment.

"The apartment was in the wildest disorder—the furniture broken and thrown about in all directions. There was only one bedstead; and from this the bed had been removed, and thrown into the middle of the floor. On a chair lay a razor, besmeared with blood. On the hearth were two or three long and thick tresses of gray human hair, also dabbled in blood, and seeming to have been pulled out by the roots. Upon the floor were found four Napoleons, an earring of topaz, three large silver spoons, three smaller of *métal d'Alger*, and two bags, containing nearly four thousand francs in gold. The drawers of a *bureau*, which stood in one corner, were open, and had been, apparently, rifled, although many articles still remained in them. A small iron safe was discovered under the *bed* (not under the bedstead). It was open, with the key still in the door. It had no contents beyond a few old letters, and other papers of little consequence.

"Of Madame L'Espanaye no traces were here seen; but an unusual quantity of soot being observed in the fireplace, a search was made in the chimney, and (horrible to relate!) the corpse of the daughter, head downwards, was dragged therefrom; it having been thus forced up the narrow aperture for a considerable distance. The body was quite warm. Upon examining it, many excoriations were perceived, no doubt occasioned by the violence with which it had been thrust up and disengaged. Upon the face were many severe scratches, and, upon the throat, dark bruises, and deep indentations of finger-nails, as if the deceased had been throttled to death.

"After a thorough investigation of every portion of the house, without farther discovery, the party made its way into a small paved yard in the rear of the building, where lay the corpse of the old lady, with her throat so entirely cut that, upon an attempt to raise her, the head fell off. The body, as well as the head, was fearfully mutilated—the former so much so as scarcely to retain any semblance of humanity.

"To this horrible mystery there is not as yet, we believe, the slightest clue."

The next day's paper had these additional particulars.

"*The Tragedy in the Rue Morgue.* Many individuals have been examined in relation to this most extraordinary and frightful affair" (the word '*affaire*' has not yet, in France, that levity of import which it conveys with us), "but nothing whatever has transpired to throw light upon it. We give below all the material testimony elicited.

"*Pauline Dubourg*, laundress, deposes that she has known both the deceased for three years, having washed for them during that period. The old lady and her daughter seemed on good terms—very affectionate towards each other. They were excellent pay. Could not speak in regard to their mode or means of living. Believed that Madame L. told fortunes for a living. Was reputed to have money put by. Never met any persons in the house when she called for the clothes or took them home. Was sure that they had no servant in employ. There appeared to be no furniture in any part of the building except in the fourth story.

"*Pierre Moreau*, tobacconist, deposes that he has been in the habit of selling small quantities of tobacco and snuff to Madame L'Espanaye for nearly four years. Was born in the neighborhood, and has always resided there. The deceased and her daughter had occupied the house in which the corpses were found, for more than six years. It was formerly occupied by a jeweler, who under-let the upper rooms to various persons. The house was the property of Madame L. She became dissatisfied with the abuse of the premises by her tenant, and moved into them herself, refusing to let any portion. The old lady was childish. Witness had seen the daughter some five or six times during the six years. The two lived an exceedingly retired life—were reputed to have money. Had heard it said among the neighbors that Madame L. told fortunes—did not believe it. Had never seen any person enter the door except the old lady and her daughter, a porter once or twice, and a physician some eight or ten times.

"Many other persons, neighbors, gave evidence to the same effect. No one was spoken of as frequenting the house. It was not known whether there were any living connections of Madame L. and her daughter. The shutters of the front windows were seldom opened. Those in the rear were always closed, with the exception of the large back room, fourth story. The house was a good house—not very old.

"*Isidore Musèt, gendarme*, deposes that he was called to the house about three o'clock in the morning, and found some twenty or thirty persons at the gateway, endeavoring to gain admittance. Forced it open, at length, with a bayonet—not with a crowbar. Had but little difficulty in getting it open, on account of its being a double or folding gate, and bolted neither at bottom nor top. The shrieks were continued until the gate was forced—and then suddenly ceased. They seemed to be screams of some person (or persons) in great agony— were loud and drawn out, not short and quick. Witness led the way upstairs. Upon reaching the first landing, heard two voices in loud and angry contention—the one a gruff voice, the other much shriller—a very strange voice. Could distinguish some words of the former, which was that of a Frenchman. Was positive that it was not a woman's voice. Could distinguish the words '*sacré*' and '*diable.*' The shrill voice was that of a foreigner. Could not be sure whether it was the voice of a man or of a woman. Could not make out what was said, but believed the language to be Spanish. The state of the room and of the bodies was described by this witness as we described them yesterday.

"*Henri Duval,* a neighbor, and by trade a silversmith, deposes that he was one of the party who first entered the house. Corroborates the testimony of Musèt in general. As soon as they forced an entrance, they reclosed the door, to keep out the crowd, which collected very fast, notwithstanding the lateness of the hour. The shrill voice, the witness thinks, was that of an Italian. Was certain it was not French. Could not be sure that it was a man's voice. It might have been a woman's. Was not acquainted with the Italian language. Could not distinguish the words, but was convinced by the intonation that the speaker was an Italian. Knew Madame L. and her daughter. Had conversed with both frequently. Was sure that the shrill voice was not that of either of the deceased.

"—— *Odenheimer restaurateur.* This witness volunteered his testimony. Not speaking French, was examined through an interpreter. Is a native of Amsterdam. Was passing the house at the time of the shrieks. They lasted for several minutes—probably ten. They were long and loud—very awful and distressing. Was one of those who entered the building. Corroborated the previous evidence in every respect but one. Was sure that the shrill voice was that of a man—of a Frenchman. Could not distinguish the words uttered. They were loud and quick—unequal—spoken apparently in fear as well as in anger. The voice was harsh—not so much shrill as harsh. Could not call it a shrill voice. The gruff voice said repeatedly 'sacré,' 'diable' and once 'mon Dieu.'

"*Jules Mignaud*, banker, of the firm of Mignaud et Fils, Rue Deloraine. Is the elder Mignaud. Madame L'Espanaye had some property. Had opened an account with his banking house in the spring of the year —— (eight years previously). Made frequent deposits in small sums. Had checked for nothing until the third day before her death, when she took out in person the sum of 4000 francs. This sum was paid in gold, and a clerk sent home with the money.

"*Adolphe Le Bon*, clerk to Mignaud et Fils, deposes that on the day in question, about noon, he accompanied Madame L'Espanaye to her residence with the 4000 francs, put up in two bags. Upon the door being opened, Mademoiselle L. appeared and took from his hands one of the bags, while the old lady relieved him of the other. He then bowed and departed. Did not see any person in the street at the time. It is a bye-street—very lonely.

"*William Bird*, tailor, deposes that he was one of the party who entered the house. Is an Englishman. Has lived in Paris two years. Was one of the first to ascend the stairs. Heard the voices in contention. The gruff voice was that of a Frenchman. Could make out several words, but cannot now remember all. Heard distinctly 'sacré' and 'mon Dieu.' There was a sound at the moment as if of several persons struggling—a scraping and scuffling sound. The shrill voice was very loud—louder than the gruff one. Is sure that it was not the voice of an Englishman. Appeared to be that of a German. Might have been a woman's voice. Does not understand German.

"Four of the above-named witnesses, being recalled, deposed that the door of the chamber in which was found the body of Mademoiselle L. was locked on the inside when the party reached it. Everything was perfectly silent—no groans or noises of any kind. Upon forcing the door no person was seen. The windows, both of the back and front room, were down and firmly fastened from within. A door between the two rooms was closed, but not locked. The door leading from the front room into the passage was locked, with the key on the inside. A small room in the front of the house, on the fourth story, at the head of the passage, was open, the door being ajar. This room was crowded with old beds, boxes, and so forth. These were carefully removed and searched. There was not an inch of any portion of the house which was not carefully searched. Sweeps were sent up and down the chimneys. The house was a four-story one, with garrets (*mansardes*). A trap-door on the roof was nailed down very securely—did not appear to have been opened for years. The time elapsing between the hearing of the voices in contention and the breaking open of the room door, was variously stated by the witnesses. Some made it as short as three minutes—some as long as five. The door was opened with difficulty.

"*Alfonzo Garcio,* undertaker, deposes that he resides in the Rue Morgue. Is a native of Spain. Was one of the party who entered the house. Did not proceed upstairs. Is nervous, and was apprehensive of the consequences of agitation. Heard the voices in contention. The gruff voice was that of a Frenchman. Could not distinguish what was said. The shrill voice was that of an Englishman—is sure of this. Does not understand the English language, but judges by the intonation.

"*Alberto Montani,* confectioner, deposes that he was among the first to ascend the stairs. Heard the voices in question. The gruff voice was that of a Frenchman. Distinguished several words. The speaker appeared to be expostulating. Could not make out the words of the shrill voice. Spoke quick and unevenly. Thinks it the voice of a Russian. Corrobates the general testimony. Is an Italian. Never conversed with a native of Russia.

"Several witnesses, recalled, here testified that the chimneys of all the rooms on the fourth story were too narrow to admit the passage of a human being. By 'sweeps' were meant cylindrical sweeping-brushes, such as are employed by those who clean chimneys. These brushes were passed up and down every flue in the house. There is no back passage by which any one could have descended while the party proceeded up stairs. The body of Mademoiselle L'Espanaye was so firmly wedged in the chimney that it could not be got down until four or five of the party united their strength.

"*Paul Dumas,* physician, deposes that he was called to view the bodies about daybreak. They were both then lying on the sacking of the bedstead in the chamber where Mademoiselle L. was found. The corpse of the young lady was much bruised and excoriated. The fact that it had been thrust up the chimney would sufficiently account for these appearances. The throat was greatly chafed. There were several deep scratches just below the chin, together with a series of livid spots which were evidently the impression of fingers. The face was fearfully discolored, and the eyeballs protruded. The tongue had been partially bitten through. A large bruise was discovered upon the pit of the stomach, produced, apparently, by the pressure of a knee. In the opinion of M. Dumas, Mademoiselle L'Espanaye had been throttled to death by some person or persons unknown. The corpse of the mother was horribly mutilated. All the bones of the right leg and arm were more or less shattered. The left *tibia* much splintered, as well as all the ribs of the left side. Whole body dreadfully

bruised and discolored. It was not possible to say how
the injuries had been inflicted. A heavy club of wood,
or a broad bar of iron—a chair—any large, heavy, and
obtuse weapon would have produced such results, if
wielded by the hands of a very powerful man. No
woman could have inflicted the blows with any weapon.
The head of the deceased, when seen by witness, was
entirely separated from the body, and was also greatly
shattered. The throat had evidently been cut with
some very sharp instrument—probably with a razor.

"*Alexandre Etienne*, surgeon, was called with M.
Dumas to view the bodies. Corroborated the testimony,
and the opinions of Mr. Dumas.

"Nothing farther of importance was elicited, although
several other persons were examined. A murder so mysterious, and so perplexing in all its particulars, was
never before committed in Paris—if indeed a murder
has been committed at all. The police are entirely at
fault—an unusual occurrence in affairs of this nature.
There is not, however, the shadow of a clue apparent."

The evening edition of the paper stated that the
greatest excitement still continued in the Quartier St.
Roch—that the premises in question had been carefully
re-searched, and fresh examinations of witnesses instituted, but all to no purpose. A postscript, however, mentioned that Adolphe Le Bon had been arrested and imprisoned—although nothing appeared to criminate him,
beyond the facts already detailed.

Dupin seemed singularly interested in the progress
of this affair—at least so I judged from his manner, for
he made no comments. It was only after the announcement that Le Bon had been imprisoned, that he asked
me my opinion respecting the murders.

I could merely agree with all Paris in considering

them an insoluble mystery. I saw no means by which it would be possible to trace the murderer.

"We must not judge of the means," said Dupin, "by this shell of an examination. The Parisian police, so much extolled for *acumen*, are cunning, but no more. There is no method in their proceedings, beyond the method of the moment. They make a vast parade of measures; but, not unfrequently, these are so ill adapted to the objects proposed, as to put us in mind of Monsieur Jourdain's calling for his *robe-de-chambre—pour mieux entendre la musique.* The results attained by them are not unfrequently surprising, but, for the most part, are brought about by simple diligence and activity. When these qualities are unavailing, their schemes fail. Vidocq, for example, was a good guesser, and a persevering man. But, without educated thought, he erred continually by the very intensity of his investigations. He impaired his vision by holding the object too close. He might see, perhaps, one or two points with unusual clearness, but in so doing he, necessarily, lost sight of the matter as a whole. Thus there is such a thing as being too profound. Truth is not always in a well. In fact, as regards the more important knowledge, I do believe that she is invariably superficial. The depth lies in the valleys where we seek her, and not upon the mountain-tops where she is found. The modes and sources of this kind of error are well typified in the contemplation of the heavenly bodies. To look at a star by glances—to view it in a side-long way, by turning towards it the exterior portions of the *retina* (more susceptible of feeble impressions of light than the interior), is to behold the star distinctly—is to have the best appreciation of its luster—a luster which grows dim just in proportion as we turn our vision *fully* upon it. A greater number of rays actually fall upon the eye in the latter case, but, in the former, there is the more refined capacity for comprehension. By undue profundity we perplex and enfeeble thought; and it is possible to make even Venus herself vanish from the firmament by a scrutiny too sustained, too concentrated, or too direct.

"As for these murders, let us enter into some examinations for ourselves, before we make up an opinion respecting them. An inquiry will afford us amusement" (I thought this an odd term, so applied, but said nothing), "and, besides, Le Bon once rendered me a service for which I am not ungrateful. We will go and see the premises with our own eyes. I know G——, the Prefect of Police, and shall have no difficulty in obtaining the necessary permission."

The permission was obtained, and we proceeded at once to the Rue Morgue. This is one of those miserable thoroughfares, which intervene between the Rue Richelieu and the Rue St. Roch. It was late in the afternoon when we reached it; as this quarter is at a great distance from that in which we resided. The house was readily found; for there were still many persons gazing up at the closed shutters, with an objectless curiosity, from the opposite side of the way. It was an ordinary Parisian house, with a gateway, on one side of which was a glazed watch-box, with a sliding panel in the window, indicating a *loge de concierge*. Before going in we walked up the street, turned down an alley, and then, again turning, passed in the rear of the building— Dupin, meanwhile, examining the whole neighborhood, as well as the house, with a minuteness of attention for which I could see no possible object.

Retracing our steps, we came again to the front of the dwelling, rang, and, having shown our credentials, were admitted by the agents in charge. We went upstairs—into the chamber where the body of Mademoiselle L'Espanaye had been found, and where both the deceased still lay. The disorders of the room had, as usual, been suffered to exist. I saw nothing beyond what had been stated in the "Gazette des Tribunaux." Dupin scrutinized everything—not excepting the bodies of the victims. We then went into the other rooms, and into the yard: a *gendarme* accompanying us throughout. The examination occupied us until dark, when we took our departure. On our way home my companion stopped in for a moment at the office of the daily papers.

I have said that the whims of my friend were manifold, and that *Je les ménageais:*—for this phrase there is no English equivalent. It was his humor, now, to decline all conversation on the subject of the murder, until about noon the next day. He then asked me, suddenly, if I had observed anything *peculiar* at the scene of the atrocity.

There was something in his manner of emphasizing the word "peculiar," which caused me to shudder, without knowing why.

"No, nothing *peculiar*," I said; "nothing more, at least, than we both saw stated in the paper.

"The 'Gazette.'" he replied, "has not entered, I fear, into the unusual horror of the thing. But dismiss the idle opinions of this print. It appears to me that this mystery is considered insoluble, for the very reason which should cause it to be regarded as easy of solution—I mean for the *outré* character of its features. The police are confounded by the seeming absence of motive —not for the murder itself—but for the atrocity of the murder. They are puzzled, too, by the seeming impossibility of reconciling the voices heard in contention, with the facts that no one was discovered upstairs but the assassinated Mademoiselle L'Espanaye, and that

there were no means of egress without the notice of the
party ascending. The wild disorder of the room; the
corpse thrust, with the head downwards, up the chimney; the frightful mutilation of the body of the old
lady; these considerations, with those just mentioned,
and others which I need not mention, have sufficed to
paralyze the powers, by putting completely at fault
the boasted *acumen,* of the government agents. They
have fallen into the gross but common error of con-
founding the unusual with the abstruse. But it is by
these deviations from the plane of the ordinary, that
reason feels its way, if at all, in its search for the true.
In investigations such as we are now pursuing, it should
not be so much asked 'what has occurred,' as 'what has
occurred that has never occurred before.' In fact, the
facility with which I shall arrive, or have arrived, at the
solution of this mystery, is in the direct ratio of its apparent insolubility in the eyes of the police."

I stared at the speaker in mute astonishment.

"I am now awaiting," continued he, looking towards
the door of our apartment—"I am now awaiting a person who, although perhaps not the perpetrator of these
butcheries, must have been in some measure implicated
in their perpetration. Of the worst portion of the crimes
committed, it is probable that he is innocent. I hope
that I am right in this supposition; for upon it I build
my expectation of reading the entire riddle. I look for
the man here—in this room—every moment. It is true
that he may not arrive; but the probability is that he
will. Should he come, it will be necessary to detain
him. Here are pistols; and we both know how to use
them when occasion demands their use."

I took the pistols, scarcely knowing what I did, or
believing what I heard, while Dupin went on, very
much as if in a soliloquy. I have already spoken of his

abstract manner at such times. His discourse was addressed to myself; but his voice, although by no means loud, had that intonation which is commonly employed in speaking to some one at a great distance. His eyes, vacant in expression, regarded only the wall.

"That the voices heard in contention," he said, "by the party upon the stairs, were not the voices of the women themselves, was fully proved by the evidence. This relieves us of all doubt upon the question whether the old lady could have first destroyed the daughter, and afterward have committed suicide. I speak of this point chiefly for the sake of method; for the strength of Madame L'Espanaye would have been utterly unequal to the task of thrusting her daughter's corpse up the chimney as it was found; and the nature of the wounds upon her own person entirely preclude the idea of self-destruction. Murder, then, has been committed by some third party; and the voices of this third party were those heard in contention. Let me now advert— not to the whole testimony respecting these voices— but to what was *peculiar* in that testimony. Did you observe anything peculiar about it?"

I remarked that, while all the witnesses agreed in supposing the gruff voice to be that of a Frenchman, there was much disagreement in regard to the shrill, or, as one individual termed it, the harsh voice.

"That was the evidence itself," said Dupin, "but it was not the peculiarity of the evidence. You have observed nothing distinctive. Yet there *was* something to be observed. The witnesses, as you remark, agreed about the gruff voice; they were here unanimous. But in regard to the shrill voice, the peculiarity is—not that they disagreed—but that, while an Italian, an Englishman, a Spaniard, a Hollander, and a Frenchman attempted to describe it, each one spoke of it as that of *a foreigner*.

Each is sure that it was not the voice of one of his own countrymen. Each likens it—not to the voice of an individual of any nation with whose language he is conversant—but the converse. The Frenchman supposes it the voice of a Spaniard, and 'might have distinguished some words *had be been acquainted with the Spanish.*' The Dutchman maintains it to have been that of a Frenchman; but we find it stated that '*not understanding French this witness was examined through an interpreter.*' The Englishman thinks it the voice of a German, and '*does not understand German.*' The Spaniard 'is sure' that it was that of an Englishman, but 'judges by the intonation' altogether, '*as he has no knowledge of the English.*' The Italian believes it the voice of a Russian, but '*has never conversed with a native of Russia.*' A second Frenchman differs, moreover, with the first, and is positive that the voice was that of an Italian; but, *not being cognizant of that tongue,* is, like the Spaniard, 'convinced by the intonation.' Now, how strangely unusual must that voice have really been, about which such testimony as this *could* have been elicited!—in whose *tones,* even, denizens of the five great divisions of Europe could recognize nothing familiar! You will say that it might have been the voice of an Asiatic—of an African. Neither Asiatics nor Africans abound in Paris; but, without denying the inference, I will now merely call your attention to three points. The voice is termed by one witness 'harsh rather than shrill.' It is represented by two others to have been 'quick and *unequal.*' No words —no sounds resembling words—were by any witness mentioned as distinguishable.

"I know not," continued Dupin, "what impression I may have made, so far, upon your own understanding; but I do not hesitate to say that legitimate deductions even from this portion of the testimony—the portion respecting the gruff and shrill voices—are in themselves sufficient to engender a suspicion which should give direction to all farther progress in the investigation of the mystery. I said 'legitimate deductions'; but my meaning is not thus fully expressed. I designed to imply that the deductions are the *sole* proper ones, and that the suspicion arises *inevitably* from them as the single result. What the suspicion is, however, I will not say just yet. I merely wish you to bear in mind that, with myself, it was sufficiently forcible to give a definite form—a certain tendency—to my inquiries in the chamber.

"Let us now transport ourselves, in fancy, to this chamber. What shall we first seek here? The means of egress employed by the murderers. It is not too much to say that neither of us believe in præternatural events. Madame and Mademoiselle L'Espanaye were not destroyed by spirits. The doers of the deed were material, and escaped materially. Then how? Fortunately, there is but one mode of reasoning upon the point, and that mode *must* lead us to a definite decision.—Let us examine, each by each, the possible means of egress. It is clear that the assassins were in the room where Mademoiselle L'Espanaye was found, or at least in the room adjoining, when the party ascended the stairs. It is then only from these two apartments that we have to seek issues. The police have laid bare the floors, the ceilings, and the masonry of the walls, in every direction. No *secret* issues could have escaped their vigilance. But not trusting to *their* eyes, I examined with my own. There were, then, *no* secret issues. Both doors leading from the rooms into the passage were securely locked, with the keys inside. Let us turn to the chimneys. These, although of ordinary width for some eight or ten feet above the hearths, will not admit, throughout their extent, the body of a large cat. The impossibility of egress, by means already stated, being thus absolute, we are reduced to the windows. Through those of the front room no one could have escaped without notice from the crowd in the street. The murderers *must* have passed, then, through those of the back room. Now, brought to this conclusion in so unequivocal a manner as we are, it is not our part, as reasoners, to reject it on account of apparent impossibilities. It is only left for us to prove that these apparent 'impossibilities' are, in reality, not such.

"There are two windows in the chamber. One of them is unobstructed by furniture, and is wholly visible. The lower portion of the other is hidden from view by the head of the unwieldy bedstead which is thrust close up against it. The former was found securely fastened from within. It resisted the utmost force of those who endeavored to raise it. A large gimlet-hole had been pierced in its frame to the left, and a very stout nail was found fitted therein, nearly to the head. Upon examining the other window, a similar nail was seen similarly fitted in it; and a vigorous attempt to raise this sash, failed also. The police were now entirely satisfied that egress had not been in these directions. And, *therefore*, it was thought a matter of supererogation to withdraw the nails and open the windows.

"My own examination was somewhat more particular, and was so for the reason I have just given—because here it was, I knew, that all apparent impossibilities *must* be proved to be not such in reality.

"I proceeded to think thus—*à posteriori*. The murderers *did* escape from one of these windows. This being so, they could not have refastened the sashes from the inside, as they were found fastened;—the consideration which put a stop, through its obviousness, to the scrutiny of the police in this quarter. Yet the sashes *were* fastened. They *must*, then, have the power of fastening themselves. There was no escape from this conclusion. I stepped to the unobstructed casement, withdrew the nail with some difficulty, and attempted to raise the sash. It resisted all my efforts, as I had anticipated. A concealed spring must, I now knew, exist; and this corroboration of my idea convinced me that my premises, at least, were correct, however mysterious still appeared the circumstances attending the nails. A careful search soon brought to light the hidden spring. I pressed it, and, satisfied with the discovery, forbore to upraise the sash.

"I now replaced the nail and regarded it attentively. A person passing out through this window might have reclosed it, and the spring would have caught—but the nail could not have been replaced. The conclusion was plain, and again narrowed in the field of my investigations. The assassins *must* have escaped through the other window. Supposing, then, the springs upon each sash to be the same, as was probable, there *must* be found a difference between the nails, or at least between the modes of their fixture. Getting upon the sacking of the bedstead, I looked over the head-board minutely at the second casement. Passing my hand down behind the board, I readily discovered and pressed the spring, which was, as I had supposed, identical in character with its neighbor. I now looked at the nail. It was as stout as the other, and apparently fitted in the same manner—driven in nearly up to the head.

"You will say that I was puzzled; but, if you think so, you must have misunderstood the nature of the inductions. To use a sporting phrase, I had not been once 'at fault.' The scent had never for an instant been lost.

There was no flaw in any link of the chain. I had traced the secret to its ultimate result,—and that result was *the nail*. It had, I say, in every respect, the appearance of its fellow in the other window; but this fact was an absolute nullity (conclusive as it might seem to be) when compared with the consideration that here, at this point, terminated the clue. 'There *must* be something wrong,' I said, 'about the nail.' I touched it; and the head, with about a quarter of an inch of the shank, came off in my fingers. The rest of the shank was in the gimlet-hole, where it had been broken off. The fracture was an old one (for its edges were incrusted with rust), and had apparently been accomplished by the blow of a hammer, which had partially imbedded, in the top of the bottom sash, the head portion of the nail. I now carefully replaced this head portion in the indentation whence I had taken it, and the resemblance to a perfect nail was complete—the fissure was invisible. Pressing the spring, I gently raised the sash for a few inches; the head went up with it, remaining firm in its bed. I closed the window, and the semblance of the whole nail was again perfect.

"The riddle, so far, was now unriddled. The assassin had escaped through the window which looked upon the bed. Dropping of its own accord upon his exit (or perhaps purposely closed), it had become fastened by the spring; and it was the retention of this spring which had been mistaken by the police for that of the nail,—farther inquiry being thus considered unnecessary.

"The next question is that of the mode of descent. Upon this point I had been satisfied in my walk with you around the building. About five feet and a half from the casement in question there runs a lightning-rod. From this rod it would have been impossible for any one to reach the window itself, to say nothing of entering it. I observed, however, that the shutters of the fourth story were of the peculiar kind called by Parisian carpenters *ferrades*—a kind rarely employed at the present day, but frequently seen upon very old mansions at Lyons and Bordeaux. They are in the form of an ordinary door (a single, not a folding door), except that the upper half is latticed or worked in open trellis—thus affording an excellent hold for the hands. In the present instance these shutters were fully three feet and a half broad. When we saw them from the rear of the house, they were both about half open—that is to say, they stood off at right angles from the wall. It is probable that the police, as well as myself, examined the back of the tenement; but, if so, in looking at these *ferrades* in the line of their breadth (as they must have done), they did not perceive this great breadth itself, or, at all events, failed to take it into due consideration. In fact, having once satisfied themselves that no egress could have been made in this quarter, they would naturally bestow here a very cursory examination. It was clear to me, however, that the shutter belonging to the window at the head of the bed, would, if swung fully back to the wall, reach to within two feet of the lightning-rod. It was also evident that, by exertion of a very unusual degree of activity and courage, an entrance into the window, from the rod, might have been thus effected.—By reaching to the distance of two feet and a half (we now suppose the shutter open to its whole extent) a robber might have taken a firm grasp upon the trellis-work. Letting go, then, his hold upon the rod, placing his feet securely against the wall, and springing boldly from it, he might have swung the shutter so as to close it, and, if we imagine the window open at the time, might even have swung himself into the room.

"I wish you to bear especially in mind that I have spoken of a *very* unusual degree of activity as requisite to success in so hazardous and so difficult a feat. It is my design to show you, first, that the thing might possibly have been accomplished:—but, secondly and *chiefly*, I wish to impress upon your understanding the *very extraordinary*—the almost præternatural character of that agility which could have accomplished it.

"You will say, no doubt, using the language of the law, that 'to make out my case' I should rather undervalue, than insist upon a full estimation of the activity required in this matter. This may be the practice in law, but it is not the usage of reason. My ultimate object is only the truth. My immediate purpose is to lead you to place in juxtaposition that *very unusual* activity of which I have just spoken, with that *very peculiar* shrill (or harsh) and *unequal* voice, about whose nationality no two persons could be found to agree, and in whose utterance no syllabification could be detected."

At these words a vague and half-formed conception of the meaning of Dupin flitted over my mind. I seemed to be upon the verge of comprehension, without power to comprehend—as men, at times, find themselves upon the brink of rememberance, without being able, in the end, to remember. My friend went on with his discourse.

"You will see," he said, "that I have shifted the question from the mode of egress to that of ingress. It was my design to suggest that both were effected in the same manner, at the same point. Let us now revert to the interior of the room. Let us survey the appearances here. The drawers of the bureau, it is said, had been rifled, although many articles of apparel still remained within them. The conclusion here is absurd. It is a mere guess—a very silly one—and no more. How are we to know that the articles found in the drawers were not all these drawers had originally contained? Madame L'Espanaye and her daughter lived an exceedingly retired life—saw no company—seldom went out— had little use for numerous changes of habiliment. Those found were at least of as good quality as any likely to be possessed by these ladies. If a thief had taken any, why did he not take the best—why did he not take all? In a word, why did he abandon four thousand francs in gold to encumber himself with a bundle of linen? The gold *was* abandoned. Nearly the whole sum mentioned by Monsieur Mignaud, the banker, was discovered, in bags, upon the floor. I wish you, therefore, to discard from your thoughts the blundering idea of *motive*, engendered in the brains of the police by that portion of the evidence which speaks of money delivered at the door of the house. Coincidences ten times as remarkable as this (the delivery of the money, and murder committed within three days upon the party receiving it), happen to all of us every hour of our lives, without attracting even momentary notice. Coincidences, in general, are great stumbling-blocks in the way of that class of thinkers who have been educated to know nothing of the theory of probabilities—that theory to which the most glorious objects of human research are indebted for the most glorious of illustration. In the present instance, had the gold been gone, the fact of its delivery three days before would have formed something more than a coincidence. But, under the real circumstances of the case, if we are to suppose gold the motive of this outrage, we must also imagine the perpetrator so vacillating an idiot as to have abandoned his gold and his motive together.

"Keeping now steadily in mind the points to which I have drawn your attention—that peculiar voice, that unusual agility, and that startling absence of motive in a murder so singularly atrocious as this—let us glance at the butchery itself. Here is a woman strangled to death by manual strength, and thrust up a chimney, head downwards. Ordinary assassins employ no such modes of murder as this. Least of all, do they thus dispose of the murdered. In the manner of thrusting the corpse up the chimney, you will admit that there was something *excessively outré*—something altogether irreconcilable with our common notions of human action, even when we suppose the actors the most depraved of men. Think, too, how great must have been that strength which could have thrust the body *up* such an aperture so forcibly that the united vigor of several persons was found barely sufficient to drag it *down!*

"Turn, now, to other indications of the employment of a vigor most marvelous. On the hearth were thick tresses—very thick tresses—of gray human hair. These had been torn out by the roots. You are aware of the great force necessary in tearing thus from the head even twenty or thirty hairs together. You saw the locks in question as well as myself. Their roots (a hideous sight!) were clotted with fragments of the flesh of the scalp—sure token of the prodigious power which had been exerted in uprooting perhaps half a million of hairs at a time. The throat of the old lady was not merely cut, but the head absolutely severed from the body: the instrument was a mere razor. I wish you also to look at the *brutal* ferocity of these deeds. Of the bruises upon the body of Madame L'Espanaye I do not speak. Monsieur Dumas, and his worthy coadjutor Monsieur Etienne, have pronounced that they were inflicted by some obtuse instrument; and so far these gentlemen are very correct. The obtuse instrument was clearly the stone pavement in the yard, upon which the victim had fallen from the window which looked in upon the bed. This idea, however simple it may now seem, escaped the police for the same reason that the breadth of the shutters escaped them—because, by the affair of the nails, their perceptions had been hermetically sealed against the possibility of the windows having ever been opened at all.

"If now, in addition to all these things, you have properly reflected upon the odd disorder of the chamber, we have gone so far as to combine the ideas of an agility astounding, a strength superhuman, a ferocity brutal, a butchery without motive, a *grotesquerie* in horror absolutely alien from humanity, and a voice foreign in tone to the ears of men of many nations, and devoid of all distinct or intelligible syllabification. What result, then, has ensued? What impression have I made upon your fancy?"

I felt a creeping of the flesh as Dupin asked me the question. "A madman," I said, "has done this deed— some raving maniac, escaped from a neighboring *Maison de Santé.*"

"In some respects," he replied, "your idea is not irrelevant. But the voices of madmen, even in their wildest paroxysms, are never found to tally with that peculiar voice heard upon the stairs. Madmen are of some nation, and their language, however incoherent in its words, has always the coherence of syllabification. Besides, the hair of a madman is not such as I now hold in my hand. I disentangled this little tuft from the rigidly clutched fingers of Madame L'Espanaye. Tell me what you can make of it."

"Dupin!" I said completely unnerved; "this hair is most unusual—this is no *human* hair."

"I have not asserted that it is," said he; "but, before we decide this point, I wish you to glance at the little sketch I have here traced upon this paper. It is a *facsimile* drawing of what has been described in one portion of the testimony as 'dark bruises, and deep indentations of fingernails,' upon the throat of Mademoiselle L'Espanaye, and in another (by Messrs. Dumas and Etienne), as a 'series of livid spots, evidently the impression of fingers.'

"You will perceive," continued my friend, spreading out the paper upon the table before us, "that this drawing gives the idea of a firm and fixed hold. There is no *slipping* apparent. Each finger has retained— possibly until the death of the victim—the fearful grasp by which it originally imbedded itself. Attempt, now, to place all your fingers, at the same time, in the respective impressions as you see them."

I made the attempt in vain.

"We are possibly not giving this matter a fair trial," he said. "The paper is spread out upon a plane surface; but the human throat is cylindrical. Here is a billet of wood, the circumference of which is about that of the throat. Wrap the drawing around it, and try the experiment again."

I did so; but the difficulty was even more obvious than before.

"This," I said, "is the mark of no human hand."

"Read now," replied Dupin, "this passage from Cuvier."

It was a minute anatomical and generally descriptive

account of the large fulvous Orang-Outang of the East
Indian Islands. The gigantic stature, the prodigious
strength and activity, the wild ferocity, and the imita-
tive propensities of these mammalia are sufficiently well
known to all. I understood the full horrors of the murder at once.

"The description of the digits," said I, as I made
an end of reading, "is in exact accordance with this
drawing. I see that no animal but an Orang-Outang, of
the species here mentioned, could have impressed the
indentations as you have traced them. This tuft of
tawny hair, too, is identical in character with that of
the beast of Cuvier. But I cannot possibly comprehend
the particulars of this frightful mystery. Besides, there
were *two* voices heard in contention, and one of them
was unquestionably the voice of a Frenchman."

"True; and you will remember an expression attributed almost unanimously, by the evidence, to this
voice,—the expression, '*mon Dieu!*' This, under the
circumstances, has been justly characterized by one of
the witnesses (Montani, the confectioner), as an expression of remonstrance or expostulation. Upon these
two words, therefore, I have mainly built my hopes of
a full solution of the riddle. A Frenchman was cognizant of the murder. It is possible—indeed it is far more
than probable—that he was innocent of all participa-
tion in the bloody transactions which took place. The
Orang-Outang may have escaped from him. He may
have traced it to the chamber; but, under the agitating
circumstances which ensued, he could never have re-
captured it. It is still at large. I will not pursue these
guesses—for I have no right to call them more—since
the shades of reflection upon which they are based are
scarcely of sufficient depth to be appreciable by my
own intellect, and since I could not pretend to make

them intelligible to the understanding of another. We will call them guesses then, and speak of them as such. If the Frenchman in question is indeed, as I suppose, innocent of this atrocity, this advertisement, which I left last night, upon our return home, at the office of 'Le Monde' (a paper devoted to the shipping interest, and much sought by sailors), will bring him to our residence."

He handed me a paper, and I read thus:

CAUGHT—*In the Bois de Boulogne, early in the morning of the — inst.* (the morning of the murder), *a very large, tawny Orang-Outang of the Bornese species. The owner* (who is ascertained to be a sailor, belonging to a Maltese vessel), *may have the animal again, upon identifying it satisfactorily, and paying a few charges arising from its capture and keeping. Call at No. —, Rue—, Faubourg St. Germain — au troisième.*

"How was it possible," I asked, "that you should know the man to be a sailor, and belonging to a Maltese vessel?"

"I do *not* know it," said Dupin. "I am not *sure* of it. Here, however, is a small piece of ribbon, which from its form, and from its greasy appearance, has evidently been used in tying the hair in one of those long *queues* of which sailors are so fond. Moreover, this knot is one which few besides sailors can tie, and is peculiar to the Maltese. I picked the ribbon up at the foot of the lightning-rod. It could not have belonged to either of the deceased. Now if, after all, I am wrong in my induction from this ribbon, that the Frenchman was a sailor belonging to a Maltese vessel, still I can have done no harm in saying what I did in the advertisement. If I am in error, he will merely suppose that I have been misled by some circumstance into which he will not take the trouble to inquire. But if I am right, a great point is gained. Cognizant although innocent of the murder, the Frenchman will naturally hesitate about replying to the advertisement—about demanding the Orang-Outang. He will reason thus:—'I am innocent; I am poor; my Orang-Outang is of great value—to one in my circumstances a fortune of itself—why should I lose it through idle apprehensions of danger? Here it is, within my grasp. It was found in the Bois de Boulogne—at a vast distance from the scene of that butchery. How can it ever be suspected that a brute beast should have done the deed? The police are at fault—they have failed to procure the slightest clue. Should they even trace the animal, it would be impossible to prove me cognizant of the murder, or to implicate me in guilt on account of that cognizance. Above all, *I am known.* The advertiser designates me as the possessor of the beast. I am not sure to what limit his knowledge may extend. Should I avoid claiming a property of so great value, which it is known that I possess, I will render the animal, at least, liable to suspicion. It is not my policy to attract attention either to myself or to the beast. I will answer the advertisement, get the Orang-Outang, and keep it close until this matter has blown over.'"

At this moment we heard a step upon the stairs.

"Be ready," said Dupin, "with your pistols, but neither use them nor show them until at a signal from myself."

The front door of the house had been left open, and the visitor had entered, without ringing, and advanced several steps upon the staircase. Now, however, he seemed to hesitate. Presently we heard him descending. Dupin was moving quickly to the door, when we again heard him coming up. He did not turn back a second time, but stepped up with decision and rapped at the door of our chamber.

"Come in," said Dupin, in a cheerful and hearty tone.

A man entered. He was a sailor, evidently,—a tall, stout, and muscular-looking person, with a certain daredevil expression of countenance, not altogether unprepossessing. His face, greatly sunburnt, was more than half hidden by whisker and *mustachio*. He had with him a huge oaken cudgel, but appeared to be otherwise unarmed. He bowed awkwardly, and bade us "good evening," in French accents, which, although somewhat Neufchatelish, were still sufficiently indicative of a Parisian origin.

"Sit down, my friend," said Dupin. "I suppose you have called about the Orang-Outang. Upon my word, I almost envy you the possession of him; a remarkably fine, and no doubt a very valuable animal. How old do you suppose him to be?"

The sailor drew a long breath, with the air of a man relieved of some intolerable burthen, and then replied, in an assured tone:

"I have no way of telling—but he can't be more than four or five years old. Have you got him here?"

"Oh no; we had no conveniences for keeping him here. He is at a livery stable in the Rue Dubourg, just by. You can get him in the morning. Of course you are prepared to identify the property?"

"To be sure I am, sir."

"I shall be sorry to part with him," said Dupin.

"I don't mean that you should be at all this trouble for nothing, sir," said the man. "Couldn't expect it. Am very willing to pay a reward for the finding of the animal—that is to say, anything in reason."

"Well," replied my friend, "that is all very fair, to be

sure. Let me think!—what should I have? Oh! I will tell you. My reward shall be this. You shall give me all the information in your power about these murders in the Rue Morgue."

Dupin said the last words in a very low tone, and very quietly. Just as quietly, too, he walked towards the door, locked it, and put the key in his pocket. He then drew a pistol from his bosom and placed it, without the least flurry, upon the table.

The sailor's face flushed up as if he were struggling with suffocation. He started to his feet and grasped his cudgel; but the next moment he fell back into his seat, trembling violently, and with the countenance of death itself. He spoke not a word. I pitied him from the bottom of my heart.

"My friend," said Dupin, in a kind tone, "you are alarming yourself unnecessarily—you are indeed. We mean you no harm whatever. I pledge you the honor of a gentleman, and of a Frenchman, that we intend you no injury. I perfectly well know that you are innocent of the atrocities in the Rue Morgue. It will not do, however, to deny that you are in some measure implicated in them. From what I have already said, you must know that I have had means of information about this matter —means of which you could never have dreamed. Now the thing stands thus. You have done nothing which you could have avoided—nothing, certainly, which renders you culpable. You were not even guilty of robbery, when you might have robbed with impunity. You have nothing to conceal. You have no reason for concealment. On the other hand, you are bound by every principle of honor to confess all you know. An innocent man is now imprisoned, charged with that crime of which you can point out the perpetrator."

The sailor had recovered his presence of mind, in a great measure, while Dupin uttered these words; but his original boldness of bearing was all gone.

"So help me God," said he, after a brief pause, "I *will* tell you all I know about this affair;—but I do not expect you to believe one half I say—I would be a fool indeed if I did. Still, I *am* innocent, and I will make a clean breast if I die for it."

What he stated was, in substance, this. He had lately made a voyage to the Indian Archipelago. A party, of which he formed one, landed at Borneo, and passed into the interior on an excursion of pleasure. Himself and a companion had captured the Orang-Outang. This companion dying, the animal fell into his own exclusive possession. After great trouble, occasioned by the intractable ferocity of his captive during the home voyage, he at length succeeded in lodging it safely at his own residence in Paris, where, not to attract towards himself the unpleasant curiosity of his neighbors, he kept it carefully secluded, until such time as it should recover from a wound in the foot, received from a splinter on board ship. His ultimate design was to sell it.

Returning home from some sailors' frolic on the night, or rather in the morning of the murder, he found the beast occupying his own bedroom, into which it had broken from a closet adjoining, where it had been, as was thought, securely confined. Razor in hand, and fully lathered, it was sitting before a looking-glass, attempting the operation of shaving, in which it had no doubt previously watched its master through the keyhole of the closet. Terrified at the sight of so dangerous a weapon in the possession of an animal so ferocious, and so well able to use it, the man, for some moments, was at a loss what to do. He had been accustomed, however, to quiet the creature, even in its fiercest moods, by the use of a whip, and to this he now resorted. Upon sight of it, the Orang-Outang sprang at once through the door of the chamber, down the stairs, and thence, through a window, unfortunately open, into the street.

The Frenchman followed in despair; the ape, razor still in hand, occasionally stopping to look back and gesticulate at its pursuer, until the latter had nearly come up with it. It then again made off. In this manner the chase continued for a long time. The streets were profoundly quiet, as it was nearly three o'clock in the morning. In passing down an alley in the rear of the Rue Morgue, the fugitive's attention was arrested by a light gleaming from the open window of Madame L'Espanaye's chamber, in the fourth story of her house. Rushing to the building, it perceived the lightning-rod, clambered up with inconceivable agility, grasped the shutter, which was thrown fully back against the wall, and, by its means, swung itself directly upon the head-board of the bed. The whole feat did not occupy a minute. The shutter was kicked open again by the Orang-Outang as it entered the room.

The sailor, in the meantime, was both rejoiced and perplexed. He had strong hopes of now recapturing the brute, as it could scarcely escape from the trap into which it had ventured, except by the rod, where it might be intercepted as it came down. On the other hand, there was much cause for anxiety as to what it might do in the house. This latter reflection urged the man still to follow the fugitive. A lightning-rod is ascended without difficulty, especially by a sailor; but, when he had arrived as high as the window, which lay far to his left, his career was stopped; the most that he could accomplish was to reach over so as to obtain a glimpse of the interior of the room. At this glimpse he nearly fell from his hold through excess of horror. Now it was that those hideous shrieks arose upon the night, which had startled from slumber the inmates of the Rue Morgue. Madame L'Espanaye and her daughter, habited in their night clothes, had apparently been arranging some papers in the iron chest already mentioned, which had been wheeled into the middle of the room. It was open, and its contents lay beside it on the floor. The victims must have been sitting with their backs toward the window; and, from the time elapsing between the ingress of the beast and the screams, it seems probable that it was not immediately perceived. The flapping-to of the shutter would naturally have been attributed to the wind.

As the sailor looked in, the gigantic animal had seized Madame L'Espanaye by the hair (which was loose, as she had been combing it), and was flourishing the razor about her face, in imitation of the motions of a barber. The daughter lay prostrate and motionless; she had swooned. The screams and struggles of the old lady (during which the hair was torn from her head) had the effect of changing the probably pacific purposes of the Orang-Outang into those of wrath. With one determined sweep of its muscular arm it nearly severed her head from her body. The sight of blood inflamed its anger into frenzy. Gnashing its teeth, and flashing fire from its eyes, it flew upon the body of the girl, and imbedded its fearful talons in her throat, retaining its grasp until she expired. Its wandering and wild glances fell at this moment upon the head of the bed, over which the face of its master, rigid with horror, was just discernible. The fury of the beast, who no doubt bore still in mind the dreaded whip, was instantly converted into fear. Conscious of having deserved punishment, it seemed desirous of concealing its bloody deeds, and skipped about the chamber in an agony of nervous agitation; throwing down and breaking the furniture as it moved, and dragging the bed from the bedstead. In conclusion, it seized first the corpse of the daughter, and thrust it up the chimney, as it was found; then that of the old lady, which it immediately hurled through the window headlong.

As the ape approached the casement with its mutilated burthen, the sailor shrank aghast to the rod, and, rather gliding than clambering down it, hurried at once home—dreading the consequences of the butchery, and gladly abandoning, in his terror, all solicitude about the fate of the Orang-Outang. The words heard by the party upon the staircase were the Frenchman's exclamations of horror and affright, co-mingled with the fiendish jabberings of the brute.

I have scarcely anything to add. The Orang-Outang must have escaped from the chamber, by the rod, just before the breaking of the door. It must have closed the window as it passed through it. It was subsequently caught by the owner himself, who obtained for it a very large sum at the *Jardin des Plantes*. Le Bon was instantly released, upon our narration of the circumstances (with some comments from Dupin) at the *bureau* of the Prefect of Police. This functionary, however well disposed to my friend, could not altogether conceal his chagrin at the turn which affairs had taken, and was fain to indulge in a sarcasm or two, about the propriety of every person minding his own business.

"Let them talk," said Dupin, who had not thought it necessary to reply. "Let him discourse; it will ease his conscience. I am satisfied with having defeated him in his own castle. Nevertheless, that he failed in the solution of this mystery, is by no means that matter for wonder which he supposes it; for, in truth, our friend the Prefect is somewhat too cunning to be profound. In

his wisdom is no *stamen*. It is all head and no body,
like the pictures of the Goddess Laverna,—or, at best,
all head and shoulders, like a codfish. But he is a good
creature after all. I like him especially for one master
stroke of cant, by which he has attained his reputation
for ingenuity. I mean the way he has *'de nier ce qui est,
et d'expliquer ce qui n'est pas.'"*

MISSIONARY JOURNEYS

FROM *Death Comes for the Archbishop*

BY *WILLA CATHER*

I

The White Mules

IN mid-March, Father Vaillant was on the road, returning from a missionary journey to Albuquerque. He was to stop at the *rancho* of a rich Mexican, Manuel Lujon, to marry his men and maid servants who were living in concubinage, and to baptize the children. There he would spend the night. To-morrow or the day after he would go on to Santa Fé, halting by the way at the Indian pueblo of Santo Domingo to hold service. There was a fine old mission church at Santo Domingo, but the Indians were of a haughty and suspicious disposition. He had said Mass there on his way to Albuquerque, nearly a week ago. By dint of canvassing from house to house, and offering medals and religious colour prints to all who came to church, he had got together a considerable congregation. It was a large and prosperous pueblo, set among clean sand-hills, with its rich irrigated farm-lands lying just below, in the valley of the Rio Grande. His congregation was quiet, dignified, attentive. They sat on the earth floor, wrapped in their best blankets, repose in every line of their strong, stubborn backs. He harangued them in such Spanish as he could command, and they listened with respect. But bring their children to be baptized, they would not. The Spaniards

93

had treated them very badly long ago, and they had been meditating upon their grievance for many generations. Father Vaillant had not baptized one infant there, but he meant to stop to-morrow and try again. Then back to his Bishop, provided he could get his horse up La Bajada Hill.

He had bought his horse from a Yankee trader and had been woefully deceived. One week's journey of from twenty to thirty miles a day had shown the beast up for a wind-broken wreck. Father Vaillant's mind was full of material cares as he approached Manuel Lujon's place beyond Bernalillo. The *rancho* was like a little town, with all its stables, corrals, and stake fences. The *casa grande* was long and low, with glass windows and bright blue doors, a *portale* running its full length, supported by blue posts. Under this *portale* the adobe wall was hung with bridles, saddles, great boots and spurs, guns and saddle-blankets, strings of red peppers, foxskins, and the skins of two great rattlesnakes.

When Father Vaillant rode in through the gateway, children came running from every direction, some with no clothing but a little shirt, and women with no shawls over their black hair came running after the children. They all disappeared when Manuel Lujon walked out of the great house, hat in hand, smiling and hospitable. He was a man of thirty-five, settled in figure and somewhat full under the chin. He greeted the priest in the name of God and put out a hand to help him alight, but Father Vaillant sprang quickly to the ground.

'God be with you, Manuel, and with your house. But where are those who are to be married?'

'The men are all in the field, Padre. There is no hurry. A little wine, a little bread, coffee, repose—and then the ceremonies.'

'A little wine, very willingly, and bread, too. But not until afterward. I meant to catch you all at dinner, but I am two hours late because my horse is bad. Have someone bring in my saddle-bags, and I will put on my vestments. Send out to the fields for your men, Señor Lujon. A man can stop work to be married.'

The swarthy host was dazed by this dispatch. 'But one moment, Padre. There are all the children to baptize; why not begin with them, if I cannot persuade you to wash the dust from your sainted brow and repose a little.'

'Take me to a place where I can wash and change my clothes, and I will be ready before you can get them here. No, I tell you, Lujon, the marriages first, the baptisms afterward; that order is but Christian. I will baptize the children to-morrow morning, and their parents will at least have been married overnight.'

Father Joseph was conducted to his chamber, and the older boys were sent running off across the fields to fetch the men. Lujon and his two daughters began constructing an altar at one end of the *sala*. Two old women came to scrub the floor, and another brought chairs and stools.

'My God, but he is ugly, the Padre!' whispered one of these to the others. 'He must be very holy. And did you see the great wart he has on his chin? My grandmother could take that away for him if she were alive, poor soul! Somebody ought to tell him about the holy mud at Chimayo. That mud might dry it up. But there is nobody left now who can take warts away.'

'No, the times are not so good any more,' the other agreed. 'And I doubt if all this marrying will make them any better. Of what use is it to marry people after they have lived together and had children? and the man is maybe thinking about another woman, like Pablo. I saw him coming out of the brush with that oldest girl of Trinidad's, only Sunday night.'

The reappearance of the priest upon the scene cut short further scandal. He knelt down before the improvised altar and began his private devotions. The women tiptoed away. Señor Lujon himself went out toward the servants' quarters to hurry the candidates for the marriage sacrament. The women were giggling and snatching up their best shawls. Some of the men had even washed their hands. The household crowded into the *sala*, and Father Vaillant married couples with great dispatch.

'To-morrow morning, the baptisms,' he announced. 'And the mothers see to it that the children are clean, and that there are sponsors for all.'

After he had resumed his travelling-clothes, Father Joseph asked his host at what hour he dined, remarking that he had been fasting since an early breakfast.

'We eat when it is ready—a little after sunset, usually. I have had a young lamb killed for your Reverence.'

Father Joseph kindled with interest. 'Ah, and how will it be cooked?'

Señor Lujon shrugged. 'Cooked? Why, they put it in a pot with chili, and some onions, I suppose.'

'Ah, that is the point. I have had too much stewed mutton. Will you permit me to go into the kitchen and cook my portion in my own way?'

Lujon waved his hand. 'My house is yours, Padre. Into the kitchen I never go—too many women. But there it is, and the woman in charge is named Rosa.'

When the Father entered the kitchen, he found a crowd of women discussing the marriages. They quickly dispersed, leaving old Rosa by her fireplace, where hung a kettle from which issued the savour of cooking mutton fat, all too familiar to Father Joseph. He found a half sheep hanging outside the door, covered with a bloody sack, and asked Rosa to heat the oven for him, announcing that he meant to roast the hind leg.

'But, Padre, I baked before the marriages. The oven is almost cold. It will take an hour to heat it, and it is only two hours till supper.'

'Very well. I can cook my roast in an hour.'

'Cook a roast in an hour!' cried the old woman. 'Mother of God, Padre, the blood will not be dried in it!'

'Not if I can help it!' said Father Joseph fiercely. 'Now hurry with the fire, my good woman.'

When the Padre carved his roast at the supper-table, the serving-girls stood behind his chair and looked with horror at the delicate stream of pink juice that followed the knife. Manuel Lujon took a slice for politeness, but he did not eat it. Father Vaillant had his *gigot* to himself.

All the men and boys sat down at the long table with the host, the women and children would eat later. Father Joseph and Lujon, at one end, had a bottle of white Bordeaux between them. It had been brought from Mexico City on mule-back, Lujon said. They were discussing the road back to Santa Fé, and when the missionary remarked that he would stop at Santo Domingo, the host asked him why he did not get a horse there. 'I am afraid you will hardly get back to Santa Fé on your own. The pueblo is famous for breeding good horses. You might make a trade.'

'No,' said Father Vaillant. 'Those Indians are of a sullen disposition. If I were to have dealings with them, they would suspect my motives. If we are to save their souls, we must make it clear that we want no profit for ourselves, as I told Father Gallegos in Albuquerque.'

Manuel Lujon laughed and glanced down the table at his men, who were all showing their white teeth. 'You said that to the Padre at Albuquerque? You have courage. He is a rich man, Padre Gallegos. All the same, I respect him. I have played poker with him. He is a great gambler and takes his losses like a man. He stops at nothing, plays like an American.'

'And I,' retorted Father Joseph, 'I have not much respect for a priest who either plays cards or manages to get rich.'

'Then you do not play?' asked Lujon. 'I am disappointed. I had hoped we could have a game after supper. The evenings are dull enough here. You do not even play dominoes?'

'Ah, that is another matter!' Father Joseph declared. 'A game of dominoes, there by the fire, with coffee, or some of that excellent grape brandy you allowed me to taste, that I would find refreshing. And tell me, Manuelito, where do you get that brandy? It is like a French liqueur.'

'It is well seasoned. It was made at Bernalillo in my grandfather's time. They make it there still, but it is not so good now.'

The next morning, after coffee, while the children were being got ready for baptism, the host took Father Vaillant through his corrals and stables to show him his stock.

He exhibited with peculiar pride two cream-coloured mules, stalled side by side. With his own hand he led them out of the stable, in order to display to advantage their handsome coats, not bluish-white, as with white horses, but a rich, deep ivory, that in shadow changed to fawn-colour. Their tails were clipped at the ends into the shape of bells.

'Their names,' said Lujon, 'are Contenta and Angelica, and they are as good as their names. It seems that God has given them intelligence. When I talk to them, they look up at me like Christians; they are very companionable. They are always ridden together and have a great affection for each other.'

Father Joseph took one by the halter and led it about. 'Ah, but they are rare creatures! I have never seen a mule or horse coloured like a young fawn before.' To his host's astonishment, the wiry little priest sprang upon Contenta's back with the agility of a grasshopper. The mule, too, was astonished. She shook herself violently, bolted toward the gate of the barnyard, and at the gate stopped suddenly. Since this did not throw her rider, she seemed satisfied, trotted back, and stood placidly beside Angelica.

'But you are a *caballero*, Father Vaillant!' Lujon exclaimed. 'I doubt if Father Gallegos would have kept his seat—though he is something of a hunter.'

'The saddle is to be my home in your country, Lujon. What an easy gait this mule has, and what a narrow back! I notice that especially. For a man with short legs, like me, it is a punishment to ride eight hours a day on a wide horse. And this I must do day after day. From here I go to Santa Fé, and, after a day in conference with the Bishop, I start for Mora.'

'For Mora?' exclaimed Lujon. 'Yes, that is far, and the roads are very bad. On your mare you will never do it. She will drop dead under you.' While he talked, the Father remained upon the mule's back, stroking her with his hand.

'Well, I have no other. God grant that she does not drop somewhere far from food and water. I can carry very little with me except my vestments and the sacred vessels.'

The Mexican had been growing more and more

thoughtful, as if he were considering something profound and not altogether cheerful. Suddenly his brow cleared, and he turned to the priest with a radiant smile, quite boyish in its simplicity.

'Father Vaillant,' he burst out in a slightly oratorical manner, 'you have made my house right with Heaven, and you charge me very little. I will do something very nice for you; I will give you Contenta for a present, and I hope to be particularly remembered in your prayers.'

Springing to the ground, Father Vaillant threw his arms about his host. 'Manuelito!' he cried, 'for this darling mule I think I could almost pray you into Heaven!'

The Mexican laughed, too, and warmly returned the embrace. Arm-in-arm they went in to begin the baptisms.

The next morning, when Lujon went to call Father Vaillant for breakfast, he found him in the barnyard, leading the two mules about and smoothing their fawn-coloured flanks, but his face was not the cheerful countenance of yesterday.

'Manuel,' he said at once, 'I cannot accept your present. I have thought upon it overnight, and I see that I cannot. The Bishop works as hard as I do, and his horse is little better than mine. You know he lost everything on his way out here, in a shipwreck at Galveston— among the rest a fine wagon he had had built for travel on these plains. I could not go about on a mule like this when my Bishop rides a common hack. It would be inappropriate. I must ride away on my old mare.'

'Yes, Padre?' Manuel looked troubled and somewhat aggrieved. Why should the Padre spoil everything? It had all been very pleasant yesterday, and he had felt like a prince of generosity. 'I doubt if she will make La

Bajada Hill,' he said slowly, shaking his head. 'Look my horses over and take the one that suits you. They are all better than yours.'

'No, no,' said Father Vaillant decidedly. 'Having seen these mules, I want nothing else. They are the colour of pearls, really! I will raise the price of marriages until I can buy this pair from you. A missionary must depend upon his mount for companionship in his lonely life. I want a mule that can look at me like a Christian, as you said of these.'

Señor Lujon sighed and looked about his barnyard as if he were trying to find some escape from this situation.

Father Joseph turned to him with vehemence. 'If I were a rich *ranchero*, like you, Manuel, I would do a splendid thing; I would furnish the two mounts that are to carry the Word of God about this heathen country, and then I would say to myself: *There go my Bishop and my Vicario, on my beautiful cream-coloured mules.*'

'So be it, Padre,' said Lujon with a mournful smile. 'But I ought to get a good many prayers. On my whole estate there is nothing I prize like those two. True, they might pine if they were parted for long. They have never been separated, and they have a great affection for each other. Mules, as you know, have strong affections. It is hard for me to give them up.'

'You will be all the happier for that, Manuelito,' Father Joseph cried heartily. 'Every time you think of these mules, you will feel pride in your good deed.'

Soon after breakfast Father Vaillant departed, riding Contenta, with Angelica trotting submissively behind, and from his gate Señor Lujon watched them disconsolately until they disappeared. He felt he had been worried out of his mules, and yet he bore no resentment. He did not doubt Father Joseph's devotedness, nor his singleness of purpose. After all, a Bishop was a Bishop,

and a Vicar was a Vicar, and it was not to their discredit
that they worked like a pair of common parish priests.
He believed he would be proud of the fact that they
rode Contenta and Angelica. Father Vaillant had forced
his hand, but he was rather glad of it.

II

The Lonely Road to Mora

The Bishop and his Vicar were riding through the
rain in the Truchas Mountains. The heavy, lead-
coloured drops were driven slantingly through the air by
an icy wind from the peak. These raindrops, Father Latour kept thinking, were the shape of tadpoles, and they
broke against his nose and cheeks, exploding with a
splash, as if they were hollow and full of air. The priests
were riding across high mountain meadows, which in a
few weeks would be green, though just now they were
slate-coloured. On every side lay ridges covered with
blue-green fir trees; above them rose the horny back-
bones of mountains. The sky was very low; purplish
lead-coloured clouds let down curtains of mist into the
valleys between the pine ridges. There was not a glimmer of white light in the dark vapours working overhead—rather, they took on the cold green of the ever-
greens. Even the white mules, their coats wet and
matted into tufts, had turned a slaty hue, and the faces
of the two priests were purple and spotted in that singular light.

Father Latour rode first, sitting straight upon his
mule, with his chin lowered just enough to keep the
drive of rain out of his eyes. Father Vaillant followed,
unable to see much—in weather like this his glasses

were of no use, and he had taken them off. He crouched down in the saddle, his shoulders well over Contenta's neck. Father Joseph's sister, Philomène, who was Mother Superior of a convent in her native town in the Puy-de-Dôme, often tried to picture her brother and Bishop Latour on these long missionary journeys of which he wrote her; she imagined the scene and saw the two priests moving through it in their cassocks, bareheaded, like the pictures of Saint Francis Xavier with which she was familiar. The reality was less picturesque—but for all that, no one could have mistaken these two men for hunters or traders. They wore clerical collars about their necks instead of neckerchiefs, and on the breast of his buckskin jacket the Bishop's silver cross hung by a silver chain.

They were on their way to Mora, the third day out, and they did not know just how far they had still to go. Since morning they had not met a traveller or seen a human habitation. They believed they were on the right trail, for they had seen no other. The first night of their journey they had spent at Santa Cruz, lying in the warm, wide valley of the Rio Grande, where the fields and gardens were already softly coloured with early spring. But since they had left the Española country behind them, they had contended first with wind and sand-storms, and now with cold. The Bishop was going to Mora to assist the Padre there in disposing of a crowd of refugees who filled his house. A new settlement in the Conejos Valley had lately been raided by Indians; many of the inhabitants were killed, and the survivors, who were originally from Mora, had managed to get back there, utterly destitute.

Before the travellers had crossed the mountain meadows, the rain turned to sleet. Their wet buckskins quickly froze, and the rattle of icy flakes struck them and bounded off. The prospect of a night in the open was not cheering. It was too wet to kindle a fire, their blankets would become soaked on the ground. As they were descending the mountain on the Mora side, the grey daylight seemed already beginning to fail, though it was only four o'clock.

Father Latour turned in his saddle and spoke over his shoulder.

'The mules are certainly very tired, Joseph. They ought to be fed.'

'Push on,' said Father Vaillant. 'We will come to shelter of some kind before night sets in.' The Vicar had been praying steadfastly while they crossed the meadows, and he felt confident that Saint Joseph would not turn a deaf ear.

Before the hour was done, they did indeed come upon a wretched adobe house, so poor and mean that they might not have seen it had it not lain close beside the trail, on the edge of a steep ravine. The stable looked more habitable than the house, and the priests thought perhaps they could spend the night in it.

As they rode up to the door, a man came out, bareheaded, and they saw to their surprise that he was not a Mexican, but an American, of a very unprepossessing type. He spoke to them in some drawling dialect they could scarcely understand and asked if they wanted to stay the night. During the few words they exchanged with him, Father Latour felt a growing reluctance to remain even for a few hours under the roof of this ugly, evil-looking fellow. He was tall, gaunt, and ill-formed, with a snake-like neck, terminating in a small, bony head. Under his close-clipped hair this repellent head showed a number of thick ridges, as if the skull joinings were overgrown by layers of superfluous bone. With its small, rudimentary ears, this head had a positively malignant look. The man seemed not more than half human, but he was the only householder on the lonely road to Mora.

The priests dismounted and asked him whether he could put their mules under shelter and give them grain feed.

'As soon as I git my coat on I will. You kin come in.'

They followed him into a room where a piñon fire blazed in the corner, and went toward it to warm their stiffened hands. Their host made an angry, snarling sound in the direction of the partition, and a woman came out of the next room. She was a Mexican.

Father Latour and Father Vaillant addressed her courteously in Spanish, greeting her in the name of the Holy Mother, as was customary. She did not open her lips, but stared at them blankly for a moment, then dropped her eyes and cowered as if she were terribly frightened. The priests looked at each other; it struck them both that this man had been abusing her in some way. Suddenly he turned on her.

'Clear off them cheers fur the strangers. They won't eat ye, if they air priests.'

She began distractedly snatching rags and wet socks and dirty clothes from the chairs. Her hands were shaking so that she dropped things. She was not old, she might have been very young, but she was probably half-witted. There was nothing in her face but blankness and fear.

Her husband put on his coat and boots, went to the door, and stopped with his hand on the latch, throwing over his shoulder a crafty, hateful glance at the bewildered woman.

'Here, you! Come right along, I'll need ye!'

She took her black shawl from a peg and followed him. Just at the door she turned and caught the eyes of the visitors, who were looking after her in compassion and perplexity. Instantly that stupid face became intense, prophetic, full of awful meaning. With her finger she pointed them away, away!—two quick thrusts into the air. Then, with a look of horror beyond anything language could convey, she threw back her head and drew the edge of her palm quickly across her distended throat—and vanished. The doorway was empty; the two priests stood staring at it, speechless. That flash of electric passion had been so swift, the warning it communicated so vivid and definite, that they were struck dumb.

Father Joseph was the first to find his tongue.

'There is no doubt of her meaning. Your pistol is loaded, Jean?'

'Yes, but I neglected to keep it dry. No matter.'

They hurried out of the house. It was still light enough to see the stable through the grey drive of rain, and they went toward it.

'Señor American,' the Bishop called, 'will you be good enough to bring out our mules?'

The man came out of the stable. 'What do you want?'

'Our mules. We have changed our minds. We will push on to Mora. And here is a dollar for your trouble.'

The man took a threatening attitude. As he looked from one to the other his head played from side to side exactly like a snake's. 'What's the matter? My house ain't good enough for ye?'

'No explanation is necessary. Go into the barn and get the mules, Father Joseph.'

'You dare go into my stable, you——priest!'

The Bishop drew his pistol. 'No profanity, Señor. We want nothing from you but to get away from your uncivil tongue. Stand where you are.'

The man was unarmed. Father Joseph came out with

the mules, which had not been unsaddled. The poor things were each munching a mouthful, but they needed no urging to be gone; they did not like this place. The moment they felt their riders on their backs they trotted quickly along the road, which dropped immediately into the arroyo. While they were descending, Father Joseph remarked that the man would certainly have a gun in the house, and that he had no wish to be shot in the back.

'Nor I. But it is growing too dark for that, unless he should follow us on horseback,' said the Bishop. 'Were there horses in the stable?'

'Only a burro.'

Father Vaillant was relying upon the protection of Saint Joseph, whose office he had fervently said that morning. The warning given them by that poor woman, with such scant opportunity, seemed evidence that some protecting power was mindful of them.

By the time they had ascended the far side of the arroyo, night had closed down and the rain was pouring harder than ever.

'I am by no means sure that we can keep in the road,' said the Bishop. 'But at least I am sure we are not being followed. We must trust to these intelligent beasts. Poor woman! He will suspect her and abuse her, I am afraid.' He kept seeing her in the darkness as he rode on, her face in the firelight, and her terrible pantomime.

They reached the town of Mora a little after midnight. The Padre's house was full of refugees, and two of them were put out of a bed in order that the Bishop and his Vicar could get into it.

In the morning a boy came from the stable and reported that he had found a crazy woman lying in the straw, and that she begged to see the two Padres who owned the white mules. She was brought in, her clothing cut to rags, her legs and face and even her hair so plastered with mud that the priests could scarcely recognize the woman who had saved their lives the night before.

She said she had never gone back to the house at all. When the two priests rode away, her husband had run to the house to get his gun, and she had plunged down a washout behind the stable into the arroyo, and had been on the way to Mora all night. She had supposed he would overtake her and kill her, but he had not. She reached the settlement before daybreak, and crept into the stable to warm herself among the animals and wait until the household was awake. Kneeling before the Bishop, she began to relate such horrible things that he stopped her and turned to the native priest.

'This is a case for the civil authorities. Is there a magistrate here?'

There was no magistrate, but there was a retired fur trapper who acted as notary and could take evidence. He was sent for, and in the interval Father Latour instructed the refugee women from Conejos to bathe this poor creature and put decent clothes on her, and to care for the cuts and scratches on her legs.

An hour later the woman, whose name was Magdalena, calmed by food and kindness, was ready to tell her story. The notary had brought along his friend, Saint Vrain, a Canadian trapper who understood Spanish better than he. The woman was known to Saint Vrain, moreover, who confirmed her statement that she was born Magdalena Valdez, at Los Ranchos de Taos, and that she was twenty-four years old. Her husband, Buck Scales, had drifted into Taos with a party of hunters from somewhere in Wyoming. All white men knew him for a dog and a degenerate—but to Mexican girls, marriage with an American meant coming up in the world. She had married him six years ago, and had been liv-

ing with him ever since in that wretched house on the
Mora trail. During that time he had robbed and murdered four travellers who had stopped there for the
night. They were all strangers, not known in the country. She had forgot their names, but one was a German
boy who spoke very little Spanish and little English; a
nice boy with blue eyes, and she had grieved for him
more than for the others. They were all buried in the
sandy soil behind the stable. She was always afraid their
bodies might wash out in a storm. Their horses Buck
had ridden off by night and sold to Indians somewhere
in the north. Magdalena had borne three children since
her marriage, and her husband had killed each of them
a few days after birth, by ways so horrible that she
could not relate it. After he killed the first baby, she
ran away from him, back to her parents at Ranchos.
He came after her and made her go home with him by
threatening harm to the old people. She was afraid to
go anywhere for help, but twice before she had managed to warn travellers away, when her husband happened to be out of the house. This time she had found
courage because, when she looked into the faces of these
two Padres, she knew they were good men, and she
thought if she ran after them they could save her. She
could not bear any more killing. She asked nothing better than to die herself, if only she could hide near a
church and a priest for a while, to make her soul right
with God.

Saint Vrain and his friend got together a search-party
at once. They rode out to Scales's place and found the
remains of four men buried under the corral behind the
stable, as the woman had said. Scales himself they captured on the road from Taos, where he had gone to look
for his wife. They brought him back to Mora, but Saint
Vrain rode on to Taos to fetch a magistrate.

There was no *calabozo* in Mora, so Scales was put
into an empty stable, under guard. This stable was soon
surrounded by a crowd of people, who loitered to hear
the blood-curdling threats the prisoner shouted against
his wife. Magdalena was kept in the Padre's house,
where she lay on a mat in the corner, begging Father
Latour to take her back to Santa Fé, so that her husband could not get at her. Though Scales was bound,
the Bishop felt alarmed for her safety. He and the American notary, who had a pistol of the new revolver model,
sat in the *sala* and kept watch over her all night.

In the morning the magistrate and his party arrived
from Taos. The notary told him the facts of the case in
the plaza, where everyone could hear. The Bishop en-
quired whether there was any place for Magdalena in
Taos, as she could not stay on here in such a state of
terror. A man dressed in buckskin hunting-clothes
stepped out of the crowd and asked to see Magdalena.
Father Latour conducted him into the room where she
lay on her mat. The stranger went up to her, removing
his hat. He bent down and put his hand on her shoulder. Although he was clearly an American, he spoke
Spanish in the native manner.

'Magdalena, don't you remember me?'

She looked up at him as out of a dark well; something became alive in her deep, haunted eyes. She
caught with both hands at his fringed buckskin knees.

'Cristobal!' she wailed. 'Oh, Cristobal!'

'I'll take you home with me, Magdalena, and you
can stay with my wife. You wouldn't be afraid in my
house, would you?'

'No, no, Cristobal, I would not be afraid with you.
I am not a wicked woman.'

He smoothed her hair. 'You're a good girl, Magdalena—always were. It will be all right. Just leave things to me.'

Then he turned to the Bishop. 'Señor Vicario, she can come to me. I live near Taos. My wife is a native woman, and she'll be good to her. That varmint won't come about my place, even if he breaks jail. He knows me. My name is Carson.'

Father Latour had looked forward to meeting the scout. He had supposed him to be a very large man, of powerful body and commanding presence. This Carson was not so tall as the Bishop himself, was very slight in frame, modest in manner, and he spoke English with a soft Southern drawl. His face was both thoughtful and alert; anxiety had drawn a permanent ridge between his blue eyes. Under his blond moustache his mouth had a singular refinement. The lips were full and delicately modelled. There was something curiously unconscious about his mouth, reflective, a little melancholy—and something that suggested a capacity for tenderness.

The Bishop felt a quick glow of pleasure in looking at the man. As he stood there in his buckskin clothes one felt in him standards, loyalties, a code which is not easily put into words, but which is instantly felt when two men who live by it come together by chance. He took the scout's hand.

'I have long wanted to meet Kit Carson,' he said, 'even before I came to New Mexico. I have been hoping you would pay me a visit at Santa Fé.'

The other smiled. 'I'm right shy, sir, and I'm always afraid of being disappointed. But I guess it will be all right from now on.'

This was the beginning of a long friendship.

On their ride back to Carson's ranch, Magdalena was

put in Father Vaillant's care, and the Bishop and the scout rode together. Carson said he had become a Catholic merely as a matter of form, as Americans usually did when they married a Mexican girl. His wife was a good woman and very devout; but religion had seemed to him pretty much a woman's affair until his last trip to California. He had been sick out there, and the Fathers at one of the missions took care of him.

'I began to see things different, and thought I might some day be a Catholic in earnest. I was brought up to think priests were rascals, and that the nuns were bad women—all the stuff they talk back in Missouri. A good many of the native priests here bear out that story. Our Padre Martínez at Taos is an old scapegrace, if ever there was one; he's got children and grandchildren in almost every settlement around here. And Padre Lucero at Arroyo Hondo is a miser, takes everything a poor man's got to give him a Christian burial.'

The Bishop discussed the needs of his people at length with Carson. He felt great confidence in his judgment. The two men were about the same age, both a little over forty, and both had been sobered and sharpened by wide experience. Carson had been guide in world-renowned explorations, but he was still almost as poor as in the days when he was a beaver trapper. He lived in a little adobe house with his Mexican wife. The great country of desert and mountain ranges between Santa Fé and the Pacific coast was not yet mapped or charted; the most reliable map of it was in Kit Carson's brain. This Missourian, whose eye was so quick to read a landscape or a human face, could not read a printed page. He could at that time barely write his own name. Yet one felt in him a quick and discriminating intelligence. That he was illiterate was an accident; he had got ahead of books, gone where the printing-press could not follow him. Out of the hardships of his boyhood—from fourteen to twenty picking up a bare living as cook or mule-driver for wagon trains, often in the service of brutal and desperate characters—he had preserved a clean sense of honour and a compassionate heart. In talking to the Bishop of poor Magdalena he said sadly: 'I used to see her in Taos when she was such a pretty girl. Ain't it a pity?'

The degenerate murderer, Buck Scales, was hanged after a short trial. Early in April the Bishop left Santa Fé on horseback and rode to St. Louis, on his way to attend the Provincial Council at Baltimore. When he returned in September, he brought back with him five courageous nuns, Sisters of Loretto, to found a school for girls in letterless Santa Fé. He sent at once for Magdalena and took her into the service of the Sisters. She became housekeeper and manager of the Sisters' kitchen. She was devoted to the nuns, and so happy in the service of the Church that when the Bishop visited the school he used to enter by the kitchen-garden in order to see her serene and handsome face. For she became beautiful, as Carson said she had been as a girl. After the blight of her horrible youth was over, she seemed to bloom again in the household of God.

THE DUKE AND THE
DAUPHIN COME ABOARD

BY MARK TWAIN

*Here is one episode from an abundant work of genius which Robert
Louis Stevenson hailed as the finest adventure-story since the Odyssey.
If today a poll were taken of all living American authors, Huckleberry
Finn, now approaching its sixtieth birthday, would certainly be voted
the American book most likely to succeed. When consulted on the
composition of this volume, that author who in the judgment of its
editor leads all the rest, made this impractical but tempting suggestion:
"I almost think that if I were making an anthology for American
soldiers, I would make a neat edition of Huckleberry Finn and let
it go at that! Thousands of them have never read it, and the thousands
who have read it will read it with a different feeling in a foreign land.
Times have changed, I know. But anyhow, I think it is still the most
American of any."*

TWO or three days and nights went by; I reckon
I might say they swum by, they slid along so
quiet and smooth and lovely. Here is the way we
put in the time. It was a monstrous big river down
there—sometimes a mile and a half wide; we run
nights, and laid up and hid daytimes; soon as night
was most gone we stopped navigating and tied up—
nearly always in the dead water under a towhead;
and then cut young cottonwoods and willows, and
hid the raft with them. Then we set out the lines.
Next we slid into the river and had a swim, so as to
freshen up and cool off; then we set down on the
sandy bottom where the water was about knee-deep,
and watched the daylight come. Not a sound any-

wheres—perfectly still—just like the whole world was asleep, only sometimes the bullfrogs a-cluttering, maybe. The first thing to see, looking away over the water, was a kind of dull line—that was the woods on t'other side; you couldn't make nothing else out; then a pale place in the sky; then more paleness spreading around; then the river softened up away off, and warn't black any more, but gray; you could see little dark spots drifting along ever so far away—trading-scows, and such things; and long black streaks—rafts; sometimes you could hear a sweep screaking; or jumbled-up voices, it was so still, and sounds come so far; and by and by you could see a streak on the water which you know by the look of the streak that there's a snag there in a swift current which breaks on it and makes that streak look that way; and you see the mist curl up off of the water, and the east reddens up, and the river, and you make out a log cabin in the edge of the woods, away on the bank on t'other side of the river, being a wood-yard, likely, and piled by them cheats so you can throw a dog through it anywheres; then the nice breeze springs up, and comes fanning you from over there, so cool and fresh and sweet to smell on account of the woods and the flowers; but sometimes not that way, because they've left dead fish laying around, gars and such, and they do get pretty rank; and next you've got the full day, and everything smiling in the sun, and the song-birds just going it!

A little smoke couldn't be noticed now, so we would take some fish off of the lines and cook up a hot breakfast. And afterwards we would watch the lonesomeness of the river, and kind of lazy along, and by and by lazy off to sleep. Wake up by and by, and look to see what done it, and maybe see a steamboat cough-

ing along up-stream, so far off towards the other side
you couldn't tell nothing about her only whether she
was a stern-wheel or side-wheel; then for about an
hour there wouldn't be nothing to hear nor nothing
to see—just solid lonesomeness. Next you'd see a
raft sliding by, away off yonder, and maybe a galoot
on it chopping, because they're most always doing
it on a raft; you'd see the ax flash and come down—
you don't hear nothing; you see that ax go up again,
and by the time it's above the man's head then you
hear the *k'chunk!*—it had took all that time to come
over the water. So we would put in the day, lazying
around, listening to the stillness. Once there was a
thick fog, and the rafts and things that went by was
beating tin pans so the steamboats wouldn't run over
them. A scow or a raft went by so close we could
hear them talking and cussing and laughing—heard
them plain; but we couldn't see no sign of them; it
made you feel crawly; it was like spirits carrying on that
way in the air. Jim said he believed it was spirits; but
I says:

"No; spirits wouldn't say, 'Dern the dern fog.'"

Soon as it was night out we shoved; when we got
her out to about the middle we let her alone, and let
her float wherever the current wanted her to; then
we lit the pipes, and dangled our legs in the water,
and talked about all kinds of things—we was always
naked, day and night, whenever the mosquitoes would
let us—the new clothes Buck's folks made for me was
too good to be comfortable, and besides I didn't go
much on clothes, nohow.

Sometimes we'd have that whole river all to ourselves for the longest time. Yonder was the banks
and the islands, across the water; and maybe a
spark—which was a candle in a cabin window; and

sometimes on the water you could see a spark or two—on a raft or a scow, you know; and maybe you could hear a fiddle or a song coming over from one of them crafts. It's lovely to live on a raft. We had the sky up there, all speckled with stars, and we used to lay on our backs and look up at them, and discuss about whether they was made or only just happened. Jim he allowed they was made, but I allowed they happened; I judged it would have took too long to *make* so many. Jim said the moon could 'a' laid them; well, that looked kind of reasonable, so I didn't say nothing against it, because I've seen a frog lay most as many, so of course it could be done. We used to watch the stars that fell, too, and see them streak down. Jim allowed they'd got spoiled and was hove out of the nest.

Once or twice of a night we would see a steamboat slipping along in the dark, and now and then she would belch a whole world of sparks up out of her chimbleys, and they would rain down in the river and look awful pretty; then she would turn a corner and her lights would wink out and her powwow shut off and leave the river still again; and by and by her waves would get to us, a long time after she was gone, and joggle the raft a bit, and after that you wouldn't hear nothing for you couldn't tell how long, except maybe frogs or something.

After midnight the people on shore went to bed, and then for two or three hours the shores was black —no more sparks in the cabin windows. These sparks was our clock—the first one that showed again meant morning was coming, so we hunted a place to hide and tie up right away.

One morning about daybreak I found a canoe and crossed over a chute to the main shore—it was only two hundred yards—and paddled about a mile up a crick amongst the cypress woods, to see if I couldn't get some berries. Just as I was passing a place where a kind of a cowpath crossed the crick, here comes a couple of men tearing up the path as tight as they could foot it. I thought I was a goner, for whenever anybody was after anybody I judged it was *me*—or maybe Jim. I was about to dig out from there in a hurry, but they was pretty close to me then, and sung out and begged me to save their lives—said they hadn't been doing nothing, and was being chased for it—said there was men and dogs a-coming. They wanted to jump right in, but I says:

"Don't you do it. I don't hear the dogs and horses yet; you've got time to crowd through the brush and get up the crick a little ways; then you take to the water and wade down to me and get in—that'll throw the dogs off the scent."

They done it, and soon as they was aboard I lit out for our towhead, and in about five or ten minutes we heard the dogs and the men away off, shouting. We heard them come along towards the crick, but couldn't see them; they seemed to stop and fool around awhile; then, as we got further and further away all the time, we couldn't hardly hear them at all; by the time we had left a mile of woods behind us and struck the river, everything was quiet, and we paddled over to the towhead and hid in the cottonwoods and was safe.

One of these fellows was about seventy or upwards, and had a bald head and very gray whiskers. He had an old battered-up slouch hat on, and a greasy blue woolen shirt, and ragged old blue jeans britches stuffed into his boot-tops, and home-knit galluses—no, he only had one. He had an old long-tailed blue jeans coat with slick brass buttons flung over his arm, and both of them had big, fat, ratty-looking carpet-bags.

The other fellow was about thirty, and dressed about as ornery. After breakfast we all laid off and talked, and the first thing that come out was that these chaps didn't know one another.

"What got you into trouble?" says the baldhead to t'other chap.

"Well, I'd been selling an article to take the tartar off the teeth—and it does take it off, too, and generly the enamel along with it—but I stayed about one night longer than I ought to, and was just in the act of sliding out when I ran across you on the trail this side of town, and you told me they were coming, and begged me to help you to get off. So I told you I was expecting trouble myself, and would scatter out *with* you. That's the whole yarn—what's yourn?"

"Well, I'd ben a-runnin' a little temperance revival thar 'bout a week, and was the pet of the women folks, big and little, for I was makin' it mighty warm for the rummies, I *tell* you, and takin' as much as five or six dollars a night—ten cents a head, children and niggers free—and business a-growin' all the time, when some-how or another a little report got around last night that I had a way of puttin' in my time with a private jug on the sly. A nigger rousted me out this mornin', and told me the people was getherin' on the quiet with their dogs and horses, and they'd be along pretty soon and give me 'bout half an hour's start, and then run me down if they could; and if they got me they'd tar and feather me and ride me on a rail, sure. I didn't wait for no breakfast—I warn't hungry."

"Old man," said the young one, "I reckon we might double-team it together; what do you think?"

"I ain't undisposed. What's your line—mainly?"

"Jour printer by trade; do a little in patent medicines; theater-actor—tragedy, you know; take a turn to mesmerism and phrenology when there's a chance; teach singing-geography school for a change; sling a lecture sometimes—oh, I do lots of things—most anything that comes handy, so it ain't work. What's your lay?"

"I've done considerble in the doctoring way in my time. Layin' on o' hands is my best holt—for cancer and paralysis, and sich things; and I k'n tell a fortune pretty good when I've got somebody along to find out the facts for me. Preachin's my line, too, and workin' camp-meetin's, and missionaryin' around."

Nobody never said anything for a while; then the young man hove a sigh and says:

"Alas!"

"What 're you alassin' about?" says the baldhead.

"To think I should have lived to be leading such a life, and be degraded down into such company." And he begun to wipe the corner of his eye with a rag.

"Dern your skin, ain't the company good enough for you?" says the baldhead, pretty pert and uppish.

"Yes, it *is* good enough for me; it's as good as I deserve; for who fetched me so low when I was so high? *I* did myself. I don't blame *you*, gentlemen —far from it; I don't blame anybody. I deserve it all. Let the cold world do its worst; one thing I know—there's a grave somewhere for me. The world may go on just as it's always done, and take everything from me—loved ones, property, everything; but it can't take that. Some day I'll lie down in it and forget it all, and my poor broken heart will be at rest." He went on a-wiping.

"Drot your pore broken heart," says the bald-head; "what are you heaving your pore broken heart at *us* f'r? *We* hain't done nothing."

"No, I know you haven't. I ain't blaming you, gentlemen. I brought myself down—yes, I did it myself. It's right I should suffer—perfectly right—I don't make any moan."

"Brought you down from whar? Whar was you brought down from?"

"Ah, you would not believe me; the world never believes—let it pass—'tis no matter. The secret of my birth—"

"The secret of your birth! Do you mean to say—"

"Gentlemen," says the young man, very solemn, "I will reveal it to you, for I feel I may have confidence in you. By rights I am a duke!"

Jim's eyes bugged out when he heard that; and I reckon mine did, too. Then the baldhead says: "No! you can't mean it?"

"Yes. My great-grandfather, eldest son of the Duke of Bridgewater, fled to this country about the end of the last century, to breathe the pure air of freedom; married here, and died, leaving a son, his own father dying about the same time. The second son of the late duke seized the titles and estates—the infant real duke was ignored. I am the lineal descendant of that infant—I am the rightful Duke of Bridgewater; and here am I, forlorn, torn from my high estate, hunted of men, despised by the cold world, ragged, worn, heartbroken, and degraded to the companionship of felons on a raft!"

Jim pitied him ever so much, and so did I. We

tried to comfort him, but he said it warn't much use, he couldn't be much comforted; said if we was a mind to acknowledge him, that would do him more good than most anything else; so we said we would, if he would tell us how. He said we ought to bow when we spoke to him, and say "Your Grace," or "My Lord," or "Your Lordship"—and he wouldn't mind it if we called him plain "Bridgewater," which, he said, was a title anyway, and not a name; and one of us ought to wait on him at dinner, and do any little thing for him he wanted done.

Well, that was all easy, so we done it. All through dinner Jim stood around and waited on him, and says, "Will yo' Grace have some o' dis or some o' dat?" and so on, and a body could see it was mighty pleasing to him.

But the old man got pretty silent by and by— didn't have much to say, and didn't look pretty comfortable over all that petting that was going on around that duke. He seemed to have something on his mind. So, along in the afternoon, he says:

"Looky here, Bilgewater," he says, "I'm nation sorry for you, but you ain't the only person that's had troubles like that."

"No?"

"No, you ain't. You ain't the only person that's ben snaked down wrongfully out'n a high place."

"Alas!"

"No, you ain't the only person that's had a secret of his birth." And, by jings, *he* begins to cry.

"Hold! What do you mean?"

"Bilgewater, kin I trust you?" says the old man, still sort of sobbing.

"To the bitter death!" He took the old man by

the hand and squeezed it, and says, "That secret of your being: speak!"

"Bilgewater, I am the late Dauphin!"

You bet you, Jim and me stared this time. Then the duke says:

"You are what?"

"Yes, my friend, it is too true—your eyes is lookin' at this very moment on the pore disappeared Dauphin, Looy the Seventeen, son of Looy the Sixteen and Marry Antonette."

"You! At your age! No! You mean you're the late Charlemagne; you must be six or seven hundred years old, at the very least."

"Trouble has done it, Bilgewater, trouble has done it; trouble has brung these gray hairs and this premature balditude. Yes, gentlemen, you see before you, in blue jeans and misery, the wanderin', exiled, trampled-on, and sufferin' rightful King of France."

Well, he cried and took on so that me and Jim didn't know hardly what to do, we was so sorry— and so glad and proud we'd got him with us, too. So we set in, like we done before with the duke, and tried to comfort *him*. But he said it warn't no use, nothing but to be dead and done with it all could do him any good; though he said it often made him feel easier and better for a while if people treated him according to his rights, and got down on one knee to speak to him, and always called him "Your Majesty," and waited on him first at meals, and didn't set down in his presence till he asked them. So Jim and me set to majestying him, and doing this and that and t'other for him, and standing up till he told us we might set down. This done him heaps of good, and so he got cheerful and comfortable. But the duke kind of soured on him, and didn't look a bit satisfied with the way things was going; still, the king acted real friendly towards him, and said the duke's great-grandfather and all the other Dukes of Bilgewater was a good deal thought of by *his* father, and was allowed to come to the palace considerable; but the duke stayed huffy a good while, till by and by the king says:

"Like as not we got to be together a blamed long time on this h-yer raft, Bilgewater, and so what's the use o' your bein' sour? It 'll only make things oncomfortable. It ain't my fault I warn't born a duke, it ain't your fault you warn't born a king—so what's the use to worry? Make the best o' things the way you find 'em, says I—that's my motto. This ain't no bad thing that we've struck here—plenty grub and an easy life—come, give us your hand, duke, and le's all be friends."

The duke done it, and Jim and me was pretty glad to see it. It took away all the uncomfortableness and we felt mighty good over it, because it would 'a' been a miserable business to have any unfriendliness on the raft; for what you want, above all things, on a raft, is for everybody to be satisfied, and feel right and kind towards the others.

It didn't take me long to make up my mind that these liars warn't no kings nor dukes at all, but just low-down humbugs and frauds. But I never said nothing, never let on; kept it to myself; it's the best way; then you don't have no quarrels, and don't get into no trouble. If they wanted us to call them kings and dukes, I hadn't no objections, 'long as it would keep peace in the family; and it warn't no use to tell Jim, so I didn't tell him. If I never learnt nothing else out of pap, I learnt that the best way to get along with his kind of people is to let them have their own way.

They asked us considerable many questions; wanted
to know what we covered up the raft that way for, and
laid by in the daytime instead of running—was Jim a
runaway nigger? Says I:

"Goodness sakes! would a runaway nigger run
south?"

No, they allowed he wouldn't. I had to account for
things some way, so I says:

"My folks was living in Pike County, in Missouri,
where I was born, and they all died off but me and pa
and my brother Ike. Pa, he'lowed he'd break up
and go down and live with Uncle Ben, who's got a
little one-horse place on the river forty-four mile below Orleans. Pa was pretty poor, and had some debts;
so when he'd squared up there warn't nothing left but
sixteen dollars and our nigger, Jim. That warn't enough
to take us fourteen hundred mile, deck passage nor no
other way. Well, when the river rose pa had a streak
of luck one day; he ketched this piece of a raft; so we
reckoned we'd go down to Orleans on it. Pa's luck
didn't hold out; a steamboat run over the forrard corner
of the raft one night, and we all went overboard and
dove under the wheel; Jim and me come up all right,
but pa was drunk, and Ike was only four years old,
so they never come up no more. Well, for the next
day or two we had considerable trouble, because people
was always coming out in skiffs and trying to take Jim
away from me, saying they believed he was a runaway
nigger. We don't run daytimes no more now; nights
they don't bother us."

The duke says:

"Leave me alone to cipher out a way so we can
run in the daytime if we want to. I'll think the thing
over—I'll invent a plan that 'll fix it. We'll let it
alone for to-day, because of course we don't want to

go by that town yonder in daylight—it mightn't be healthy."

Towards night it begun to darken up and look like rain; the heat-lightning was squirting around low down in the sky, and the leaves was beginning to shiver—it was going to be pretty ugly, it was easy to see that. So the duke and the king went to over-hauling our wigwam, to see what the beds was like. My bed was a straw tick—better than Jim's, which was a corn-shuck tick; there's always cobs around about in a shuck tick, and they poke into you and hurt; and when you roll over the dry shucks sound like you was rolling over in a pile of dead leaves; it makes such a rustling that you wake up. Well, the duke allowed he would take my bed; but the king allowed he wouldn't. He says:

"I should 'a' reckoned the difference in rank would a sejested to you that a corn-shuck bed warn't just fitten for me to sleep on. Your Grace 'll take the shuck bed yourself."

Jim and me was in a sweat again for a minute, being afraid there was going to be some more trouble amongst them; so we was pretty glad when the duke says:

"'Tis my fate to be always ground into the mire under the iron heel of oppression. Misfortune has broken my once haughty spirit; I yield, I submit; 'tis my fate. I am alone in the world—let me suffer; I can bear it."

We got away as soon as it was good and dark. The king told us to stand well out towards the middle of the river, and not show a light till we got a long ways below the town. We come in sight of the little bunch of lights by and by—that was the town, you know—and slid by, about a half a mile out, all right. When we was three-quarters of a mile below we hoisted up our signal lantern; and about ten o'clock it come on to rain and blow and thunder and lighten like everything; so the king told us to both stay on watch till the weather got better; then him and the duke crawled into the wigwam and turned in for the night. It was my watch below till twelve, but I wouldn't 'a' turned in anyway if I'd had a bed, because a body don't see such a storm as that every day in the week, not by a long sight. My souls, how the wind did scream along! And every second or two there'd come a glare that lit up the white-caps for a half a mile around, and you'd see the islands looking dusty through the rain, and the trees thrashing around in the wind; then comes a *h-whack!*—bum! bum! bumble-umble-um-bum-bum-bum-bum-bum—and the thunder would go rumbling and grumbling away, and quit—and then *rip* comes another flash and another sockdolager. The waves most washed me off the raft sometimes, but I hadn't any clothes on, and didn't mind. We didn't have no trouble about snags; the lightning was glaring and flittering around so constant that we could see them plenty soon enough to throw her head this way or that and miss them.

I had the middle watch, you know, but I was pretty sleepy by that time, so Jim he said he would stand the first half of it for me; he was always mighty good that way, Jim was. I crawled into the wigwam, but the king and the duke had their legs sprawled around so there warn't no show for me; so I laid outside—I didn't mind the rain, because it was warm, and the waves warn't running so high now. About two they come up again, though, and Jim was going to call me; but he changed his mind, because he reckoned they warn't high enough yet to do any harm; but he was mistaken about that, for pretty soon all of a sudden along comes a regular ripper and washed me overboard. It most killed Jim a-laughing. He was the easiest nigger to laugh that ever was, anyway.

I took the watch, and Jim he laid down and snored away; and by and by the storm let up for good and all; and the first cabin-light that showed I rousted him out, and we slid the raft into hiding-quarters for the day.

The king got out an old ratty deck of cards after breakfast, and him and the duke played seven-up awhile, five cents a game. Then they got tired of it and allowed they would "lay out a campaign," as they called it. The duke went down into his carpetbag, and fetched up a lot of little printed bills and read them out loud. One bill said, "The celebrated Dr. Armand de Montalban, of Paris," would "lecture on the Science of Phrenology" at such and such a place, on the blank day of blank, at ten cents admission, and "furnish charts of character at twenty-five cents apiece." The duke said that was *him*. In another bill he was the "world-renowned Shakespearian tragedian, Garrick the Younger, of Drury Lane, London." In other bills he had a lot of other names and done other wonderful things, like finding water and gold with a "divining-rod," "dissipating witch spells," and so on. By and by he says:

"But the histrionic muse is the darling. Have you ever trod the boards, Royalty?"

"No," says the king.

"You shall, then, before you're three days older, Fallen Grandeur," says the duke. "The first good town we come to we'll hire a hall and do the sword-fight in 'Richard III.' and the balcony scene in 'Romeo and Juliet.' How does that strike you?"

"I'm in, up to the hub, for anything that will pay,

Bilgewater; but, you see, I don't know nothing about play-actin', and hain't ever seen much of it. I was too small when pap used to have 'em at the palace. Do you reckon you can learn me?"

"Easy!"

"All right. I'm jist a-freezin' for something fresh, anyway. Le's commence right away."

So the duke he told him all about who Romeo was and who Juliet was, and said he was used to being Romeo, so the king could be Juliet.

"But if Juliet's such a young gal, duke, my peeled head and my white whiskers is goin' to look oncommon odd on her, maybe."

"No, don't you worry; these country jakes won't ever think of that. Besides, you know, you'll be in costume, and that makes all the difference in the world; Juliet's in a balcony, enjoying the moonlight before she goes to bed, and she's got on her nightgown and her ruffled nightcap. Here are the costumes for the parts."

He got out two or three curtain-calico suits, which he said was meedyevil armor for Richard III. and t'other chap, and a long white cotton nightshirt and a ruffled nightcap to match. The king was satisfied; so the duke got out his book and read the parts over in the most splendid spread-eagle way, prancing around and acting at the same time, to show how it had got to be done; then he give the book to the king and told him to get his part by heart.

There was a little one-horse town about three mile down the bend, and after dinner the duke said he had ciphered out his idea about how to run in daylight without it being dangersome for Jim; so he allowed he would go down to the town and fix that thing. The king allowed he would go, too, and see if he couldn't strike something. We was out of coffee, so Jim said I better go along with them in the canoe and get some.

When we got there there warn't nobody stirring; streets empty, and perfectly dead and still, like Sunday. We found a sick nigger sunning himself in a back yard, and he said everybody that warn't too young or too sick or too old was gone to campmeeting, about two mile back in the woods. The king got the directions, and allowed he'd go and work that camp-meeting for all it was worth, and I might go, too.

The duke said what he was after was a printingoffice. We found it; a little bit of a concern, up over a carpenter-shop—carpenters and printers all gone to the meeting, and no doors locked. It was a dirty, littered-up place, and had ink-marks, and handbills with pictures of horses and runaway niggers on them, all over the walls. The duke shed his coat and said he was all right now. So me and the king lit out for the camp-meeting.

We got there in about a half an hour fairly dripping, for it was a most awful hot day. There was as much as a thousand people there from twenty mile around. The woods was full of teams and wagons, hitched everywheres, feeding out of the wagon-troughs and stomping to keep off the flies. There was sheds made out of poles and roofed over with branches, where they had lemonade and gingerbread to sell, and piles of watermelons and green corn and such-like truck.

The preaching was going on under the same kinds of sheds, only they was bigger and held crowds of people. The benches was made out of outside slabs of logs, with holes bored in the round side to drive sticks into for legs. They didn't have no backs. The preachers had high platforms to stand on at one end of the sheds. The women had on sun-bonnets; and some had linsey-woolsey frocks, some gingham ones, and a few of the young ones had on calico. Some of the young men was barefooted, and some of the children didn't have on any clothes but just a tow-linen shirt. Some of the old women was knitting, and some of the young folks was courting on the sly.

The first shed we come to the preacher was lining out a hymn. He lined out two lines, everybody sung it, and it was kind of grand to hear it, there was so many of them and they done it in such a rousing way; then he lined out two more for them to sing—and so on. The people woke up more and more, and sung louder and louder; and towards the end some begun to groan, and some begun to shout. Then the preacher begun to preach, and begun in earnest, too; and went weaving first to one side of the platform and then the other, and then a-leaning down over the front of it, with his arms and his body going all the time, and shouting his words out with all his might; and every now and then he would hold up his Bible and spread it open, and kind of pass it around this way and that, shouting, "It's the brazen serpent in the wilderness! Look upon it and live!" And people would shout out, "Glory!— A-a-men!" And so he went on, and the people groaning and crying and saying amen:

"Oh, come to the mourners' bench! come, black with sin! (amen!) come, sick and sore! (amen!) come, lame and halt and blind! (amen!) come, pore and needy, sunk in shame! (a-a-men!) come, all that's worn and soiled and suffering!—come with a broken spirit! come with a contrite heart! come in your rags and sin and dirt! the waters that cleanse is free, the door of heaven stands open—oh, enter in and be at rest!" (a-a-men! glory, glory hallelujah!)

And so on. You couldn't make out what the preacher said any more, on account of the shouting and crying. Folks got up everywheres in the crowd, and worked their way just by main strength to the mourners' bench, with the tears running down their faces; and when all the mourners had got up there to the front benches in a crowd, they sung and shouted and flung themselves down on the straw, just crazy and wild.

Well, the first I knowed the king got a-going, and you could hear him over everybody; and next he went a-charging up onto the platform, and the preacher he begged him to speak to the people, and he done it. He told them he was a pirate—been a pirate for thirty years out in the Indian Ocean—and his crew was thinned out considerable last spring in a fight, and he was home now to take out some fresh men, and thanks to goodness he'd been robbed last night and put ashore off of a steamboat without a cent, and he was glad of it; it was the blessedest thing that ever happened to him, because he was a changed man now, and happy for the first time in his life; and, poor as he was, he was going to start right off and work his way back to the Indian Ocean, and put in the rest of his life trying to turn the pirates into the true path; for he could do it better than anybody else, being acquainted with all pirate crews in that ocean; and though it would take him a long time to get there without money, he would get there anyway, and every time he convinced a pirate he would say to him, "Don't you thank me, don't you give me no credit; it all belongs to them dear people in Pokeville camp-meeting, natural brothers and benefactors of the race, and that dear preacher there, the truest friend a pirate ever had!"

And then he busted into tears, and so did everybody. Then somebody sings out, "Take up a collection for him, take up a collection!" Well, a half a dozen made a jump to do it, but somebody sings out, "Let *him* pass the hat around!" Then everybody said it, the preacher too.

So the king went all through the crowd with his hat, swabbing his eyes, and blessing the people and praising them and thanking them for being so good to the poor pirates away off there; and every little while the prettiest kind of girls, with the tears running down their cheeks, would up and ask him would he let them kiss him for to remember him by; and he always done it; and some of them he hugged and kissed as many as five or six times—and he was invited to stay a week; and everybody wanted him to live in their houses, and said they'd think it was an honor; but he said as this was the last day of the camp-meeting he couldn't do no good, and besides he was in a sweat to get to the Indian Ocean right off and go to work on the pirates.

When we got back to the raft and he come to count up he found he had collected eighty-seven dollars and seventy-five cents. And then he had fetched away a three-gallon jug of whisky, too, that he found under a wagon when he was starting home through the woods. The king said, take it all around, it laid over any day he'd ever put in in the missionarying line. He said it warn't no use talking, heathens don't amount to shucks alongside of pirates to work a camp-meeting with.

The duke was thinking *he'd* been doing pretty well till the king come to show up, but after that he didn't think so so much. He had set up and printed off two little jobs for farmers in that printing-office—horse bills —and took the money, four dollars. And he had got in ten dollars' worth of advertisements for the paper, which he said he would put in for four dollars if they would pay in advance—so they done it. The price of the paper was two dollars a year, but he took in three subscriptions for half a dollar apiece on condition of them paying him in advance; they were going to pay in cordwood and onions as usual, but he said he had just bought the concern and knocked down the price as low as he could afford it, and was going to run it for cash. He set up a little piece of poetry, which he made, himself, out of his own head—three verses—kind of sweet and saddish—the name of it was, "Yes, crush, cold world, this breaking heart"—and he left that all set up and ready to print in the paper, and didn't charge nothing for it. Well, he took in nine dollars and a half, and said he'd done a pretty square day's work for it.

Then he showed us another little job he'd printed and hadn't charged for, because it was for us. It had a picture of a runaway nigger with a bundle on a stick over his shoulder, and "$200 reward" under it. The reading was all about Jim and just described him to a dot. It said he run away from St. Jacques's plantation, forty mile below New Orleans, last winter, and likely went north, and whoever would catch him and send him back he could have the reward and expenses.

"Now," says the duke, "after to-night we can run in the daytime if we want to. Whenever we see anybody coming we can tie Jim hand and foot with a rope, and lay him in the wigwam and show this handbill and say we captured him up the river, and were too poor to travel on a steamboat, so we got this little raft on credit from our friends and are going down to get the reward. Handcuffs and chains would look still better on Jim, but it wouldn't go well with the story of us being so poor. Too much like jewelry. Ropes are the correct thing—we must preserve the unities, as we say on the boards."

We all said the duke was pretty smart, and there couldn't be no trouble about running daytimes. We judged we could make miles enough that night to get out of the reach of the powwow we reckoned the duke's work in the printing-office was going to make in that little town; then we could boom right along if we wanted to.

We laid low and kept still, and never shoved out till nearly ten o'clock; then we slid by, pretty wide away from the town, and didn't hoist our lantern till we was clear out of sight of it.

When Jim called me to take the watch at four in the morning, he says:

"Huck, does you reck'n we gwyne to run acrost any mo' kings on dis trip?"

"No," I says, "I reckon not."

"Well," says he, "dat's all right, den. I doan' mine one er two kings, but dat's enough. Dis one's powerful drunk, en de duke ain' much better."

I found Jim had been trying to get him to talk French, so he could hear what it was like; but he said he had been in this country so long, and had so much trouble, he'd forgot it.

It was after sun-up now, but we went right on and didn't tie up. The king and the duke turned out by and by looking pretty rusty; but after they'd jumped over-board and took a swim it chippered them up a good deal. After breakfast the king he took a seat on the cor-ner of the raft, and pulled off his boots and rolled up his britches, and let his legs dangle in the water, so as to be comfortable, and lit his pipe, and went to getting his "Romeo and Juliet" by heart. When he had got it pretty good him and the duke begun to practise it together. The duke had to learn him over and over again how to say every speech; and he made him sigh, and put his hand on his heart, and after a while he said he done it

pretty well; "only," he says, "you mustn't bellow out
Romeo! that way, like a bull—you must say it soft and
sick and languishy, so—Ro-o-o-meo! that is the idea; for
Juliet's a dear sweet mere child of a girl, you know, and
she doesn't bray like a jackass."

Well, next they got out a couple of long swords that
the duke made out of oak laths, and begun to practise
the sword-fight—the duke called himself Richard III.;
and the way they laid on and pranced around the raft
was grand to see. But by and by the king tripped and
fell overboard, and after that they took a rest, and had
a talk about all kinds of adventures they'd had in other
times along the river.

After dinner the duke says:

"Well, Capet, we'll want to make this a first-class
show, you know, so I guess we'll add a little more to it.
We want a little something to answer encores with, anyway."

"What's onkores, Bilgewater?"

The duke told him, and then says:

"I'll answer by doing the Highland fling or the sailor's
hornpipe; and you—well, let me see—oh, I've got it—
you can do Hamlet's soliloquy."

"Hamlet's which?"

"Hamlet's soliloquy, you know; the most celebrated
thing in Shakespeare. Ah, it's sublime, sublime! Always
fetches the house. I haven't got it in the book—I've only
got one volume—but I reckon I can piece it out from
memory. I'll just walk up and down a minute, and see if
I can call it back from recollection's vaults."

So he went to marching up and down, thinking, and
frowning horrible every now and then; then he would
hoist up his eyebrows; next he would squeeze his hand
on his forehead and stagger back and kind of moan;
next he would sigh, and next he'd let on to drop a tear.

It was beautiful to see him. By and by he got it. He told us to give attention. Then he strikes a most noble attitude, with one leg shoved forwards, and his arms stretched away up, and his head tilted back, looking up at the sky; and then he begins to rip and rave and grit his teeth; and after that, all through his speech, he howled, and spread around, and swelled up his chest, and just knocked the spots out of any acting ever *I* see before. This is the speech—I learned it, easy enough, while he was learning it to the king:

To be, or not to be; that is the bare bodkin
That makes calamity of so long life;
For who would fardels bear, till Birnam Wood do come
    to Dunsinane,
But that the fear of something after death
Murders the innocent sleep,
Great nature's second course,
And makes us rather sling the arrows of outrageous
    fortune
Than fly to others that we know not of.
There's the respect must give us pause:
Wake Duncan with thy knocking! I would thou couldst;
For who would bear the whips and scorns of time,
The oppressor's wrong, the proud man's contumely,
The law's delay, and the quietus which his pangs might
    take,
In the dead waste and middle of the night, when church-
    yards yawn
In customary suits of solemn black,
But that the undiscovered country from whose bourne
    no traveler returns,
Breathes forth contagion on the world,
And thus the native hue of resolution, like the poor cat
    i' the adage,
Is sicklied o'er with care,
And all the clouds that lowered o'er our housetops,
With this regard their currents turn awry,

And lose the name of action.
'Tis a consummation devoutly to be wished. But soft
     you, the fair Ophelia:
Ope not thy ponderous and marble jaws,
But get thee to a nunnery—go!

Well, the old man he liked that speech, and he mighty
soon got it so he could do it first rate. It seemed like he
was just born for it; and when he had his hand in and
was excited, it was perfectly lovely the way he would
rip and tear and rair up behind when he was getting it
off.

The first chance we got the duke he had some show-
bills printed; and after that, for two or three days as
we floated along, the raft was a most uncommon lively
place, for there warn't nothing but sword-fighting and
rehearsing—as the duke called it—going on all the time.
One morning, when we was pretty well down the state
of Arkansaw, we come in sight of a little one-horse town
in a big bend; so we tied up about three-quarters of a
mile above it, in the mouth of a crick which was shut in
like a tunnel by the cypress trees, and all of us but Jim
took the canoe and went down there to see if there was
any chance in that place for our show.

We struck it mighty lucky; there was going to be a
circus there that afternoon, and the country-people was
already beginning to come in, in all kinds of old shackly
wagons, and on horses. The circus would leave before
night, so our show would have a pretty good chance. The
duke he hired the court-house, and we went around and
stuck up our bills. They read like this:

Shaksperean Revival ! ! !
Wonderful Attraction!
For One Night Only!
The world renowned tragedians,

David Garrick the younger, of Drury Lane Theatre,
London, and
Edmund Kean the elder, of the Royal Haymarket
Theatre, Whitechapel, Pudding Lane, Picca-
dilly, London, and the Royal Continental
Theatres, in their sublime
Shaksperean Spectacle entitled
The Balcony Scene
in
Romeo and Juliet ! ! !

Romeo ....Mr. Garrick
Juliet ....Mr. Kean
Assisted by the whole strength of the company!
New costumes, new scenery, new appointments!
Also:
The thrilling, masterly, and blood-curdling
Broad-sword conflict
In Richard III. ! ! !

Richard III..........................Mr. Garrick
Richmond ....Mr. Kean
Also
(by special request)
Hamlet's Immortal Soliloquy ! !
By the Illustrious Kean!
Done by him 300 consecutive nights in Paris!
For One Night Only,
On account of imperative European engagements!
Admission 25 cents; children and servants, 10 cents.

Then we went loafing around town. The stores and
houses was most all old, shackly, dried-up frame concerns that hadn't ever been painted; they was set up
three or four foot above ground on stilts, so as to be out
of reach of the water when the river was overflowed.
The houses had little gardens around them, but they
didn't seem to raise hardly anything in them but
jimpson-weeds, and sunflowers, and ash-piles, and old
curled-up boots and shoes, and pieces of bottles, and

rags, and played-out tinware. The fences was made of different kinds of boards, nailed on at different times; and they leaned every which way, and had gates that didn't generly have but one hinge—a leather one. Some of the fences had been whitewashed some time or another, but the duke said it was in Columbus's time, like enough. There was generly hogs in the garden, and people driving them out.

All the stores was along one street. They had white domestic awnings in front, and the country-people hitched their horses to the awning-posts. There was empty dry-goods boxes under the awnings, and loafers roosting on them all day long, whittling them with their Barlow knives; and chawing tobacco, and gaping and yawning and stretching—a mighty ornery lot. They generly had on yellow straw hats most as wide as an umbrella, but didn't wear no coats nor waistcoats; they called one another Bill, and Buck, and Hank, and Joe, and Andy, and talked lazy and drawly, and used considerable many cuss-words. There was as many as one loafer leaning up against every awning-post, and he most always had his hands in his britches pockets, except when he fetched them out to lend a chaw of tobacco or scratch. What a body was hearing amongst them all the time was:

"Gimme a chaw 'v tobacker, Hank."

"Cain't; I hain't got but one chaw left. Ask Bill."

Maybe Bill he gives him a chaw; maybe he lies and says he ain't got none. Some of them kinds of loafers never has a cent in the world, nor a chaw of tobacco of their own. They get all their chawing by borrowing; they say to a fellow, "I wisht you'd len' me a chaw, Jack, I jist this minute give Ben Thompson the last chaw I had"—which is a lie pretty much every time; it don't fool nobody but a stranger; but Jack ain't no stranger, so he says:

"*You* give him a chaw, did you? So did your sister's cat's grandmother. You pay me back the chaws you've awready borry'd off'n me, Lafe Buckner, then I'll loan you one or two ton of it, and won't charge you no back intrust, nuther."

"Well, I *did* pay you back some of it wunst."

"Yes, you did—'bout six chaws. You borry'd store tobacker and paid back nigger-head."

Store tobacco is flat black plug, but these fellows mostly chaws the natural leaf twisted. When they borrow a chaw they don't generly cut it off with a knife, but set the plug in between their teeth, and gnaw with their teeth and tug at the plug with their hands till they get it in two; then sometimes the one that owns the tobacco looks mournful at it when it's handed back, and says, sarcastic:

"Here, gimme the *chaw*, and you take the *plug*."

All the streets and lanes was just mud; they warn't nothing else *but* mud—mud as black as tar and nigh about a foot deep in some places, and two or three inches deep in *all* the places. The hogs loafed and grunted around everywheres. You'd see a muddy sow and a litter of pigs come lazying along the street and whollop herself right down in the way, where folks had to walk around her, and she'd stretch out and shut her eyes and wave her ears whilst the pigs was milking her, and look as happy as if she was on salary. And pretty soon you'd hear a loafer sing out, "Hi! *so* boy! sick him, Tige!" and away the sow would go, squealing most horrible, with a dog or two swinging to each ear, and three or four dozen more a-coming; and then you would see all the loafers get up and watch the thing out of sight, and laugh at the fun and look grateful for the noise. Then they'd settle back again till there was a dog-fight. There couldn't anything wake them up all over, and make them happy all over, like a dog-fight—unless it might be putting turpentine on a stray dog and setting fire to him, or tying a tin pan to his tail and see him run himself to death.

On the river-front some of the houses was sticking out over the bank, and they was bowed and bent, and about ready to tumble in. The people had moved out of them. The bank was caved away under one corner of some others, and that corner was hanging over. People lived in them yet, but it was dangersome, because sometimes a strip of land as wide as a house caves in at a time. Sometimes a belt of land a quarter of a mile deep will start in and cave along and cave along till it all caves into the river in one summer. Such a town as that has to be always moving back, and back, and back, because the river's always gnawing at it.

The nearer it got to noon that day the thicker and thicker was the wagons and horses in the streets, and more coming all the time. Families fetched their dinners with them from the country, and eat them in the wagons. There was considerable whisky-drinking going on, and I seen three fights. By and by somebody sings out:

"Here comes old Boggs!—in from the country for his little old monthly drunk; here he comes, boys!"

All the loafers looked glad; I reckoned they was used to having fun out of Boggs. One of them says:

"Wonder who he's a-gwyne to chaw up this time. If he'd a-chawed up all the men he's ben a-gwyne to chaw up in the last twenty year he'd have considerable ruputation now."

Another one says, "I wisht old Boggs 'd threaten me, 'cuz then I'd know I warn't gwyne to die for a thousan' year."

Boggs comes a-tearing along on his horse, whooping and yelling like an Injun, and singing out:

"Cler the track, thar. I'm on the waw-path, and the price uv coffins is a-gwyne to raise."

He was drunk, and weaving about in his saddle; he was over fifty year old, and had a very red face. Everybody yelled at him and laughed at him and sassed him, and he sassed back, and said he'd attend to them and lay them out in their regular turns, but he couldn't wait now because he'd come to town to kill old Colonel Sherburn, and his motto was, "Meat first, and spoon vittles to top off on."

He see me, and rode up and says:

"Whar'd you come f'm, boy? You prepared to die?"

Then he rode on. I was scared, but a man says:

"He don't mean nothing; he's always a-carryin' on like that when he's drunk. He's the best-naturedest old fool in Arkansaw—never hurt nobody, drunk nor sober."

Boggs rode up before the biggest store in town, and bent his head down so he could see under the curtain of the awning and yells:

"Come out here, Sherburn! Come out and meet the man you've swindled. You're the houn' I'm after, and I'm a-gwyne to have you, too!"

And so he went on, calling Sherburn everything he could lay his tongue to, and the whole street packed with people listening and laughing and going on. By and by a proud-looking man about fifty-five— and he was a heap the best-dressed man in that town, too—steps out of the store, and the crowd drops back on each side to let him come. He says to Boggs, might ca'm and slow—he says:

"I'm tired of this, but I'll endure it till one o'clock. Till one o'clock, mind—no longer. If you open your mouth against me only once after that time you can't travel so far but I will find you."

Then he turns and goes in. The crowd looked mighty sober; nobody stirred, and there warn't no more laughing. Boggs rode off blackguarding Sherburn as loud as he could yell, all down the street; and pretty soon back he comes and stops before the store, still keeping it up. Some men crowded around him and tried to get him to shut up, but he wouldn't; they told him it would be one o'clock in about fifteen minutes, and so he *must* go home—he must go right away. But it didn't do no good. He cussed away with all his might, and throwed his hat down in the mud and rode over it, and pretty soon away he went a-raging down the street again, with his gray hair a-flying. Everybody that could get a chance at him tried their best to coax him off of his horse so they could lock him up and get him sober; but it warn't no use—up the street he would tear again, and give Sherburn another cussing. By and by somebody says:

"Go for his daughter!—quick, go for his daughter; sometimes he'll listen to her. If anybody can persuade him, she can."

So somebody started on a run. I walked down street a ways and stopped. In about five or ten minutes here comes Boggs again, but not on his horse. He was a-reeling across the street towards me, bareheaded, with a friend on both sides of him a-holt of his arms and hurrying him along. He was quiet, and looked uneasy; and he warn't hanging back any, but was doing some of the hurrying himself. Somebody sings out:

"Boggs!"

I looked over there to see who said it, and it was that Colonel Sherburn. He was standing perfectly still in the street, and had a pistol raised in his right hand—not aiming it, but holding it out with the barrel tilted up towards the sky. The same second I see a young girl coming on the run, and two men with her. Boggs and the men turned round to see who called him, and when they see the pistol the men jumped to one side, and the pistol-barrel come down slow and steady to a level—both barrels cocked. Boggs throws up both of his hands and says, "O Lord, don't shoot!" Bang! goes the first shot, and he staggers back, clawing at the air—bang! goes the second one, and he tumbles backward onto the ground, heavy and solid, with his arms spread out. That young girl screamed out and comes rushing, and down she throws herself on her father, crying, and saying, "Oh, he's killed him, he's killed him!" The crowd closed up around them, and shouldered and jammed one another, with their necks stretched, trying to see, and people on the inside trying to shove them back and shouting, "Back, back! give him air, give him air!"

Colonel Sherburn he tossed his pistol onto the ground, and turned around on his heels and walked off.

They took Boggs to a little drug store, the crowd pressing around just the same, and the whole town following, and I rushed and got a good place at the window, where I was close to him and could see in. They laid him on the floor and put one large Bible under his head, and opened another one and spread it on his breast; but they tore open his shirt first, and I seen where one of the bullets went in. He

made about a dozen long gasps, his breast lifting
the Bible up when he drawed in his breath, and
letting it down again when he breathed it out—and
after that he laid still; he was dead. Then they
pulled his daughter away from him, screaming and
crying, and took her off. She was about sixteen, and
very sweet and gentle looking, but awful pale and
scared.

Well, pretty soon the whole town was there, squirm-
ing and scrouging and pushing and shoving to get at
the window and have a look, but people that had the
places wouldn't give them up, and folks behind them
was saying all the time, "Say, now, you've looked
enough, you fellows; 'tain't right and 'tain't fair for you
to stay thar all the time, and never give nobody a
chance; other folks has their rights as well as you."

There was considerable jawing back, so I slid out,
thinking maybe there was going to be trouble. The
streets was full, and everybody was excited. Everybody that seen the shooting was telling how it happened, and there was a big crowd packed around
each one of these fellows, stretching their necks and
listening. One long, lanky man, with long hair and
a big white fur stovepipe hat on the back of his
head, and a crooked-handled cane, marked out the
places on the ground where Boggs stood and where
Sherburn stood, and the people following him around
from one place to t'other and watching everything
he done, and bobbing their heads to show they understood, and stooping a little and resting their hands
on their thighs to watch him mark the places on
the ground with his cane; and then he stood up
straight and stiff where Sherburn had stood, frowning
and having his hat-brim down over his eyes, and
sung out, "Boggs!" and then fetched his cane down

slow to a level, and says "Bang!" staggered backwards, says "Bang!" again, and fell down flat on his
back. The people that had seen the thing said he
done it perfect; said it was just exactly the way it all
happened. Then as much as a dozen people got out
their bottles and treated him.

Well, by and by somebody said Sherburn ought
to be lynched. In about a minute everybody was
saying it; so away they went, mad and yelling, and
snatching down every clothes-line they come to to do
the hanging with.

They swarmed up towards Sherburn's house,
a-whooping and raging like Injuns, and everything
had to clear the way or get run over and tromped to
mush, and it was awful to see. Children was heeling it
ahead of the mob, screaming and trying to get out of
the way; and every window along the road was full
of women's heads, and there was nigger boys in every
tree, and bucks and wenches looking over every fence;
and as soon as the mob would get nearly to them they
would break and skaddle back out of reach. Lots of the
women and girls was crying and taking on, scared most
to death.

They swarmed up in front of Sherburn's palings
as thick as they could jam together, and you couldn't
hear yourself think for the noise. It was a little twenty-
foot yard. Some sung out "Tear down the fence! tear
down the fence!" Then there was a racket of ripping and
tearing and smashing, and down she goes, and the front
wall of the crowd begins to roll in like a wave.

Just then Sherburn steps out onto the roof of his
little front porch, with a double-barrel gun in his
hand, and takes his stand, perfectly ca'm and de-

liberate, not saying a word. The racket stopped, and the wave sucked back.

Sherburn never said a word—just stood there, looking down. The stillness was awful creepy and uncomfortable. Sherburn run his eye slow along the crowd; and wherever it struck the people tried a little to outgaze him, but they couldn't; they dropped their eyes and looked sneaky. Then pretty soon Sherburn sort of laughed; not the pleasant kind, but the kind that makes you feel like when you are eating bread that's got sand in it.

Then he says, slow and scornful:

"The idea of *you* lynching anybody! It's amusing. The idea of you thinking you had pluck enough to lynch a *man!* Because you're brave enough to tar and feather poor friendless cast-out women that come along here, did that make you think you had grit enough to lay your hands on a *man?* Why, a *man's* safe in the hands of ten thousand of your kind—as long as it's daytime and you're not behind him.

"Do I know you? I know you clear through. I was born and raised in the South, and I've lived in the North; so I know the average all around. The average man's a coward. In the North he lets anybody walk over him that wants to, and goes home and prays for a humble spirit to bear it. In the South one man, all by himself, has stopped a stage full of men in the daytime, and robbed the lot. Your newspapers call you a brave people so much that you think you *are* braver than any other people—whereas you're just *as* brave, and no braver. Why don't your juries hang murderers? Because they're afraid the man's friends will shoot them in the back, in the dark—and it's just what they *would* do.

"So they always acquit; and then a *man* goes in

the night, with a hundred masked cowards at his
back, and lynches the rascal. Your mistake is, that
you didn't bring a man with you; that's one mistake,
and the other is that you didn't come in the dark
and fetch your masks. You brought *part* of a man—
Buck Harkness, there—and if you hadn't had him to
start you, you'd 'a' taken it out in blowing.

"You didn't want to come. The average man don't
like trouble and danger. *You* don't like trouble and
danger. But if only *half* a man—like Buck Harkness,
there—shouts 'Lynch him! lynch him!' you're afraid to
back down—afraid you'll be found out to be what you
are—*cowards*—and so you raise a yell, and hang your-
selves onto that half-a-man's coat-tail, and come raging
up here, swearing what big things you're going to do.
The pitifulest thing out is a mob; that's what an army is
—a mob; they don't fight with courage that's born in
them, but with courage that's borrowed from their mass,
and from their officers. But a mob without any *man* at
the head of it is *beneath* pitifulness. Now the thing for
you to do is to droop your tails and go home and crawl
in a hole. If any real lynching's going to be done it will
be done in the dark, Southern fashion; and when they
come they'll bring their masks, and fetch a *man* along.
Now *leave*—and take your half-a-man with you"—
tossing his gun up across his left arm and cocking it
when he says this.

The crowd washed back sudden, and then broke all
apart, and went tearing off every which way, and Buck
Harkness he heeled it after them, looking tolerable
cheap. I could 'a' stayed if I wanted to, but I didn't
want to.

I went to the circus and loafed around the back side
till the watchman went by, and then dived in under the
tent. I had my twenty-dollar gold piece and some other

money, but I reckoned I better save it, because there
ain't no telling how soon you are going to need it, away
from home and amongst strangers that way. You can'
be too careful. I ain't opposed to spending money or
circuses when there ain't no other way, but there ain't no
use in *wasting* it on them.

It was a real bully circus. It was the splendides
sight that ever was when they all come riding in, two
and two, and gentleman and lady, side by side, the
men just in their drawers and undershirts, and no shoe
nor stirrups, and resting their hands on their thighs easy
and comfortable—there must 'a' been twenty of them
—and every lady with a lovely complexion, and per
fectly beautiful, and looking just like a gang of rea
sure-enough queens, and dressed in clothes that cos
millions of dollars, and just littered with diamonds. I
was a powerful fine sight; I never see anything so lovely
And then one by one they got up and stood, and wen
a-weaving around the ring so gentle and wavy and
graceful, the men looking ever so tall and airy and
straight, with their heads bobbing and skimming along
away up there under the tent-roof, and every lady's rose
leafy dress flapping soft and silky around her hips, and
she looking like the most loveliest parasol.

And then faster and faster they went, all of them
dancing, first one foot out in the air and then the other
the horses leaning more and more, and the ringmaste
going round and round the center pole, cracking hi
whip and shouting "Hi!—hi!" and the clown cracking
jokes behind him; and by and by all hands dropped the
reins, and every lady put her knuckles on her hips and
every gentleman folded his arms, and then how th
horses did lean over and hump themselves! And so on
after the other they all skipped off into the ring, and
made the sweetest bow I ever see, and then scampered

out, and everybody clapped their hands and went just about wild.

Well, all through the circus they done the most astonishing things; and all the time that clown carried on so it most killed the people. The ringmaster couldn't ever say a word to him but he was back at him quick as a wink with the funniest things a body ever said; and how he ever *could* think of so many of them, and so sudden and so pat, was what I couldn't no way understand. Why, I couldn't 'a' thought of them in a year. And by and by a drunken man tried to get into the ring —said he wanted to ride; said he could ride as well as anybody that ever was. They argued and tried to keep him out, but he wouldn't listen, and the whole show come to a standstill. Then the people begun to holler at him and make fun of him, and that made him mad, and he begun to rip and tear; so that stirred up the people, and a lot of men begun to pile down off of the benches and swarm toward the ring, saying, "Knock him down! throw him out!" and one or two women begun to scream. So, then, the ringmaster he made a little speech, and said he hoped there wouldn't be no disturbance, and if the man would promise he wouldn't make no more trouble he would let him ride if he thought he could stay on the horse. So everybody laughed and said all right, and the man got on. The minute he was on, the horse begun to rip and tear and jump and cavort around, with two circus men hanging on to his bridle trying to hold him, and the drunken man hanging on to his neck, and his heels flying in the air every jump, and the whole crowd of people standing up shouting and laughing till tears rolled down. And at last, sure enough, all the circus men could do, the horse broke loose, and away he went like the very nation, round and round the ring, with that sot laying down on him and hanging to his neck, with first one leg hanging most to the ground on one side, and then t'other one on t'other side, and the people just crazy. It warn't funny to me, though; I was all of a tremble to see his danger. But pretty soon he struggled up astraddle and grabbed the bridle, a-reeling this way and that; and the next minute he sprung up and dropped the bridle and stood! and the horse a-going like a house afire, too. He just stood up there, a-sailing around as easy and comfortable as if he warn't ever drunk in his life—and then he begun to pull off his clothes and sling them. He shed them so thick they kind of clogged up the air, and altogether he shed seventeen suits. And, then, there he was, slim and handsome, and dressed the gaudiest and prettiest you ever saw, and he lit into that horse with his whip and made him fairly hum—and finally skipped off, and made his bow and danced off to the dressing-room, and everybody just a-howling with pleasure and astonishment.

Then the ringmaster he see how he had been fooled, and he *was* the sickest ringmaster you ever see, I reckon. Why, it was one of his own men! He had got up that joke all out of his own head, and never let on to nobody. Well, I felt sheepish enough to be took in so, but I wouldn't 'a' been in that ringmaster's place, not for a thousand dollars. I don't know; there may be bullier circuses than what that one was, but I never struck them yet. Anyways, it was plenty good enough for *me;* and wherever I run across it, it can have all of *my* custom every time.

Well, that night we had *our* show; but there warn't only about twelve people there—just enough to pay expenses. And they laughed all the time, and that made the duke mad; and everybody left, anyway, before the show was over, but one boy which was asleep. So the duke said these Arkansaw lunkheads couldn't come up

o Shakespeare; what they wanted was low comedy—
nd maybe something ruther worse than low comedy,
e reckoned. He said he could size their style. So next
norning he got some big sheets of wrapping-paper and
ome black paint, and drawed off some handbills, and
tuck them up all over the village. The bills said:

AT THE COURT HOUSE!
FOR 3 NIGHTS ONLY!
The World-Renowned Tragedians
DAVID GARRICK THE YOUNGER!
AND
EDMUND KEAN THE ELDER!
*Of the London and Continental
Theatres,*
In their Thrilling Tragedy of
THE KING'S CAMELEOPARD,
OR
THE ROYAL NONESUCH ! ! !
Admission 50 cents.

Then at the bottom was the biggest line of all, which
aid:

LADIES AND CHILDREN NOT ADMITTED

"There," says he, "if that line don't fetch them, I
lon't know Arkansaw!"

Well, all day him and the king was hard at it, rigging
ip a stage and a curtain and a row of candles for foot-
ights; and that night the house was jam full of men
n no time. When the place couldn't hold no more, the
luke he quit tending door and went around the back
vay and come onto the stage and stood up before the
curtain and made a little speech, and praised up this
ragedy, and said it was the most thrillingest one that

ever was; and so he went on a-bragging about th
tragedy, and about Edmund Kean the Elder, which wa
to play the main principal part in it; and at last whe
he'd got everybody's expectations up high enough, h
rolled up the curtain, and the next minute the kin
come a-prancing out on all fours, naked; and he wa
painted all over, ring-streaked-and-striped, all sorts o
colors, as splendid as a rainbow. And—but never min
the rest of his outfit; it was just wild, but it was awfu
funny. The people most killed themselves laughing; an
when the king got done capering and capered off behin
the scenes, they roared and clapped and stormed an
haw-hawed till he come back and done it over again
and after that they made him do it another time. Wel
it would make a cow laugh to see the shines that ol
idiot cut.

Then the duke he lets the curtain down, and bows t
the people, and says the great tragedy will be per
formed only two nights more, on accounts of pressin
London engagements, where the seats is all sold alread
for it in Drury Lane; and then he makes them anothe
bow, and says if he has succeeded in pleasing them an
instructing them, he will be deeply obleeged if the
will mention it to their friends and get them to com
and see it.

Twenty people sings out:

"What, is it over? Is that *all?*"

The duke says yes. Then there was a fine time. Every
body sings out, "Sold!" and rose up mad, and wa
a-going for that stage and them tragedians. But a big
fine-looking man jumps up on a bench and shouts:

"Hold on! Just a word, gentlemen." They stoppe
to listen. "We are sold—mighty badly sold. But we
don't want to be the laughing-stock of this whole town
I reckon, and never hear the last of this thing as long

as we live. *No.* What we want is to go out of here quiet, and talk this show up, and sell the *rest* of the town! Then we'll all be in the same boat. Ain't that sensible?" ("You bet it is!—the jedge is right!" everybody sings out.) "All right, then—not a word about any sell. Go along home, and advise everybody to come and see the tragedy."

Next day you couldn't hear nothing around that town but how splendid that show was. House was jammed again that night, and we sold this crowd the same way. When me and the king and the duke got home to the raft we all had a supper; and by and by, about midnight, they made Jim and me back her out and float her down the middle of the river, and fetch her in and hide her about two mile below town.

The third night the house was crammed again— and they warn't new-comers this time, but people that was at the show the other two nights. I stood by the duke at the door, and I see that every man that went in had his pockets bulging, or something muffled up under his coat—and I see it warn't no perfumery, neither, not by a long sight. I smelt sickly eggs by the barrel, and rotten cabbages, and such things; and if I know the signs of a dead cat being around, and I bet I do, there was sixty-four of them went in. I shoved in there for a minute, but it was too various for me; I couldn't stand it. Well, when the place couldn't hold no more people the duke he give a fellow a quarter and told him to tend door for him a minute, and then he started around for the stage door, I after him; but the minute we turned the corner and was in the dark he says:

"Walk fast now till you get away from the houses, and then shin for the raft like the dickens was after you!"

I done it, and he done the same. We struck the raft

at the same time, and in less than two seconds we was
gliding down-stream, all dark and still, and edging towards the middle of the river, nobody saying a word.
I reckoned the poor king was in for a gaudy time of it
with the audience, but nothing of the sort; pretty soon he
crawls out from under the wigwam, and says:

"Well, how'd the old thing pan out this time, duke?"
He hadn't been up-town at all.

We never showed a light till we was about ten mile
below the village. Then we lit up and had a supper,
and the king and the duke fairly laughed their bones
loose over the way they'd served them people. The duke
says:

"Greenhorns, flatheads! *I* knew the first house would
keep mum and let the rest of the town get roped in;
and I knew they'd lay for us the third night, and consider it was *their* turn now. Well, it *is* their turn, and
I'd give something to know how much they'd take for it.
I *would* just like to know how they're putting in their
opportunity. They can turn it into a picnic if they want
to—they brought plenty provisions."

Them rapscallions took in four hundred and sixty-five
dollars in that three nights. I never see money hauled
in by the wagon-load like that before.

By and by, when they was asleep and snoring, Jim
says:

"Don't it s'prise you de way dem kings carries on,
Huck?"

"No," I says, "it don't."

"Why don't it, Huck?"

"Well, it don't, because it's in the breed. I reckon
they're all alike."

"But, Huck, dese kings o' ourn is reglar rapscallions;
dat's jist what dey is; dey's reglar rapscallions."

"Well, that's what I'm a-saying; all kings is mostly rapscallions, as fur as I can make out."

"Is dat so?"

"You read about them once—you'll see. Look at Henry the Eighth; this 'n' 's a Sunday-school Superintendent to *him*. And look at Charles Second, and Louis Fourteen, and Louis Fifteen, and James Second, and Edward Second, and Richard Third, and forty more; besides all them Saxon heptarchies that used to rip around so in old times and raise Cain. My, you ought to seen old Henry the Eight when he was in bloom. He *was* a blossom. He used to marry a new wife every day, and chop off her head next morning. And he would do it just as indifferent as if he was ordering up eggs. 'Fetch up Nell Gwynn,' he says. They fetch her up. Next morning, 'Chop off her head!' And they chop it off. 'Fetch up Jane Shore,' he says; and up she comes. Next morning, 'Chop off her head'—and they chop it off. 'Ring up Fair Rosamun.' Fair Rosamun answers the bell. Next morning, 'Chop off her head.' And he made every one of them tell him a tale every night; and he kept that up till he had hogged a thousand and one tales that way, and then he put them all in a book, and called it Domesday Book—which was a good name and stated the case. You don't know kings, Jim, but I know them; and this old rip of ourn is one of the cleanest I've struck in history. Well, Henry he takes a notion he wants to get up some trouble with this country. How does he go at it—give notice?—give the country a show? No. All of a sudden he heaves all the tea in Boston Harbor overboard, and whacks out a declaration of independence, and dares them to come on. That was *his* style—he never give anybody a chance. He had suspicions of his father, the Duke of Wellington. Well, what did he do?

Ask him to show up? No—drownded him in a butt of mamsey, like a cat. S'pose people left money laying around where he was—what did he do? He collared it. S'pose he contracted to do a thing, and you paid him, and didn't set down there and see that he done it— what did he do? He always done the other thing. S'pose he opened his mouth—what then? If he didn't shut it up powerful quick he'd lose a lie every time. That's the kind of a bug Henry was; and if we'd 'a' had him along 'stead of our kings he'd 'a' fooled that town a heap worse than ourn done. I don't say that ourn is lambs, because they ain't, when you come right down to the cold facts; but they ain't nothing to *that* old ram, anyway. All I say is, kings is kings, and you got to make allowances. Take them all around, they're a mighty ornery lot. It's the way they're raised."

"But dis one do *smell* so like de nation, Huck."

"Well, they all do, Jim. *We* can't help the way a king smells; history don't tell no way."

"Now de duke, he's a tolerable likely man in some ways."

"Yes, a duke's different. But not very different. This one's a middling hard lot for a duke. When he's drunk there ain't no near-sighted man could tell him from a king."

"Well, anyways, I doan' hanker for no mo' un um, Huck. Dese is all I kin stan'."

"It's the way I feel, too, Jim. But we've got them on our hands, and we got to remember what they are, and make allowances. Sometimes I wish we could hear of a country that's out of kings."

What was the use to tell Jim these warn't real kings and dukes? It wouldn't 'a' done no good; and, besides, it was just as I said: you couldn't tell them from the real kind.

THE OUTCASTS
OF POKER FLAT

BY BRET HARTE

AS Mr. John Oakhurst, gambler, stepped into the main street of Poker Flat on the morning of the twenty-third of November, 1850, he was conscious of a change in its moral atmosphere since the preceding night. Two or three men, conversing earnestly together, ceased as he approached, and exchanged significant glances. There was a Sabbath lull in the air, which, in a settlement unused to Sabbath influences, looked ominous.

Mr. Oakhurst's calm, handsome face betrayed small concern of these indications. Whether he was conscious of any predisposing cause, was another question. "I reckon they're after somebody," he reflected; "likely it's me." He returned to his pocket the handkerchief with which he had been whipping away the red dust of Poker Flat from his neat boots, and quietly discharged his mind of any further conjecture.

In point of fact, Poker Flat was "after somebody." It had lately suffered the loss of several thousand dollars, two valuable horses, and a prominent citizen. It was experiencing a spasm of virtuous reaction, quite as lawless and ungovernable as any of the acts that had provoked it. A secret committee had determined to rid the town of all improper persons. This was done permanently in regard of two men who were then hanging from the boughs of a sycamore in the gulch, and temporarily in the banishment of certain other objectionable characters. I regret to say that some of these were ladies. It is but due to the sex, however, to state that their impropriety was professional, and it was only in such easily established standards of evil that Poker Flat ventured to sit in judgment.

Mr. Oakhurst was right in supposing that he was included in this category. A few of the committee had urged hanging him as a possible example, and a sure method of reimbursing themselves from his pockets of the sums he had won from them. "It's agin justice," said Jim Wheeler, "to let this yer young man from Roaring Camp—an entire stranger—carry away our money." But a crude sentiment of equity residing in the breasts of those who had been fortunate enough to win from Mr. Oakhurst overruled this narrower local prejudice.

Mr. Oakhurst received his sentence with philosophic calmness, none the less coolly that he·was aware of the hesitation of his judges. He was too much of a gambler not to accept Fate. With him life was at best an uncertain game, and he recognized the usual percentage in favor of the dealer.

A body of armed men accompanied the deported wickedness of Poker Flat to the outskirts of the settlement. Besides Mr. Oakhurst, who was known to be a coolly desperate man, and for those intimidation the armed escort was intended, the expatriated party consisted of a young woman familiarly known as "The Duchess"; another, who had gained the infelicitous title of "Mother Shipton"; and "Uncle Billy," a suspected sluice-robber and confirmed drunkard. The cavalcade provoked no comments from the spectators, nor was any word uttered by the escort. Only, when the gulch which marked the uttermost limit of Poker Flat was reached, the leader spoke briefly and to the point. The exiles were forbidden to return at the peril of their lives.

As the escort disappeared, their pent-up feelings found vent in a few hysterical tears from the Duchess, some bad language from Mother Shipton, and a Parthian volley of expletives from Uncle Billy. The philosophic Oakhurst alone remained still. He listened calmly to Mother Shipton's desire to cut somebody's heart out, to the repeated statements of the Duchess that she would die on the road, and to the alarming oaths that seemed to be bumped out of Uncle Billy as he rode forward. With the easy good humor characteristic of his class, he insisted upon exchanging his own riding-horse, Five Spot, for the sorry mule which the Duchess rode. But even this act did not draw the party into any closer sympathy. The young woman readjusted her somewhat draggled plumes with a feeble, faded coquetry; Mother Shipton eyed the possessor of Five Spot with malevolence, and Uncle Billy included the whole party in one sweeping anathema.

The road to Sandy Bar—a camp that, not having as yet experienced the regenerating influences of Poker Flat, consequently seemed to offer some invitation to the emigrants—lay over a steep mountain range. It was distant a day's severe journey. In that advanced season, the party soon passed out of the moist, temperate regions of the foothills into the dry, cold, bracing air of the Sierras. The trail was narrow and difficult. At noon the Duchess, rolling out of her saddle upon the ground, declared her intention of going no farther, and the party halted.

The spot was singularly wild and impressive. A wooded amphitheater, surrounded on three sides by precipitous cliffs of naked granite, sloped gently toward the crest of another precipice that overlooked the valley. It was undoubtedly the most suitable spot for a camp, had camping been advisable. But Mr. Oakhurst knew that scarcely half the journey to Sandy Bar was accomplished, and the party were not equipped or provisioned for delay. This fact he pointed out to his companions curtly, with a philosophic commentary on the folly of "throwing up their hand before the game was played out." But they were furnished with liquor, which in this emergency stood them in place of food, fuel, rest, and prescience. In spite of his remonstrances, it was not long before they were more or less under its influence. Uncle Billy passed rapidly from a bellicose state into one of stupor, the Duchess became maudlin, and Mother Shipton snored. Mr. Oakhurst alone remained erect, leaning against a rock, calmly surveying them.

Mr. Oakhurst did not drink. It interfered with a profession which required coolness, impassiveness, and presence of mind, and, in his own language, he "couldn't afford it." As he gazed at his recumbent fellow-exiles, the loneliness begotten of his pariah-trade, his habits of life, his very vices, for the first time seriously oppressed him. He bestirred himself in dusting his black clothes, washing his hands and face, and other acts characteristic of his studiously neat habits, and for a moment forgot his annoyance. The thought of deserting his weaker and more pitiable companions never perhaps occurred to him. Yet he could not help feeling the want of that excitement which, singularly enough, was most conducive to that calm equanimity for which he was notorious. He looked at the gloomy walls that rose a thousand feet sheer above the circling pines around him; at the sky, ominously clouded; at the valley below, already deepening into shadow. And, doing so, suddenly he heard his own name called.

A horseman slowly ascended the trail. In the fresh, open face of the new-comer Mr. Oakhurst recognized Tom Simson, otherwise known as "The Innocent" of

Sandy Bar. He had met him some months before over a "little game," and had, with perfect equanimity, won the entire fortune—amounting to some forty dollars—of that guileless youth. After the game was finished, Mr. Oakhurst drew the youthful speculator behind the door and thus addressed him: "Tommy, you're a good little man, but you can't gamble worth a cent. Don't try it over again." He then handed him his money back, pushed him gently from the room, and so made a devoted slave of Tom Simson.

There was a remembrance of this in his boyish and enthusiastic greeting of Mr. Oakhurst. He had started, he said, to go to Poker Flat to seek his fortune. "Alone?" No, not exactly alone; in fact—a giggle—he had run away with Piney Woods. Didn't Mr. Oakhurst remember Piney? She that used to wait on the table at the Temperance House? They had been engaged a long time, but old Jake Woods had objected, and so they had run away, and were going to Poker Flat to be married, and here they were. And they were tired out, and how lucky it was they had found a place to camp and company. All this the Innocent delivered rapidly, while Piney—a stout, comely damsel of fifteen—emerged from behind the pine-tree, where she had been blushing unseen, and rode to the side of her lover.

Mr. Oakhurst seldom troubled himself with sentiment, still less with propriety; but he had a vague idea that the situation was not felicitous. He retained, however, his presence of mind sufficiently to kick Uncle Billy, who was about to say something, and Uncle Billy was sober enough to recognize in Mr. Oakhurst's kick a superior power that would not bear trifling. He then endeavored to dissuade Tom Simson from delaying further, but in vain. He even pointed out the fact that there was no provision, nor means of making a camp.

But, unluckily, the Innocent met this objection by assuring the party that he was provided with an extra mule loaded with provisions, and by the discovery of a rude attempt at a log-house near the trail. "Piney can stay with Mrs. Oakhurst," said the Innocent, pointing to the Duchess, "and I can shift for myself."

Nothing but Mr. Oakhurst's admonishing foot saved Uncle Billy from bursting into a roar of laughter. As it was, he felt compelled to retire up the canyon until he could recover his gravity. There he confided the joke to the tall pine trees, with many slaps of his leg, contortions of his face, and the usual profanity. But when he returned to the party, he found them seated by a fire—for the air had grown strangely chill and the sky overcast—in apparently amicable conversation. Piney was actually talking in an impulsive, girlish fashion to the Duchess, who was listening with an interest and animation she had not shown for many days. The Innocent was holding forth, apparently with equal effect, to Mr. Oakhurst and Mother Shipton, who was actually relaxing into amiability. "Is this yer a d—d picnic?" said Uncle Billy, with inward scorn, as he surveyed the sylvan group, the glancing fire-light, and the tethered animals in the foreground. Suddenly an idea mingled with the alcoholic fumes that disturbed his brain. It was apparently of a jocular nature, for he felt impelled to slap his leg again and cram his fist into his mouth.

As the shadows crept slowly up the mountain, a slight breeze rocked the tops of the pine-trees, and moaned through their long and gloomy aisles. The ruined cabin, patched and covered with pine boughs, was set apart for the ladies. As the lovers parted, they unaffectedly exchanged a kiss, so honest and sincere that it might have been heard above the swaying pines. The frail Duchess and the malevolent Mother Shipton were probably too stunned to remark upon this last evidence of simplicity, and so turned without a word to the hut. The fire was replenished, the men lay down before the door, and in a few minutes were asleep.

Mr. Oakhurst was a light sleeper. Toward morning he awoke benumbed and cold. As he stirred the dying fire, the wind, which was now blowing strongly, brought to his cheek that which caused the blood to leave it—snow!

He started to his feet with the intention of awakening the sleepers, for there was no time to lose. But turning to where Uncle Billy had been lying, he found him gone. A suspicion leaped to his brain and a curse to his lips. He ran to the spot where the mules had been tethered; they were no longer there. The tracks were already rapidly disappearing in the snow.

The momentary excitement brought Mr. Oakhurst back to the fire with his usual calm. He did not waken the sleepers. The Innocent slumbered peacefully, with a smile on his good humored, freckled face; the virgin Piney slept beside her frailer sisters as sweetly as though attended by celestial guardians, and Mr. Oakhurst, drawing his blanket over his shoulders, stroked his mustachios and waited for the dawn. It came slowly in the whirling mist of snowflakes, that dazzled and confused the eye. What could be seen of the landscape appeared magically changed. He looked over the valley, and summed up the present and future in two words—"Snowed in!"

A careful inventory of the provisions, which, fortunately for the party, had been stored within the hut, and so escaped the felonious fingers of Uncle Billy, disclosed the fact that with care and prudence they might last ten days longer. "That is," said Mr. Oakhurst, *sotto voce* to the Innocent, "if you're willing to board us. If you ain't—and perhaps you'd better not—you can wait till Uncle Billy gets back with provisions." For some occult reason, Mr. Oakhurst, could not bring himself to disclose Uncle Billy's rascality, and so offered the hypothesis that he had wandered from the camp and had accidentally stampeded the animals. He dropped a warning to the Duchess and Mother Shipton, who of course knew the facts of their associate's defection. "They'll find out the truth about us *all,* when they find out anything," he added, significantly, "and there's no good frightening them now."

Tom Simson not only put all his worldly store at the disposal of Mr. Oakhurst, but seemed to enjoy the prospect of their enforced seclusion. "We'll have a good camp for a week, and then the snow'll melt, and we'll all go back together." The cheerful gayety of the young man and Mr. Oakhurst's calm infected the others. The Innocent, with the aid of pine boughs, extemporized a thatch for the roofless cabin, and the Duchess directed Piney in the rearrangement of the interior with a taste and tact that opened the blue eyes of that provincial maiden to their fullest extent.

"I reckon now you're used to fine things at Poker Flat," said Piney. The Duchess turned away sharply to conceal something that reddened her cheek through its professional tint, and Mother Shipton requested Piney not to "chatter." But when Mr. Oakhurst returned from a weary search for the trail, he heard the sound of happy laughter echoed from the rocks. He stopped in some alarm, and his thoughts first naturally reverted to the whisky, which he had prudently *cached*. "And yet it don't somehow sound like whisky," said the gambler. It was not until he caught sight of the blazing fire through the still blinding storm, and the group around it, that he settled to the conviction that it was "square fun."

Whether Mr. Oakhurst had *cached* his cards with the whisky as something debarred the free access of the community, I cannot say. It was certain that, in Mother Shipton's words, he "didn't say cards once" during the evening. Haply the time was beguiled by an accordion, produced somewhat ostentatiously by Tom Simson, from his pack. Notwithstanding some difficulties attending the manipulation of this instrument, Piney Woods managed to pluck several reluctant melodies from its keys, to an accompaniment by the Innocent on a pair of bone castinets. But the crowning festivity of the evening was reached in a rude camp-meeting hymn, which the lovers, joining hands, sang with great earnestness and vociferation. I fear that a certain defiant tone and Covenanter's swing to its chorus, rather than any devotional quality, caused it speedily to infect the others, who at last joined in the refrain:

> I'm proud to live in the service of the Lord,
> And I'm bound to die in His army.

The pines rocked, the storm eddied and whirled above the miserable group, and the flames of their altar leaped heavenward, as if in token of the vow.

At midnight the storm abated, the rolling clouds parted, and the stars glittered keenly above the sleeping camp. Mr. Oakhurst, whose professional habits had enabled him to live on the smallest possible amount of sleep, in dividing the watch with Tom Simson, somehow managed to take upon himself the greater part of that duty. He excused himself to the Innocent, by saying that he had "often been a week without sleep." "Doing what?" asked Tom. "Poker!" replied Oakhurst, sententiously, "when a man gets a streak of luck—nigger-luck—he don't get tired. The luck gives in first. Luck," continued the gambler, reflectively, "is a mighty queer thing. All you know about it for certain is that it's bound to change. And it's finding out when it's going to change that makes you. We've had a streak of bad luck since we left Poker Flat—you come along, and slap you get into it, too. If you can hold your cards right along you're all right. For," added the gambler, with cheerful irrelevance,

> "I'm proud to live in the service of the Lord,
> And I'm bound to die in His army."

The third day came, and the sun, looking through the white-curtained valley, saw the outcasts divide their slowly decreasing store of provisions for the morning meal. It was one of the peculiarities of that mountain climate that its rays diffused a kindly warmth over the wintry landscape, as if in regretful commiseration of the past. But it revealed drift on drift of snow piled high around the hut; a hopeless, uncharted, trackless sea of white lying below the rocky shores to which the castaways still clung. Through the marvelously clear air, the smoke of the pastoral village of Poker Flat rose miles away. Mother Shipton saw it, and from a remote pinnacle of her rocky fastness, hurled in that direction a final malediction. It was her last vituperative attempt, and perhaps for that reason was invested with a certain degree of sublimity. It did her good, she privately informed the Duchess. "Just to go out there and cuss, and see." She then set herself to the task of amusing "the child," as she and the Duchess were pleased to call Piney. Piney was no chicken, but it was a soothing and ingenious theory of the pair thus to account for the fact that she didn't swear and wasn't improper.

When night crept up again through the gorges, the reedy notes of the accordion rose and fell in fitful spasms and long-drawn gasps by the flickering camp-fire. But music failed to fill entirely the aching void left by insufficient food, and a new diversion was proposed by Piney—story-telling. Neither Mr. Oakhurst nor his female companions caring to relate their personal experiences, this plan would have failed, too, but for the Innocent. Some months before he had chanced upon a stray copy of Mr. Pope's ingenious translation of the Iliad. He now proposed to narrate the principal incidents of that poem—having thoroughly mastered the argument and fairly forgotten the words—in the current vernacular of Sandy Bar. And so for the rest of that night the Homeric demigods again walked the earth. Trojan bully and wily Greek wrestled in the winds, and the great pines in the canyon seemed to bow to the wrath of the son of Peleus. Mr. Oakhurst listened with quiet satisfaction. Most especially was he interested in the fate of "Ash-heels," as the Innocent persisted in denominating the "swift-footed Achilles."

So with small food and much of Homer and the accordion, a week passed over the heads of the outcasts. The sun again forsook them, and again from leaden skies the snowflakes were sifted over the land. Day by day closer around them drew the snowy circle, until at last they looked from their prison over drifted walls of dazzling white, that towered twenty feet above their heads. It became more and more difficult to replenish their fires, even from the fallen trees beside them, now half-hidden in the drifts. And yet no one complained. The lovers turned from the dreary prospect and looked into each other's eyes, and were happy. Mr. Oakhurst settled himself coolly to the losing game before him. The Duchess, more cheerful than she had

been, assumed the care of Piney. Only Mother Shipton—once the strongest of the party—seemed to sicken
and fade. At midnight on the tenth day she called
Oakhurst to her side. "I'm going," she said, in a voice
of querulous weakness, "but don't say anything about
it. Don't waken the kids. Take the bundle from under
my head and open it." Mr. Oakhurst did so. It contained Mother Shipton's rations for the last week, untouched. "Give 'em to the child," she said, pointing to
the sleeping Piney. "You've starved yourself," said the
gambler. "That's what they call it," said the woman,
querulously, as she lay down again, and, turning her
face to the wall, passed quietly away.

The accordion and the bones were put aside that day,
and Homer was forgotten. When the body of Mother
Shipton had been committed to the snow, Mr. Oakhurst
took the Innocent aside, and showed him a pair of
snowshoes, which he had fashioned from the old pack-
saddle. "There's one chance in a hundred to save her
yet," he said, pointing to Piney; "but it's there," he
added, pointing toward Poker Flat. "If you can reach
there in two days she's safe." "And you?" asked Tom
Simson. "I'll stay here," was the curt reply.

The lovers parted with a long embrace. "You are not
going, too?" said the Duchess, as she saw Mr. Oakhurst
apparently waiting to accompany him. "As far as the
canyon," he replied. He turned suddenly, and kissed the
Duchess, leaving her pallid face aflame, and her trembling limbs rigid with amazement.

Night came, but not Mr. Oakhurst. It brought the
storm again and the whirling snow. Then the Duchess,
feeding the fire, found that some one had quietly piled
beside the hut enough fuel to last a few days longer.
The tears rose to her eyes, but she hid them from Piney.

The women slept but little. In the morning, looking into each other's faces, they read their fate. Neither spoke; but Piney, accepting the position of the stronger, drew near and placed her arm around the Duchess's waist. They kept this attitude for the rest of the day. That night the storm reached its greatest fury, and, rending asunder the protecting pines, invaded the very hut.

Toward morning they found themselves unable to feed the fire, which gradually died away. As the embers slowly blackened, the Duchess crept closer to Piney, and broke the silence of many hours: "Piney, can you pray?" "No, dear," said Piney, simply. The Duchess without knowing exactly why, felt relieved, and, putting her head upon Piney's shoulder, spoke no more. And so reclining, the younger and purer pillowing the head of her soiled sister upon her virgin breast, they fell asleep.

The wind lulled as if it feared to waken them. Feathery drifts of snow, shaken from the long pine boughs, flew like white-winged birds, and settled about them as they slept. The moon through the rifted clouds looked down upon what had been the camp. But all human stain, all trace of earthly travail, was hidden beneath the spotless mantle mercifully flung from above.

They slept all that day and the next, nor did they waken when voices and footsteps broke the silence of the camp. And when pitying fingers brushed the snow from their wan faces, you could scarcely have told from the equal peace that dwelt upon them, which was she that had sinned. Even the Law of Poker Flat recognized this, and turned away, leaving them still locked in each other's arms.

But at the head of the gulch, on one of the largest

pine trees, they found the deuce of clubs pinned to the bark with a bowie knife. It bore the following, written in pencil, in a firm hand:

✝

BENEATH THIS TREE
LIES THE BODY
OF
JOHN OAKHURST,
WHO STRUCK A STREAK OF BAD LUCK
ON THE 23D OF NOVEMBER, 1850,
AND
HANDED IN HIS CHECKS
ON THE 7TH OF DECEMBER, 1850.

✝

And pulseless and cold, with a Derringer by his side and a bullet in his heart, though still calm as in life, beneath the snow lay he who was at once the strongest and yet the weakest of the outcasts of Poker Flat.

A PREACHER GOES TO WAR

BY JOHN W. THOMASON, JR.

OF the Rev. Praxiteles Swan, it is related elsewhere how he rode out from Virginia to Texas in the days before the war, ordained to preach the Gospel after the style of the Methodist Episcopal Church, South; and how he came, on a blooded mare, with salvation in his saddlebags, to establish himself on the front rank of the battle line Methodism maintained against the powers of darkness in those parts. They relate also that he was redheaded and slabsided, and pretty nearly as tall, and as loud in the mouth, as Gen. Sam Houston. In the Rutersville District at Washington on the Brazos, he immediately thrashed the two toughest men in the community, commandeered a saloon for his tabernacle, and married the local heiress. Forthwith, he preached and practised a militant religion immensely appealing to East Texas of that ardent time. The years passed over him, and he entered into the legends and the folk tales of the region, for he was of the material from which the narrators make such things. You will find his acts set forth in certain old books; and the elders of my youth remembered him, particularly Uncle Jimmy Farrow, the Quantrill raider, who taught me the refinements of squirrel hunting by Patterson Lake; and my uncles, who fought the war in the Fifth Texas Volunteer Infantry, Confederate States Provisional Army.

From these sources, then, and from old letters in a cowhide trunk, I make this story. Praxiteles Swan was a thoughtful man and liked to analyze his personal acts. He says somewhere that the first important decision in his life was that which led him to turn his back on the tempestuous blue-blood uncle in Virginia, who brought him up, and to enter the Methodist ministry. For this decision, he felt, he had a basis of high conviction and sound scriptural precept, and he was proud of it. The second, however, he considered to have been forced upon him by no less an event than the War of the Southern Confederacy, and he was never quite certain that it carried a blessing with it.

But as for this story: The opening of the year 1861 found him in health and high condition, his circumstances better than a bishop's in most respects; a lean column of a man, red-maned and red-bearded. Named presiding elder for the Huntsville District in 1859, he had brought his family to a farm a few miles west of that pleasant little town, so that the children might have advantage of the schools which caused Huntsville to be called, in those days, the Athens of Texas. Mrs. Swan's money had provided the farm, her Negroes worked it, and she herself, Praxiteles said with pride, ran it as well as a man. For the Swans were folks who got ahead. Praxiteles himself had ever an eye for horseflesh, and talent for occasional judicious horse trading, and saw nothing wrong about it, any more than he saw evil for his cloth in hunting and fishing. Nor did he see why he shouldn't wear a good coat and ride a good horse on his pastoral rounds, and he did both all his life. While he conceded the spirituality of his colleagues, he privately considered most of them a shiftless lot; he was never able to associate starvation, even the genteel starvation of the Methodist preacher, with a state of grace. That was the year the state seceded from the Federal Union.

The war was seen far in advance by knowledgeable

men, and there were signs and portents, such as go before great events. The old folks, white and black, still remember the comet blazing in the sky, about the winter of '59 and '60; it had a tail shaped like a sword; and they recall the other omens also. When man met, throughout the South, they talked politics, and the women showed an uneasy interest, and every scrap of newspaper that penetrated to the settlements was read to tatters. Not a few of the preachers took sides and held forth from their pulpits on a tariff for revenue only, and states' rights, and brave little South Carolina. But Praxiteles Swan was not one of these; he despised politicians, and notably lacked patience with fools. He considered that preachers should abjure the things of this world, and that his Lord and Master was not in politics, and that war talk was idle and wicked. Such sentiments got him into continual argument, because tempers were running high all over the South, and Praxiteles, for all his weight and inches and red hair, was more than once forced to support his principles with his hands.

Indeed, his conduct had come to a point of issue before the last East Texas Conference of 1860. Praxiteles' presiding elder—a divine famous for his warlike sentiments, who ate fire to public admiration all over his district, and then went to California when the war broke out and stayed there—publicly cited Brother Swan for fighting—this to the scandal of the cloth. And it is one of the stories they tell: How the deliberations of the conference on the unchristian violence of Brother Swan were guided tactfully by the bishop, because Praxiteles, with his white face and flaming hair and dilated nostrils, was rather frightening. The evidence allowed no doubt that Brother Swan had, in fact, whaled the daylights out of a Mr. Ellers, of Old Waverly: and the bishop announced, uneasily: "Brother Swan must be admonished before the conference, and have prayer offered for him." They relate that the accused stood up, with the effect of a tree standing, and the bishop added hastily that Brother Abner Smedes would offer the prayer "for our dearly beloved brother, yonder." Praxiteles sat down and Brother Smedes rose; he was oldest and gentlest of them all; his hair was white as carded wool, and he was round and pink and benevolent. He stood and raised a face of beatitude and a smooth voice, saying: "O Lord! Brother Swan has been a-fightin' again. We're mighty sorry about this, Lord. We know he oughtn' to be a-fightin' like this all the time, and we hope, O Lord! you'll help him not to, any more. But if he does have to fight, O Lord, please, Seh, arrange it so he'll whup!"

After that, Praxiteles, not at all chastened, was sent into the North Texas Conference to fill the pulpit of a furloughed preacher, and the North Texas counties were close enough to Kansas to be infected with the Free Soil violence which was tearing the border to pieces. In February, Texas seceded from the Union and joined the Confederacy. Praxiteles Swan was one of the two Methodist preachers sitting on the Gainesville citizens' committee to try the bushwhackers who killed Col. Bill Young in Cooke County, and that committee tranquilized the section by hanging forty-eight men on the same tree, as it is told, and in the same day. This event, more than any other, forced Praxiteles Swan to turn his thoughts from his calling, his family and his brood mares.

The entries in his journal indicate a certain agony of spirit; he didn't believe in secession, but he wanted to do what was right: "I am still visiting, praying, and preaching as hard as I can, with fear and trembling.

. . . The people are so absorbed in the 'Crisis' that they have forgotten they have souls. . . . I think the moral crisis in this country is much greater than the political. . . . I am going to throw a few Bum shells into my congregation this very Sunday. . . ." Everywhere he went, that winter, prominent gentlemen were raising military companies and regiments. The divine who served the Galveston charge wrote him in winged words: "If Lincoln's fleet should come now . . . I am satisfied that their blood will make the grass come up a foot higher on our prairie here. . . . I shall die a true patriot and a soldier of the Cross, the gun in hand and Christ within my heart. . . ." This letter further stated that the writer was joining the MacDonald Rangers.

Praxiteles asked about the Rangers of a state militia officer in Houston, and learned that they were frontier guards; the authorities were apprehensive for the western regions of the state. Praxiteles shrugged and went his way; the approach of war, he reflected, brought out a lot of human nature. I find in this part of his diary references which, on examination, prove to be from the more sanguinary passages of the Old Testament. Praxiteles was an Old Testament man; the New Testament was for his softer moods, and he had few soft moods that one can verify. It should be added that there was no pressure on him, nor any preacher, to bear arms. The old South held its preachers high and rarely sat in judgment on their conduct. But he realized presently that he was one crying "Peace, peace," when there was no peace.

The thing came clear for him one raw March evening, after his return to Huntsville; the children, having done their lessons—young Prax, the oldest, was deep in the *Commentaries of Cæsar* and most insistent to discover the age at which Roman boys were allowed to go to war—had yawned off to bed; the two girls were tucked away; and Mrs. Swan was reading, with much indignation, a book by a Mrs. Stowe called *Uncle Tom's Cabin,* which had come into the community—although Mrs. Swan wasn't a reading woman, really. Praxiteles, since supper, had walked up and down before the fire, his face withdrawn and shadowed, his brows knitted.

Now he stopped pacing, and faced his wife. "Mrs. Swan, the thing is clear to me. I have wrestled, as Jacob on Peniel, and I have my answer. I must join this war."

"Yes, Mr. Prax," she replied, not lifting her eyes from the page. "Yes, Mr. Prax. I thought you would."

"You thought I would!" His tone implied that she had taken a liberty, thinking about his actions. "It is a plain duty. Our young men in these camps of instruction are sheep without a shepherd, if I ever saw any in my life. Most of them are from Christian homes, but there are godless young hellions at large among them. And the officers—I declare to you, Mrs. Swan, I don't believe the officers, especially the majors and colonels, do a thing but drink whisky and chew tobacco! And the generals!" He stopped to search a usually adequate vocabulary, without success. "I am no part of a soldier. I am a man of peace. I don't pretend to understand the politics of the affair. But there can be no dispensation of grace on the godless and the wrathful, and who wins must have God on his side! Where, then"—his great voice mounted and the flame fluttered in the lamp—"is the preacher's place but in the forefront of the fight? I mean, the unremitting war we wage against Apollyon and his host."

Mrs. Swan rose deliberately, went to the fireplace and laid the Stowe book well back on the logs. She returned to her chair, and you saw that she was repressing sentiments of extraordinary violence. "Don't you preach at me, Mr. Swan," she told him. "I knew you were going to the war, one way or another. You couldn't see a fuss as big as that and not get yourself into it. It was just a question in my mind, when you'd choose to join. I've got your clothes together, ready to go in the portmanteau, and——"

"Woman, you're crazy!" Praxiteles had never heard such language from her in eighteen years of married life. This dutiful and tender wife of his——"Woman, the events happening have upset you! What is this book you burn? What——"

"Nothing's upset me," Mrs. Swan told him evenly. "As to that Stowe hussy, I'd like to have my fingers"—— she crooked and flexed her strong, well-kept hands——"in her back hair for about two minutes! Pah!" She came as near spitting as a refined female might, and not do so. "I'll not vex myself discussing it. But why don't they let us alone, those Yankees? I tell you, Mr. Swan, if I was a man, I'd have gone myself before now——indeed I would." Mrs. Swan's black eyes snapped and her nostrils dilated, and she breathed strongly through her nose. She straightened herself in her chair, and you observed that she still had a figure. "I wish the Yankee nation was in the Bad Place, John Brown and that Garrison man and all," she stated, "and that I could help send them there! Well, go on and preach to your young men, Mr. Prax. I can take care of things here. But," she concluded darkly, "I don't think you'll be preaching very long." She sought with fumbling hands for her sewing basket. All at once her eyes were bright with tears, but Praxiteles observed that they were tears of pure rage. The woman Stowe's book was burning unwillingly, with a great smoke and a strong smell of glue. Come to think of it, he'd heard the book mentioned, although he discouraged among his flocks the reading of secular works—novels and such. Would that be the spark that had struck such fire from this meek wife of his bosom? She had never spoken so to him before; had been, all these years, a jewel among women. Now . . . *Jael— Jael—Jael*. The text came to him: "Blessed above women shall Jael . . . be. . . . She put her hand to the nail, and her right hand to the workmen's hammer; and with the hammer she smote Sisera, she smote off his head, when she had pierced and stricken through his temples."

Praxiteles Swan turned and leaned against the mantel, and poked *Uncle Tom's Cabin* deeper into the logs; now it burned more strongly. He looked again at his wife over his arm. Her eyes were the eyes of one seeing visions.

"My dear," he said gently, almost timidly. "My dear."

She got up and came over to him. "Mr. Prax," she said, "you're a good man and you've been a good husband to me all these years. I was never in a war, but women know all about war—women who bear men-children know all about war. This war will be terrible. I only hope it's finished before young Prax is old enough to go. But if it's not, I'll send him too."

He told her, presently, that she was overwrought; it was time they had the evening lesson and sought their rest, and he picked up his Bible. First he looked for that eloquent passage in which Paul, a bachelor, discusses matrimony, but he changed his mind and read aloud the ninety-first psalm, which is a good psalm for a man going away to war; and the prayer he prayed that night was Mizpah—Laban's "The Lord watch between me and thee when we are absent one from another."

The next day, Elder Swan set out for Houston, to

enroll himself as chaplain in the Fifth Texas Regiment of Volunteer Infantry. As far as Montgomery he had a fellow traveller, his friend, Gen. Sam Houston, lately ejected from the governor's chair at Austin, after he had declined to take the oath of allegiance to the Confederacy. The vast old general was in great form, his eyes bright with some scheme he had, and he talked for forty miles. One passage Praxiteles was to remember all his life, although he never saw Sam Houston again.

"All the young men are going to this war, Elder, and you, who are old enough to know better, are going with them. And old Sam Houston tells you, Elder, that it is madness. *Quem Deus vult perdere*— As the Gadarene swine, you rush on destruction! And you who live will see your substance wasted, your women and children homeless, your very social order destroyed. Elder, the day will come—and you will see it—oh, a chaplain seldom gets hurt—you'll see people draw the nails from those cotton sheds out there to fasten planks above their heads against the elements! You'll see gentlefolk working with their hands where your Negroes work now— only a damned sight harder. Remember, in those days, that old Sam warned ye and you would not hear."

II

Of the Texas Brigade which served with the Army of Northern Virginia many books have been written, some of them still available in the older libraries. There were the First, Fourth and Fifth Regiments, assembled from thirty-two militia companies over the eastern portion of the state in early 1861. The Fourth and Fifth formed at Houston and were sworn in by a picturesque Old Army officer named Earl Van Dorn, then major, C. S. A. In August they were ordered to Virginia, and marched through Eastern Texas and Western Louisiana to New Iberia on the Teche, a twelve-day march in the hottest and unhealthiest season of the year, which stripped away their weaklings before they reached the railhead. They arrived in Richmond, already very tough men, in September. The First Texas came in a little later by a sort of unofficial movement still unexplained in the annals; it was John Bell Hood's word that the First Texas simply straggled to the front.

They were sent to the army on the Alexandria Line— as the loose irregular front from Winchester down through the plains of Manassas, Fredericksburg and Yorktown was called—and were brigaded with the 18th Georgia and Hampton's Legion, under the famous fire-eater, General Wigfall. Their time passed without alarms, in drills and instruction; the war was urbane and far away. It was by no means certain, after the sweeping victory at Manassas in July, that there would be any fighting with the North. It was generally believed that the mudsills were well whipped, and would presently go home; although Praxiteles Swan, from his travels in the North, didn't think so himself.

Praxiteles Swan made the march to New Iberia, and the steam-car ride thereafter. He was a great help to the colonel in minor disciplinary matters, and his regiment left no trail of wrecked barrooms along the road to Richmond, as did certain other formations whose misdeeds are even now embalmed in the official records. At the Richmond camp of instruction, up river by the fairgrounds, he became interested in drills and bought himself a *Gilham's Manual*. He also added to his field library the *Commentaries of Cæsar* and Xenophon's books. But the best soldier of them all, he considered, was Joshua; he had Joshua by heart. What he saw of the Provisional Government—the Jeff Davis Government it was beginning to be called—did not impress him. He renewed no old acquaintances in Richmond. He had, he conceded, completely severed himself from his beginnings; that soft drawl of the Texans made him homesick, not for his Virginia birthplace, but for the East Texas hills and the Trinity bottom lands where Mrs. Swan and his children waited for him. Up at Charlottesville there still must live, he supposed, the furious old uncle who had brought him up, and thrown him out when he joined the ministry. No word from the uncle, all the years since he went out to Texas; the old rascal would be in a fine humor over this war, although too old to serve in it. One day, while Praxiteles played with the idea of asking leave to visit him, he learned, casually, that the gentleman was dead—dead of a thundering apoplexy induced by the news that Gen. Joe Johnston failed to pursue the broken foe after the Battle of Manassas. Also, that he had left his property—which was considerable—to a nephew who ran off to Texas some years back. Praxiteles took furlough and went to Charlottesville, and made himself known to the lawyers who were tracing him in Texas; such was the lighthearted inefficiency of the Confederate postal service that their letters would be another year finding him.

When the uncle's affairs were settled, the Reverend Praxiteles Swan was a well-to-do man, as such things went in that section. He inherited three fat Piedmont farms, some blooded stock, and a hundred slaves. Praxiteles did not hesitate over the slaves. He considered the institution legal and ethical, but prohibitively wasteful. He had no intention, he stated, of undertaking the upkeep of a parcel of lazy, heavy-eating blacks, nor did he care for the hiring-out system. He directed the legal gentlemen to manumit the able-bodied and their families as fast as work could be found for them, and he arranged living quarters and kitchen gardens for the few incapables in the back areas of the great house, which he would hold.

The farms rented readily, for it looked as though the armies would need a lot of wheat, and farmers were increasing their acreages. The horses offered no problem. Confederate remount officers snapped at them, and Praxiteles saved two for his personal use—a thoroughbred bay mare, and a strong young gelding, three-quarter strain, that promised well. There was some cash, too; the old colonel had thought highly of gold. Praxiteles put as much as he considered patriotic in Confederate bonds, and set aside a respectable sum for soldier uses. He bought no tracts; he considered that tracts did no good to anybody, and he argued the matter hotly and publicly with a Presbyterian divine in the post office at Charlottesville, to the great delight of the bystanders. His business concluded, he stood bare-headed for a space in the keen November wind by his uncle's grave, under the cedar trees in the garden, where the old gentleman loved to sit through hot afternoons. He found no feeling save a mild regret, and his uncle, he was convinced, lay securely in hell. Then he returned to his regiment and found the army going into winter quarters, after the genteel fashion of that war.

The Texas Brigade was building huts on the hills by Dumfries, with the flats of Quantico Creek below and the Potomac making a great shimmering loop toward the east. Four men would join forces and run up a windowless shack with log walls, chinked against the wind. Chimneys were contrived of stones and mud and sticks. Bunks of rough-hewed timber flanked the fireplaces inside, and doors were hung on rawhide hinges. The huts were loosely grouped by regiments. The Texans were weather-tight in no time, although Hood and the West P'int inspectors grumbled continually that the shacks were out of dress.

Regimental duty was light; the brigade was in a support echelon of the Alexandria Line. Since the enemy was snug in winter quarters, too, no unpleasantness was anticipated before spring. The regiment did its turn on picket and grand guard, but the cavalry was having all the fun, or so the reports went; and the skeptical Texans, horse-riding folks to a man, began to hear stories about a fantastical cavalier called, amusingly, Jeb Stuart. Now and then they saw some bedraggled Yankee prisoners, plucked up by his troopers. But their only enemy, save winter and rough weather, was a regiment of New York Fire Zouaves which lived across the river on the Maryland shore; clear days, you could see the splash of color they made when they drilled, for they went gloriously in red and yellow.

It became the fashion for the men of the two commands to perpetrate small outrages on one another; venturous souls crossed the river by night in rowboats to this end, and now and then did not return. January, the river froze—the Potomac is a big river down there—and the thick ice ran out so far from each bank that men could approach to shouting distance and insult one another. The New Yorkers were easily first at such games; the provincials from the Trinity bottom could not approach the glib obscenities of the Bowery, and had to content themselves with promising to cover the earth with the ring-streaked and striped bodies of the Fire Zouaves, did they ever get a chance at them. Oddly enough, the Fifth Texas and the Zouaves came face to face along Young's Branch, about sunset the last day of Second Manassas, the August following, but that is another story, remembered more in Texas than in New York. Praxiteles deplored the presence of the New Yorkers, it made the men swear so.

If time in winter quarters fell heavy on the young soldiers—how wistfully, through three winters to come, some of them would look back upon that season when the war was new—the chaplains found sufficient employment. Praxiteles Swan jousted tirelessly at the devil of the camps, which is a particularly insidious devil, beguiling men with applejack and playing cards. Many of the war stories about him date from this time, and his journal gives further evidence to the effect that he was never idle. It was not in him to be idle.

My uncles had their narratives of these months: How he stopped a fight between two sergeants by plucking up the combatants and knocking their heads together. How he discouraged a blasphemer by immersing him in a horse trough, and then—it being freezing weather —conducting the man to his quarters and wrapping him in his own blankets while the fellow's clothes dried, Praxiteles admonishing him the while—that man was a talented swearer, but he always looked over his shoulder, afterward, before he expressed himself, and they say it spoiled his style—and the time he walked in on a game of brag, table stakes, blandly swept the money into his pockets, waited, from his great height, for objections, thanked the players for their charity, and turned the loot over to the brigade surgeon for hospital extras. In the army, also, he always was the material of which legend is made.

His own diary contains frank notes on people afterwards famous. Joseph E. Johnston, the commanding general in those parts, he considered a formalist; and he did not then nor later subscribe to the Old Army viewpoint which rated Joe Johnston at the top of the list. On Longstreet, he withheld his opinion, but came to regard him as a man who knew his business; and he never indulged in the hue and cry that clouded Longstreet's fame after the war. Brig. Gen. J. E. B. Stuart interested him because of his known piety; everybody knew Stuart, who seemed as ubiquitous as the wind, but Praxiteles held that he was too young and gay for responsibilities. Praxiteles never liked the cavalry. The officer most prominent in the Texas Brigade was Colonel Hood, the West Pointer who commanded the Fourth Texas and who, when General Wigfall discovered the atmosphere of the Confederate Senate more congenial to his talents than the tented field, was given the brigade.

This Hood was a great one for soldiering, and loved parades; had his men out in all weathers, tramping around. Praxiteles did not approve of him; he was by rumor a loose liver; a vessel, in fact, of wrath; and the chaplain of the Fifth considered his example terribly dangerous to the young men of his charge. Hood was a tall, high-shouldered Kentuckian, with long arms and legs and a big-boned frame, his face smothered in a straw-colored beard. There was a droop to the set of his pale blue eyes that gave him a curious, diffident, mournful look, like a regretful Viking, but never was an appearance more deceptive. Of him, Praxiteles would write more hereafter.

His journal tells, too, of the conference the chaplains of the brigade held to determine the proper station for a chaplain during battle—a question much debated by the Southern prelates. The doctrine of the Old Army held that the chaplain was a noncombatant, and might properly, at most, engage himself in the care of the

wounded around the field hospitals, and with the
ghostly consolation of those about to die. The Provisional Army of the Confederate States was, however, as
little bound by doctrine as any ever mustered for war,
and the militia soldiers looked with cold suspicion upon
anything emanating from West Point. Thus numerous
views were expounded.

A Brother Alpheus Murk, of a Cotton State brigade,
stated that the presence of a chaplain among troops
engaged in combat did the troops no good, and further,
was exceedingly harmful to the health of the chaplain's
soul. He had served with a volunteer regiment at Buena
Vista in the Mexican War, and he related that the oaths
and blasphemies of the soldiers were so appalling, he
did not consider himself in a state of grace for at least
eleven months thereafter, although he wore down the
very springs of his knees with prayer. Several divines
present at First Manassas, were inclined to agree with
Brother Murk. Praxiteles' contribution was that he'd
never been in a battle and couldn't form an opinion
until events brought him opportunity to observe. As
affairs turned out, there were zealous brothers who,
later on, would be catching up musket and cartridge
box to pitch in with the boys, when battle joined. There
were others who, for reasons cogent to themselves,
would avoid violence and place themselves well to the
rear of the army trains and the reserve artillery until
the unpleasantness should be over, enduring with Christian fortitude the caustic comment of the uninstructed.
And you would find padres at every station in between.
The conference, after prolonged discussion, resolved
that a chaplain's battle station was where his services
were most needed. And matters stayed exactly where
they were before. Deliberations were terminated by
sudden orders to move south.

III

If you remember the records, the early spring of
1862 brought a great stirring throughout the armies.
McClellan was accumulating a force in front of Washington, which, said the Federal city newspapers—sold
daily to the Confederate outposts of the Alexandria
Line, and read with much interest through the camps—
would presently descend upon the Rebellion like the
wolf on the fold. Praxiteles Swan, by the way, took
this for his text on a Sunday about the first of March,
and predicted that, did they come, their fate would be
one with the Assyrian's. It was much admired in the
Texas Brigade, to whom Elder Swan explained the
allusion in detail. A little later, the scouts of the Potomac shore reported long columns of transports, blue
with Yankees, filing downstream.

Gen. Joe Johnston, ever sensitive of his flanks, destroyed half a year's accumulation of stores between
Manassas and Fredericksburg—a sin and a waste, inviting the rebuke of the Almighty, declared Praxiteles,
watching a fine meat packery burn—and retired on
Richmond. The Texans moved from their winter
quarters the eighth of March, over hills sodden under
a late fall of snow, and tramped to Fredericksburg,
where they lay for a month, and had the grim news of
Shiloh; there were many Texas regiments in the
Western army. It was in Fredericksburg that there
arose and clung to the Texas Brigade the reputation
for chicken stealing, which, as other of its characteristics, became famous and is remembered to this day.
There is something about it in the chaplain's diary;
he mentions that the Lord blessed them with an abundance of nourishing food in the hospitable city on the
Rappahannock, and adds: "Thou shalt not muzzle

the ox when he treadeth out the corn." Nobody, then or afterward, was able to interest Praxiteles in the small peccadilloes of men on active service.

From Fredericksburg the brigade marched to York-town through rain and mud, only to march back up the Peninsula to Richmond, much bewildered by such tactics. They lay in reserve when Longstreet turned so savagely upon McClellan at Williamsburg, and only one of the regiments, the Fourth, was really engaged in the affair at Eltham's Landing, on the York, where they chased Franklin to his gunboats and saw their quartermaster struck dead off his horse by a stray bullet. So far, they had hardly seen a Yankee, save those incredible Zouaves, and the war was dull. Then they went up-country under General Whiting, with Law's Georgians, on a wild-goose chase toward the Valley of Virginia, where one Stonewall Jackson was shaking the bushes mightily, so that they had reason to anticipate real employment. But they did not so much as hear Jackson's bugles. Following fast, aimless marches and uneventful bivouacs, they turned east from the Blue Ridge, along roads suddenly heavy with strange troops, and proceeded by rail and by hard marching in the direction of Richmond. It was late June, and hot weather.

There was still enough of the circuit rider in Praxiteles Swan for him to note the direction and duration of each day's march, but he appears to have been thoroughly bored, and noted little more. You see known names about the end of June, '62: Gordonsville, Fredericks Hall, the Ashcake Road, Hanover Courthouse. The entry for the twenty-sixth says they lay near a church, Pole Green—or was it Hundley's Corner?—and a battle seemed to be going on, southward some miles. A little skirmishing for them on the Totopotomoy.

Very hot weather; rumors of big events. He was writing his wife to dispatch, by first safe means available, his linen dusters! His uniform frock coat, with the crosses on the lapels, was oppressive. From the light of campfires in the sky that night, many troops were lying in the neighborhood of Richmond. A number of the men had asked for a discourse in the bivouac, and he talked on remission of sins and on the campaigns of Joshua.

If he had known it, that was the first of the Seven Days' Battle before Richmond; in the afternoon, Ambrose Hill's brigades had crossed the Chickahominy at Mechanicsville, and thrown themselves upon Fitz-John Porter's corps, while Lee prepared a major destruction for McClellan. But Jackson did not strike that day.

The morning of the twenty-seventh, the Texans gulped hasty coffee and half-seared dough cakes, then stood interminably in fours, and marched and countermarched vexatiously by blind wood roads in the heat and the dust, to stand again. Southward and to the right there was a lot of shooting, an angry sound of musketry that rose and fell, a continual growling of guns, and now and then a far faint yelling. Nobody knew anything; staff officers galloped with more than the usual air of mystery, to conceal the fact that they knew nothing, either; a dingy general officer rode by, men saying, "There goes old Jackson," and he was not cheered. Small insects bit and buzzed. Praxiteles' mare grew restive and hot, which concerned him. Mid-afternoon, the brigade moved again, closer to the noise; they could see smoke rising over a line of trees up the road; despondent walking wounded passed, and D. H. Hill's North Carolinians came from the south and went by with an air of going somewhere. Hill's regiments made a brave show, their flags uncased and their bayonets shining.

The Texans were all grumbling. General Hood rode along the column, and sat his horse near Praxiteles Swan, at the head of the Fifth, his eyes speculative on the smoke yonder. He had, Praxiteles considered, a fine appearance on a horse. Horses jingled on the road, horses well housed and in high condition—no jaded army nags, these—and Praxiteles Swan watched his brigadier trot to meet a neat iron-gray officer on a stout iron-gray gelding. Hood doffed his hat with a cavalier sweep, and the other general returned graceful salutation and spoke quietly and earnestly, pointing toward the lazy curling smoke above the trees. The battle grew louder as the day declined; it ran off for miles toward the south; it achieved something of a monstrous rhythm—wild yelling that pulsated through a staccato raving of musketry, on a steady underchord of cannon thunder. Up at this end, as the musketry fell a little, they could hear a deep, cadenced shouting; that would be the voice of the enemy. "They-uns don't jest open their throats and yell, like our boys. But they're gettin' mighty loud over there, ain't they?"

Balthis' Battery, well known to the brigade, waiting these hours down the road, trotted smartly out across the field and went into action, firing at something beyond the trees; the brigade watched with friendly interest. While Praxiteles craned his neck in that direction, and reassured his mare, orders pealed down from the head of the column. It went fours-left into line, flowed over the worm fence and obliqued across the field to the right of the guns, and through the screen of timber. Painfully thin timber, when you got into it. The regiments debouched in some disarray upon their first set battlefield. Just clear of the trees they halted and dressed their ranks, and while this was being meticulously accomplished by the officers, the regimental chaplain of the Fifth felt mighty solemn. He watched the color bearers strip the oilskin covers from the colors; the heavy red folds of the battle flags shook out, appeared to preen themselves as birds; and the color sergeant of the First Texas elevated higher than the rest the fine state flag presented by the ladies of Brenham; the white and blue and red were as fresh as when the ladies cut them from their Sunday dresses last spring.

A zealot in the First yelled, "Ya-a-a-i-i-ih! Ya-a-a-i-i-ih! The Lone Star!" but he was firmly squelched by a duty-struck major.

Praxiteles felt a great surge of heat through all his bones. He broadened himself and sat erect on his mare. "Terrible as an army with banners—" Just then his regiment, the Fifth, faced to the right and departed at a trot, trailing arms. "We're going into it," he decided, and looked to the rear for a sapling, to tie his mare. Didn't want her hurt. Find a safe place for her, and catch up with the command on foot. Why, he reflected angrily, hadn't that question been decided, about the proper station of the chaplain in battle? He wanted to do what was right.

While he stood, undecided, flinching unconsciously from the noises in the air, Colonel Robertson's nigger trotted back, dragging at the bridle of the colonel's big flea-bitten gray. Praxiteles knew the boy, and flung him his reins, and, so to speak, girded up his loins to go after his regiment. But now the Fifth was out of sight in the woods, the brigade had taken ground to the right, and he was, he saw, behind the Fourth Texas Regiment—boys from the old Rutersville district of the East Texas Conference.

He halted to consider, and General Hood appeared from a flank on foot, his shadow reaching immensely before him in the low sun.

The general strode to the front and center of the Fourth, his sword flashed out in a bright curve, and he said, in that blunt carrying voice of his: "Fourth Texas! When I was your colonel, I promised that I would lead you in your first charge! I am keeping my promise!" He turned his head to the left, then to the right, as a hawk looks. "Brigade, attention! Right shoulder—shift!"

Every man could hear him, for the ripple of arms ran promptly down through Hampton's Legion, on the far left. That malignant could sway a camp meeting like an archangel's horn, thought Praxiteles, with envy.

"No man to fire until I give the order!" bayed Hood —the general had learned at Eltham's Landing that the Texans would not go into battle without loading and capping their pieces, no matter what orders he gave— "For-r-r-wa-a-rd!"

The brigade gave itself a jerk and lurched ahead, and Praxiteles followed, because he could think of nothing else to do. But a charge, now—and he a preacher with a family, and getting toward forty years— The men looked white under their tanned hides, and they leaned a little, as men lean against heavy rain. Almost at once the enemy was in view, on a hill across a valley, and Praxiteles, watching with concern the Yankee line, saw a purposeful agitation in the nearest part of it—a movement of gun teams and cannon.

Things howled in the air overhead, and the brigade bowed like wheat beneath the wind; explosions occurred in the immediate rear. The howling came again, and the set of fours in front of Praxiteles disintegrated violently. The air was full of hissing particles and a rank smell, and what looked like a bad sawmill accident littered the ground; there was some screaming, and officers and sergeants bawled angry exhortations. An ashen, frantic individual, his face drawn to a point, detached himself from the regiment and caromed into Praxiteles, leaping like a jack rabbit toward the rear. Praxiteles caught the soldier by the collar and shook him until his teeth rattled, thanking his Maker for the fortifying sight of a man more frightened than himself.

" 'The devil damn thee black, thou whey-faced loon!' " he quoted between his teeth—hadn't thought of Shakespeare for years—funny how apt the tag was. "You—" He recognized a notable card sharper of the Fourth Texas, a famous frequenter of the Dumfries stills. "Jim Hicks, get up in your place before I wring your neck!"

He administered two swinging slaps and a kick, and High Private Hicks, slobbering, sought safety in the ranks. To left and right, gray jackets were flung flat, or lay wriggling, in the trail of the regiment. There were spiteful singing sounds—musketry, personal shooting. But the line was going forward over the inequalities of an old field, and the flags had the appearance of brave swooping eagles. It came into his head: "Her young ones also suck up blood: and where the slain are, there is she," but he did not know that he roared from Habakkuk at the capacity of a pair of lungs as powerful as Hood's. "They are terrible and dreadful"—the words came to him, and a jet of arterial blood slopped against his chest, as a man, shot through the neck, spun against him; he eased the fellow down, started to kneel, and saw the line was going on without him.

Boy from Big Sandy, in San Jacinto County—it seemed more important to keep up with that line. "Let the dead bury their dead—" He had to run.

Out in front, General Hood had faced about to the regiment; he held his saber lightly in both hands, at arm's length, level with his shoulders, and he walked backwards, chiding the Fourth: "The guide is left! . . . Dress on the colors, damn you to everlasting hell! . . . Up on the right there . . . up in the center!" He stepped unerringly backward, and his eye penetrated even to the file closers, where Praxiteles now marched.

A lot of men were getting hit; the brigade was at the bottom of the slope and began to climb. There was a line of men lying down in a dead space. They caught at the legs of the Texans and whined in the accents of the Deep South: "Bettah not go on up theh! It's hell an' damnation up theh!" but a young officer rose among them and waved his sword and screamed, "Fifteenth Alabama, will yo' let these heah Texicans go wheh yuh won't go?" and shouldered himself into the Texas line.

Again Hood's voice dominated. How had they come so close? Nearly in shotgun range among some shattered peach trees.

"Halt!" the general's sword made another flashing arc. "Fix . . . bayonets!" Most of the men did it. "Fire!" Hood must have capered sideways, for his voice came next out of the sudden smoke from the right of the regiment. Praxiteles reflected afterward that, once the advance started, he saw nothing and thought of nothing except what was directly in front of him. However, the regiment seemed to explode, and then the compelling voice blared. "Charge!" and all the bugles in the world rang in his word.

The men raised a high, thin, angry scream, and ran

forward, only a few of them trying to bite cartridge and reload. They burst out of the fog of their own firing upon the raw earth of a fresh-dug trench, tenanted by crumpled dead men in dusty blue clothes. There was a confused blue mass in front of them—men in short jackets toiling at guns, men in frock coats waving silly swords and mouthing—more noise than Praxiteles had imagined in the world. One clump of blue stood solid and their Springfields spoke fierce and sharp in the ambiguous tumult; something caught at the skirt of Praxiteles' coat, and three men seemed to wind themselves around his legs. He sensed a suspension of movement; here were stanch Northern men standing firm to fight. But in a flicker of thought, Praxiteles knew that his personal antagonists, right there, were as men who had emptied their pieces into the head of a flock of geese—now they had to reload. How the musket came into his hand he did not notice, but it was there, and he broke a sergeant's skull with it. What followed after that, he never remembered clearly; there were some cavalry riding out of the smoke, who tumbled in hideous ruin at his very feet. He heard an officer, his leg under his fallen horse, say in clear disgusted tone, "But I'm Captain Chambliss, and we served together in the old Second, and he'll want to see me."

Himself, he was aware of fading light and of blue backs turned so that you couldn't see the buttons, and he shouted a supplication, "Sun, stand thou still upon Gibeon; and thou, Moon, in the valley of Ajalon!"

Over the plateau the flat rays of the sun made the smoke and dust all murky red. Beyond, the deep woods of the Chickahominy bottom invited fugitives and checked pursuit. The panting soldiers slowed down and stopped. One looted a knapsack; another went among

the fallen, searching pockets; a third, with a tasseled
meerschaum pipe in a shaking hand, asked every man
he met for a smidgeon of tobacco. It was all confusion
and "garments rolled in blood," as Isaiah put it; but it
appeared to Praxiteles Swan that, anyway, his side had
won. He leaned on the musket barrel and felt faint and
empty. The sodden stain across his coat sickened him.
How did the musket get broken? And the breech was
smeared with what must be blood and brains from a
towheaded man. Soldiers stopped to stare at him.
General Hood, the light behind him, rode up, gigantic
against the west, his horse stepping delicately, avoiding
unspeakable things. He saw Praxiteles' gray frock coat.

He said, "You, there! You're an officer! Get these
rapscallions into formation! Assemble your men, sir!
No time for— Why!" His teeth showed in his beard,
"It's the big parson! What you doing here, preacher?"

"Sir," Praxiteles told him, suddenly shaken, "may
He of Galilee forgive me, but from this day hence-
forward, I serve the God of Battles, the greatest of
commanders. Tell me what you want these young men
to do and they will do it."

"Get them into line," Hood told him soberly. "Get
them—get them, that is, straightened out, by companies.
All the damned field officers seem to be shot. Do the
best you can, Elder, and when I find an officer, I'll send
him along."

Praxiteles Swan, sometime shepherd of the best-
thought-of Methodist flocks in East Texas, inflated his
chest and let out a roar. Men stopped what they were
doing and listened. "All right, you scabrous sons of
Belial! Cease from that grave robbing and come unto
me! The curse of Achan on you, who turned aside to
plunder! . . . You, young man—I mean you with the
flag—stand right here and wave that flag! Come

around here, you—" He tried to remember, but didn't, the commands in *Gilham's Manual*. "Huddle! Jehovah confound you, huddle! I would have you stay not, 'but pursue after your enemies, and smite the hindmost of them.'" He menaced them with the dreadful clotted musket barrel, and soldiers moved to assemble themselves, obedient. Even stray South Carolinians of Hampton's, high-chinned heroes from the proper side of Church Street, began to sort themselves into squads, well disposed and heedful.

General Hood gathered his horse; he wanted to find Whiting or D. H. Hill or Jackson, and get a pursuit started. "Elder," he said immensely pleased, "old Stonewall couldn't have put it better. 'Stay not . . . and smite the hindmost of them!' Go right ahead with what you're doing! You don't need any officer. And when I get my brigade headquarters set up, you come see me. I'm going to snatch that cross off your coat and put a star on it—well, captain's bars, anyway."

Again Praxiteles Swan felt that surge of heat along his bones. "General, I'll come," he said. And he added, to himself, "I'll be bound, Mrs. Swan will be right pleased when she hears about it!"

UNCLE REMUS

BY JOEL CHANDLER HARRIS

I

"UNCLE REMUS," said the little boy one evening, when he had found the old man with little
or nothing to do, "did the fox kill and eat the rabbit
when he caught him with the Tar-Baby?"

"Law, honey, ain't I tell you 'bout dat?" replied the
old darkey, chuckling slyly. "I 'clar ter grashus I ought
er tole you dat, but old man Nod wuz ridin' on my eye-
leds 'twel a leetle mo'n I'd a dis'member'd my own
name, en den on to dat here come yo' mammy hollerin'
atter you.

"W'at I tell you w'en I fus' begin? I tole you Brer
Rabbit wuz a monstus soon creetur; leas'ways dat's wa't
I laid out fer ter tell you. Well, den, honey, don't you go
en make no udder calkalashuns, kaze in dem days Brer
Rabbit en his fambly wuz at de head er de gang w'en
enny racket wuz on han', en dar dey stayed. 'Fo' you
begins fer ter wipe yo' eyes 'bout Brer Rabbit, you wait
en see whar'bouts Brer Rabbit gwineter fetch up at. But
dat's needer yer ner dar.

"W'en Brer Fox fine Brer Rabbit mixt up wid de Tar-
Baby, he feel mighty good, en he roll on de groun' en
laff. Bimeby he up'n say, sezee:

"'Well, I speck I got you dis time, Brer Rabbit,'
sezee: 'maybe I ain't, but I speck I is. You been runnin'
roun' here sassin' atter me a mighty long time, but I
speck you done come ter de een' er de row. You bin
cuttin' up yo' capers en bouncin' 'roun' in dis neighber-

hood ontwel you come ter b'leeve yo'se'f de boss er de whole gang. En den youer allers some'rs whar you got no bizness,' sez Brer Fox, sezee. 'Who ax you fer ter come en strike up a 'quaintance wid dish yer Tar-Baby? En who stuck you up dar whar you iz? Nobody in de roun' worril. You des tuck en jam yo'se'f on dat Tar-Baby widout waitin' fer enny invite,' sez Brer Fox, sezee, 'en dar you is, en dar you'll stay twel I fixes up a bresh-pile and fires her up, kaze I'm gwineter bobbycue you dis day, sho,' sez Brer Fox, sezee.

"Den Brer Rabbit talk mighty 'umble.

"'I don't keer w'at you do wid me, Brer Fox, sezee, 'so you don't fling me in dat brier-patch. Roas' me, Brer Fox, sezee, 'but don't fling me in dat brier-patch,' sezee.

"'Hit's so much trouble fer ter kindle a fier,' sez Brer Fox, sezee, 'dat I speck I'll hatter hang you,' sezee.

"'Hang me des ez high as you please, Brer Fox,' sez Brer Rabbit, sezee, 'but do fer de Lord's sake don't fling me in dat brier-patch,' sezee.

"'I ain't got no string,' sez Brer Fox, sezee, 'en now I speck I'll hatter drown you,' sezee.

"'Drown me dez ez deep ez you please, Brer Fox,' sez Brer Rabbit, sezee, 'but do don't fling me in dat brier-patch,' sezee.

"'Dey ain't no water nigh,' sez Brer Fox, sezee, 'en now I speck I'll hatter skin you,' sezee.

"'Skin me, Brer Fox,' sez Brer Rabbit, sezee, 'snatch out my eyeballs, t'ar out my years by de roots, en cut off my legs,' sezee, 'but do please, Brer Fox, don't fling me in dat brier-patch,' sezee.

"Co'se Brer Fox wanter hurt Brer Rabbit bad ez he kin, so he cotch 'im by de behime legs en slung 'im right in de middle er de brier-patch. Dar wuz a con-siderbul flutter whar Brer Rabbit struck de bushes, en Brer Fox sorter hang 'roun' fer ter see w'at wuz gwineter happen. Bimeby he hear somebody call 'im, en way up de hill he see Brer Rabbit settin' cross-legged on a chinkapin log koamin' de pitch outen his har wid a chip. Den Brer Fox know dat he bin swop off mighty bad. Brer Rabbit wuz bleedzed fer ter fling back some er his sass, en he holler out:

"'Bred en bawn in a brier-patch, Brer Fox—bred en bawn in a brier-patch!' en wid dat he skip out des es lively ez a cricket in de embers."

II

"DIDN'T the fox *never* catch the rabbit, Uncle Remus?" asked the little boy the next evening.

"He come mighty nigh it, honey, sho's you born— Brer Fox did. One day atter Brer Rabbit fool 'im wid dat calamus root, Brer Fox went ter wuk en got 'im some tar, en mix it wid some turkentime, en fix up a contrapshun wat he call a Tar-Baby, en he tuck dish yer Tar-Baby en he sot 'er in de big road, en den he lay off in de bushes fer to see wat he news wuz gwineter be. En he didn't hatter wait long, nudder, kaze bimeby here come Brer Rabbit pacin' down de road—lippity-clippity, clippity-lippity—dez ez sassy ez a jay-bird. Brer Fox, he lay low. Brer Rabbit come prancin' 'long twel he spy de Tar-Baby, en den he fotch up on his be-hime legs like he wuz 'stonished. De Tar-Baby, she sot dar, she did, en Brer Fox, he lay low.

"'Mawnin'!' sez Brer Rabbit, sezee—'nice wedder dis mawnin',' sezee.

"Tar-Baby ain't sayin' nothin', en Brer Fox, he lay low.

"'How duz yo' sym'tums seem ter segashuate?' sez Brer Rabbit, sezee.

"Brer Fox, he wink his eye slow, en lay low, en de Tar-Baby, she ain't sayin' nothin'.

"'How you come on, den? Is you deaf?' sez Brer Rabbit, sezee. 'Kaze if you is, I kin holler louder,' sezee.

"Tar-Baby stay still, en Brer Fox, he lay low.

"'Youer stuck up, dat's w'at you is,' says Brer Rabbit, sezee, 'en I'm gwineter kyore you, dat's w'at I'm a gwineter do,' sezee.

"Brer Fox, he sorter chuckle in his stummuck, he did, but Tar-Baby ain't sayin' nothin'.

"'I'm gwineter larn you howter talk ter 'specttubble fokes ef hit's de las' ack,' sez Brer Rabbit, sezee. 'Ef you don't take off dat hat en tell me howdy, I'm gwineter bus' you wide open,' sezee.

"Tar-Baby stay still, en Brer Fox, he lay low.

"Brer Rabbit keep on axin' 'im, en de Tar-Baby, she keep on sayin' nothin', twel present'y Brer Rabbit draw back wid his fis, he did, en blip he tuck 'er side er de head. Right dar's whar he broke his merlasses jug. His fis' stuck, en he can't pull loose. De tar hilt 'im. But Tar-Baby, she stay still, en Brer Fox, he lay low.

"'Ef you don't lemme loose, I'll knock you agin,' sez Brer Rabbit, sezee, en wid dat he fotch 'er a wipe wid de udder han', en dat stuck. Tar-Baby, she ain't sayin' nothin', en Brer Fox, he lay low.

"'Tu'n me loose, fo' I kick de natal stuffin' outen you,' sez Brer Rabbit, sezee, but de Tar-Baby, she ain't sayin' nothin'. She des hilt on, en den Brer Rabbit lose de use er his feet in de same way. Brer Fox, he lay low. Den Brer Rabbit squall out dat ef de Tar-Baby don't tu'n 'im loose he butt 'er chanksided. En den he butted, en his head got stuck. Den Brer Fox, he sa'ntered fort', lookin' des ez innercent ez one er yo' mammy's mockin'-birds.

"'Howdy, Brer Rabbit,' sez Brer Fox, sezee. 'You look

sorter stuck up dis mawnin',' sezee, en den he rolled on de groun', en laughed en laughed twel he couldn't laugh no mo'. 'I speck you'll take dinner wid me dis time, Brer Rabbit. I done laid in some calamus root, en I ain't gwineter take no skuse,' sez Brer Fox, sezee."

Here Uncle Remus paused, and drew a two-pound yam out of the ashes.

"Did the fox eat the rabbit?" asked the little boy to whom the story had been told.

"Dat's all de fur de tale goes," replied the old man. "He mout, en den agin he moutent. Some say Jedge B'ar come 'long en loosed 'im—some say he didn't. I hear Miss Sally callin'. You better run 'long."

A LAST WILL

BY WILLISTON FISH

This famous invention, soon adrift from its moorings in an 1898 issue of Harper's Weekly (since deceased), has often been reprinted as solemn fact and as such is now a permanent part of American folklore. In 1915 Irving Berlin turned it into a song called "When I Leave the World Behind."

IN THE NAME OF GOD, AMEN. I, Charles Lounsbury being of sound and disposing mind and memory, do now make and publish this my LAST WILL AND TESTAMENT, in order, as justly as I may, to distribute my interests in the world among succeeding men.

And first, that part of my business which is known in the law and recognized in the sheep-bound volumes as my property, being inconsiderable and of none account, I make no account of it in this my will. My right to live, being a life estate, is not at my disposal; but these things excepted, all else in the world I now proceed to devise and bequeath.

Item: And first, I give to good fathers and mothers, but in trust for their children, nevertheless, all good little words of praise and all quaint pet names, and I charge said persons to use them justly and generously as the needs of their children shall require.

Item: I leave to children exclusively, but only for the life of their childhood, all and every, the dandelions of the fields and the daisies thereof, and the right to play among them freely, according to the custom of children, warning them at the same time against the thistles. And I devise to children the yellow shores

of creeks and the golden sands beneath the waters
thereof, with the dragon-flies that skim the surface
of said waters, and the odors of the willows that dip
into said waters and the white clouds that float high
over the giant trees. And I leave to children the long,
long days to be merry in, in a thousand ways, and
the Night and Moon and the train of the Milky Way
to wonder at, but subject, nevertheless, to the rights
hereinafter given to lovers; and I give to each child
the right to choose a star that shall be his, and I direct
that the child's father shall tell him the name of it,
in order that the child shall always remember the name
of the star after he has learned and forgotten astronomy.

Item: I devise to boys jointly, all the useful idle fields
and commons where ball may be played, and all snow-
clad hills where one may coast, and all streams and
ponds where one may skate, to have and to hold the
same for the period of their boyhood. And all meadows
with the clover-blooms and butterflies thereof; and
all woods with their appurtenances of squirrels and
whirring birds and echoes and strange noises; and all
distant places which may be visited, together with the
adventures there found, I do give to said boys to be
theirs. And I give to said boys each his own place at
the fireside at night, with all pictures that may be
seen in the burning wood or coal, to enjoy without
let or hindrance and without any incumbrance of
cares.

Item: To lovers I devise their imaginary world, with
whatever they may need, as the stars of the sky,
the red, red roses by the wall, the snow of the haw-
thorn, the sweet strain of music, and aught else that
they may desire, to figure to each other the lasting-
ness and beauty of their love.

Item: To young men jointly, being joined in a brave

mad crowd, I devise and bequeath all boisterous, inspiring sports of rivalry. I give them the disdain of weakness and undaunted confidence in their own strength. Though they are rude and rough, I leave to them alone the power of making lasting friendships and possessing companions; and to them exclusively I give all merry and brave choruses to sing, with smooth voices to troll them forth.

Item: And to those who are no longer children or youths or lovers I leave Memory, and I leave to them the volumes of the poems of Burns and Shakespeare, and of other poets, if there are others, to the end that they may live the old days over again fully and freely, without tithe or diminution; and to those who are no longer children or youths or lovers I leave, too, the knowledge of what a rare, rare world it is.

ONE ARROWHEAD DAY

FROM *Ma Pettingill*

BY HARRY LEON WILSON

IT BEGAN with the wonted incitement to murder. A wooden staff projects some five feet above the topmost roof peak of the Arrowhead ranch house, and to this staff is affixed a bell of brazen malignity. At five-thirty each morning the cord controlling this engine of discord is jerked madly and forever by Lew Wee, our Chinese chef. It is believed by those compelled to obey the horrid summons that this is Lew Wee's one moment of gladness in a spoiled life. The sound of the noon bell, the caressing call of the night bell—these he must know to be welcome. The morning clangour he must know to be a tragedy of foulest import. It is undeniably rung with a keener relish. There will be some effort at rhythm with the other bells, but that morning bell jangles in a broken frenzy of clangs, ruthlessly prolonged, devilish to the last insulting stroke. Surely one without malice could manage this waking bell more tactfully.

A reckless Chinaman, then, takes his life in his hands each morning at five-thirty. Something like a dozen men are alarmed from deep sleep to half-awakened incredulity, in which they believe the bell to be a dream bell and try to dream on of something noiseless. Ten seconds later these startled men have become demons, with their nice warm feet on the icy floor of the bunkhouse, and with prayers of simple fervour that the so-and-so Chink may be struck dead while his hand is still on the rope. This prayer is never answered; so something like a dozen men dress hurriedly and reach the Arrowhead kitchen hurriedly, meaning to perform instantly there a gracious deed which Providence has thus far unaccountably left undone.

That the Arrowhead annals are, as yet, unspiced with a crime of violence is due, I consider, to Lew Wee's superb control of his facial muscles. His expression when he maniacally yanks the bell cord is believed by his victims to be one of hellish glee; so they eagerly seek each morning for one little remaining trace of this. The tiniest hint would suffice. But they encounter only a rather sad-faced, middle-aged Chinaman, with immovable eyes and a strained devotion to delicate tasks, of whom it is impossible to believe that ever a ray of joy gladdened his life.

There is a secondary reason why the spirit of Lew Wee has not long since been disembodied by able hands: His static Gorgon face stays the first murderous impulse; then his genial kitchen aroma overpowers their higher natures and the deed of high justice is weakly postponed. This genial kitchen aroma is warm, and composed cunningly from steaming coffee and frying ham or beef, together with eggs and hot cakes almost as large as the enamelled iron plates from which they are eaten. It is no contemptible combination on a frosty morning. No wonder strong men forget the simple act of manslaughter they come there to achieve and sit sullenly down to be pandered to by him who was erst their torturer.

On a morning in late May, when I had been invited to fare abroad with my hostess, Mrs. Lysander John Pettengill—who would breakfast in her own apartment— I joined this assemblage of thwarted murderers as they doggedly ate. It is a grim business, that ranch breakfast. Two paling lamps struggle with the dawn, now edging in, and the half light is held low in tone by smoke from the cake griddle, so that no man may see another too plainly. But no man wishes to see another. He stares dully into his own plate and eats with stern aversion. We might be so many strangers in a strange place, aloof, suspicious, bitter, not to say truculent.

No quip or jest will lighten the gloom. Necessary requests for the sugar or the milk or the stewed apples are phrased with a curtly formal civility. We shall be other men at noon or at night, vastly other, sunnier men, with abundance of quip and jest and playful sally with the acid personal tang. But from warm beds of repose! We avoid each other's eyes, and one's subdued "please pass that sirup pitcher!" is but tolerated like some boorish profanation of a church service.

The simple truth, of course, is that this is the one hour of the day when we are face to face with the evil visage of life unmasked; our little rosy illusions of yestereve are stale and crumpled. Not until we are well out in the sun, with the second cigarette going good, shall we again become credulous about life and safe to address. It is no meal to linger over. We grimly rise from the wrecked table and clatter out.

Only one of us—that matchless optimist, Sandy Sawtelle—sounds a flat note in the symphony of disillusion. His humanness rebounds more quickly than ours, who will not fawn upon life for twenty minutes yet. Sandy comes back to the table from the hook whence he had lifted his hat. He holds aloft a solitary hot cake and addresses Lew Wee in his best Anglo-Chinese, and with humorous intent:

"I think take-um hot cake, nail over big knot hole in bunk-house—last damn long time better than sheet iron!"

Swiftly departing pessimists accord no praise or attention to this ill-timed sketch; least of all Lew Wee, who it is meant to insult. His face retains the sad impassivity of a granite cliff as yet beyond the dawn.

Now I am out by the saddle rack under the poplars, where two horses are tied. Ma Pettengill's long-barrelled roan is saddled. My own fleabitten gray, Dandy Jim, is clad only in the rope by which he was led up from the caviata. I approach him with the respectful attention his reputed character merits and try to ascertain his mood of the moment. He is a middle-aged horse, apparently of sterling character, and in my presence has always conducted himself as a horse should. But the shadow of scandal has been flung athwart him. I have been assured that he has a hideous genius for cinch binding. Listening at first without proper alarm, it has been disclosed to me that a cinch binder ain't any joke, by a darned sight! A cinch binder will stand up straight and lean over backward on me. If I'm there when he hits the ground I'll wish I wasn't——if I am able to wish anything at all and don't simply have to be shipped off to wherever my family wants it to take place.

I am further enlightened: Dandy Jim ain't so likely to start acting if not saddled when too cold. If I saddle him then he will be expecting to have more fun out of it than I have any right to. But if the sun is well up, why, sometimes a baby could handle him. So for three weeks I have saddled Dandy Jim with the utmost circumspection and with the sun well up. Now the sun is not well up. Shall I still survive? I pause to wish that the range of high hills on the east may be instantly levelled. The land will then be worth something and the sun will be farther up. But nothing of a topographical nature ensues. The hills remain to obscure the sun.

And the brute has to be saddled. The mood of that grim breakfast, voiceless, tense, high with portent, is still upon me.

I approach and speak harshly to the potential cinch binder, telling him to get over there! He does not; so I let it pass. After all, he is only a horse. Why should I terrorize him? I bridle him with a manner far from harsh. He doesn't like the taste of the bit—not seasoned right, or something. But at last he takes it without biting my fingers off; which shows that the horse has no mind to speak of.

I look him calmly in the eye for a moment; then pull his head about, so that I can look him calmly in the other eye for a moment. This is to show the animal that he has met his master and had better not try any of that cinch-binding stuff if he knows when he's well off. Still, I treat him fairly. I smooth his back of little vegetable bits that cling there, shake out the saddle blanket and tenderly adjust it. Whistling carelessly I swing up the saddle. Dandy Jim flinches pitifully when it rests upon him and reaches swiftly round to bite my arm off. I think this is quite perfunctory on his part. He must have learned long since that he will never really bite any one's arm off. His neck is not enough like a swan's.

I adjust saddle and blanket carefully from both sides, pulling the blanket well up under the horn of the saddle and making sure that it sets comfortably. One should be considerate of the feelings of a dumb beast placed at one's mercy. Then I reach for the cinch, pass it twice through the rings, and delicately draw it up the merest trifle. Dandy Jim shudders and moans pathetically. He wishes to convey the impression that his ribs have been sprung. This, of course, is nonsense. I measureably increase the pressure. Dandy Jim again registers consternation, coughs feebly, and rolls his eyes round appealingly, as if wondering whether the world is to sit, without heart, and watch a poor defenseless horse being slain. He is about to expire.

I now lead him gently about by the bridle. It occurs to me that a horse with this curious mania for binding cinches or cinching binders—or, in other words, a cinch binder—will be as willing to indulge in his favourite sport with the saddle unoccupied as otherwise. He may like it even better with no one up there; and I know I will. Nothing happens, except that Dandy Jim stumbles stiffly and pretends to be lame. The sun is not yet well up; still, it is a lot better. Perhaps danger for the day is over. I again lead the dangerous beast——

"What you humouring that old skate for?"

Ma Pettengill, arrayed in olive-drab shirt and breeches, leather puttees, and the wide-brimmed hat of her calling with the four careful dents in the top, observed me with friendly curiosity as she ties a corduroy coat to the back of her saddle.

Hereupon I explained my tactful handling of the reputed cinch binder. It evoked the first cheerful sound I had heard that day:

Ma Pettengill laughed heartily.

"That old hair trunk never had the jazz to be any cinch binder. Who told you he was?"

I named names—all I could remember. Almost everyone on the ranch had passed me the friendly warning, and never had I saddled the brute without a thrill.

"Sure! Them chuckleheads always got to tell everybody something. It's a wonder they ain't sent you in to the Chink to borrow his meat auger, or out to the blacksmith shop for a left-handed monkey wrench, or something. Come on!"

So that was it! Just another bit of stale ranch humour
—alleged humour—as if it could be at all funny to have
me saddle this wreck with the tenderest solicitude morning after morning!

"Just one moment!" I said briskly.

I think Dandy Jim realized that everything of a tender nature between us was over. Some curious and quite
charming respect I had been wont to show him was
now gone out of my manner. He began to do deep
breathing exercises before I touched the cinch. I pulled
with the strength of a fearless man. Dandy Jim forthwith inflated his chest like a gentleman having his photo-
graph taken in a bathing suit. I waited, apparently
foiled. I stepped back, spoke to Ma Pettengill of the
day's promise, and seemed carelessly to forget what I
was there for. Slowly Dandy Jim deflated himself; and
then, on the fair and just instant, I pulled. I pulled hard
and long. The game was won. Dandy Jim had now the
waist of that matron wearing the Sveltina corset, over
in the part of the magazine where the stories die away.
I fearlessly bestrode him and the day was on.

I opened something less than a hundred gates, so that
we could take our way through the lower fields. Ma
Pettengill said she must see this here Tilton and this
here Snell, and have that two hundred yards of fence
built like they had agreed to, as man to man; and no
more of this here nonsense of putting it off from day to
day.

She was going to talk straight to them because, come
Thursday, she had to turn a herd of beef cattle into that
field.

Then I opened a few dozen more gates and we were
down on the flats. Here the lady spied a coyote, furtively skirting some willows on our left. So, for a few

merry miles, we played the game of coyote. It is a simple game to learn, but requires a trained eye. When one player sees a coyote the other becomes indebted to him in the sum of one dollar.

This sport dispelled the early morning gloom that had beset me. I won a dollar almost immediately. It may have been the same coyote, as my opponent painfully suggested; but it showed at a different breach in the willows, and I was firm.

Then the game went fiercely against me. Ma Pettengill detected coyotes at the far edges of fields—so far that I would have ignored them for jack rabbits had I observed them at all. I claimed an occasional close one; but these were few. The outlook was again not cheering. It was an excellent morning for distant coyotes, and presently I owed Mrs. Lysander John Pettengill seven dollars, she having won two double-headers in succession. This ride was costing me too much a mile. Being so utterly outclassed I was resolving to demand a handicap, but was saved from this ignominy by our imminent arrival at the abode of this here Tilton, who presently sauntered out of a feeding corral and chewed a straw at us idly.

We soon took all that out of him. The air went something like this:

MRS. L. J. P.—brightly: Morning, Chester! Say, look here! About that gap in the fence across Stony Creek field—I got to turn a beef herd in there Thursday.

TILTON—crouching luxuriously on one knee still chewing the straw: Well, now, about that little job— I tell you, Mis' Pett'ngill; I been kind o' holdin' off account o' Snell bein' rushed with his final plowin'. He claims——

Mrs. L. J. P.—still brightly: Oh, that's all right! Snell will be over there, with his men, to-morrow morning at seven o'clock. He said you'd have to be there, too.

Tilton—alarmed, he rises, takes straw from his mouth, examines the chewed end with dismay and casts it from him; removes his hat, looks at this dubiously, burnishes it with a sleeve, and sighs: To-morrow morning! You don't mean to-morrow——

Mrs. L. J. P.—carefully yet rapidly: To-morrow morning at seven o'clock. You don't want to throw Snell down on this; and he's going to be there. How many men can you take?

Tilton—dazed: Now—now lemme see!

Mrs. L. J. P.—quickly: You can take Chris and Shorty and Jake and yourself. Any one else?

Tilton—swept over the falls: Why, no'm; I don't guess there's any other I could spare, account of——

Mrs. L. J. P.—almost sweetly: All right, then. To-morrow; seven sharp.

Tilton—from the whirlpool, helplessly: Yes'm! Yes'm!

Mrs. L. J. P.: Morning!

We ride on. Tilton fades back toward the corral; he has forgotten to replace his hat.

I now decided to make a little conversation rather than have the stupid and ruinous game of coyote for a pastime.

"I thought you hadn't seen Snell yet."

"I haven't; not since he promised his half of the job two weeks ago."

"But you just told Tilton——"

"Well, Snell is going to be there, ain't he?"

"How do you know?"

"I'm going to tell him now."

And the woman did even so. If you wish the scene with Snell go back and read the scene with Tilton, changing the names. Nothing else need you change. Snell was hitching two mules to a wood wagon; but he heard the same speeches and made approximately the same replies. And the deed was done.

"There now!" boomed Mrs. Talleyrand as we rode beyond earshot of the dazed and lingering Snell. "Them two men been trying for two weeks to agree on a day to do this trifling job. They wasn't able; so I agreed on a day myself. Anything wrong with it?"

"You said you were going to talk straight to them."

"Ain't I just talked straight to Snell? Tilton will be there, won't he?"

"How about the way you talked to Tilton before you saw Snell?"

"Well, my lands! How you talk! You got to have a foundation to build on, haven't you?"

I saw it as a feat beyond my prowess to convict this woman in her own eyes of a dubious and considering veracity. So I merely wondered, in tones that would easily reach her, how the gentlemen might relish her diplomacy when they discovered it on the morrow. I preceded the word diplomacy with a slight and very affected cough.

The lady replied that they would never discover her diplomacy, not coughing in the least before the word. She said each of them would be so mad at the other for setting a day that they would talk little. They would simply build fence. She added that a woman in this business had to be looking for the worst of it all the time. She was bound to get the elbow if she didn't use her common sense.

I ignored her casuistry, for she was now rolling a ciga-rette with an air of insufferable probity. I gave her up and played a new game of smashing horseflies as they settled on my mount. Dandy Jim plays the game ably. When a big fly settles on his nose he holds his head round so I can reach it. He does not flinch at the terrific smash of my hat across his face. If a fly alights on his neck or shoulder, and I do not remark it, he turns his head slightly toward me and winks, so I can stalk and pot it. He is very crafty here. If the fly is on his right side he turns and winks his left eye at me so the insect will not observe him. And yet there are people who say horses don't reason.

I now opened fifty more gates and we left the cool green of the fields for a dusty side road that skirts the base of the mesa. We jogged along in silence, which I presently heard stir with the faint, sweet strain of a violin; an air that rose and wailed and fell again, on a violin played with a certain back-country expertness. The road bent to show us its source. We were abreast of the forlorn little shack of a dry-farmer, weathered and patched, set a dozen yards from the road and surrounded by hard-packed earth. Before the open door basked children and pigs and a few spiritless chickens.

All the children ran to the door when we halted and called to someone within. The fiddle played on with no faltering, but a woman came out—a gaunt and tattered woman who was yet curiously cheerful. The children lurked in her wake as she came to us and peered from beyond her while we did our business.

Our business was that the redskin, Laura, official laundress of the Arrowhead, had lately attended an evening affair in the valley at which the hitherto smart tipple of Jamaica ginger had been supplanted by a novel and potent beverage, Nature's own remedy for chills, dyspepsia, deafness, rheumatism, despair, car-

uncles, jaundice, and ennui. Laura had partaken
ʀeely and yet again of this delectable brew, and now
ᵤffered not only from a sprained wrist but from deten-
ᵢon, having suffered arrest on complaint of the tribal
ᵢster who had been nearest to her when she sprained
ₑr wrist. Therefore, if Mrs. Dave Pickens wanted to
ᵢme over to-morrow and wash for us, all right; she
ᵤld bring her oldest girl to help.

Mrs. Dave thereupon turned her head languidly to-
ard the ignoble dwelling and called: "Dave!" Then
ᵧain, for the fiddle stayed not: "Dave! Oh, Dave!"

The fiddle ceased to moan—complainingly it seemed
ᵢ me—and Dave framed his graceful figure in the door-
ᵃy. He was one appealing droop, from his moustache
ᵢ his moccasin-clad feet. He wore an air of elegant
isure, but was otherwise not fussily arrayed.

"Dave, Mis' Pett'ngill says there's now a day's washin'
ᵢ do over to her place to-morrow. What think?"

Dave deliberated, then pondered, then thought, then
ᵣoke:

"Well, I d'no', Addie; I d'no' as I got any objections
you ain't. I d'no' but it's all the same to me."

Hereupon we meanly put something in Dave's unsus-
ᵉcting way, too.

"You must want a day's work yourself," called out
ᵃ Pettengill. "You go up to Snell's about six in the
ᵢorning and he'll need you to help do some fencing
ᵢ that gap in Stony Creek field. If he don't need
ᵤ Tilton will. One of 'em is bound to be short a
ᵃn."

"Fencin'?" said Dave with noticeable disrelish.

"You reckon we better both leave the place at once?"
ᵤggested Mrs. Dave.

"That's so," said Dave brightly. "Mebbe I——"

"Nonsense!" boomed Ma Pettengill, dispelling h
brightness. "Addie can drop you at Snell's when sh
comes over to Arrowhead. Now that's settled!"

And we rode off as unvoiced expostulations wei
gathering. I began to wonder whether it must, through
out a beautiful day, be the stern mission of this woma
to put tribulation upon her neighbours. She was be
coming a fell destroyer. The sun was well up.
thirsted. Also, breakfast seemed to have been a thin
in the remote past.

We now rode three torrid miles up a narrow gree
slit in the hills for a scant ten minutes of talk with
most uninteresting person, whose sole claim to notic
seemed to be that he had gone and fenced the wron
water hole over back of Horsefly Mountain, where w
have a summer range. The talk was quick and pointe
and buttressed with a blue-print map, and the too-hast
fencer was left helpless after a pitiful essay at quibblin
We rode off saying that he could do just as he like
about sending someone over right away to take tha
fence down, because we had already took it down th
minute we set eyes on it. We was just letting hir
know so he needn't waste any more wire and posts an
time in committing felonious depredations that woul
get him nothing but high trouble if he was so minde
Another scalp to our belt!

I now briefly recalled to the woman that we ha
stopped at no peaceful home that morning save to wrec
its peace. I said I was getting into the spirit of th
ride myself. I suggested that at the next ranch w
passed we should stop and set fire to the haystack
just to crown the day's brutalities with something real
splendid. I also said I was starving to death in a lan
of plenty.

Ma Pettengill gazed aloft at the sun and said it wa

half-past twelve. I looked at my watch and said the sun was over ten minutes slow, which was probably due to the heavy continuous gunfire on the Western Front. This neat bit went for just nothing. As we rode on I fondly recalled that last cold hot cake which Sandy Sawtelle had sacrificed to his gift for debased whimsy. I also recalled other items of that gloomy repast, wondering how I could so weakly have quit when I did.

We rode now under a sun that retained its old fervour if not its velocity. We traversed an endless lane between fields, in one of which grazed a herd of the Arrowhead cattle. These I was made to contemplate for many valuable moments. I had to be told that I was regarding the swallow-fork herd, pure-breds that for one reason or another—the chief being careless help—had not been registered. The omission was denoted by the swallow fork in the left ear.

The owner looked upon them with fond calculation. She was fondly calculating that they would have been worth about fifty per cent. more to her with ears unmutilated. She grew resentful that their true worth should not be acclaimed by the world. In the sight of heaven they were pure-breds; so why should they suffer through the oversight of a herd boss that hadn't anywhere near such distinguished ancestry? And so on, as the lady says.

We left the lane at last and were on the county road, but headed away from the Arrowhead and food. No doubt there remained other homes for us to wreck. We mounted a rise and the road fell from us in a long, gentle slope. And then a mile beyond, where the slope ended, I beheld a most inviting tiny pleasance in this overwhelming welter of ranch land, with its more or less grim business of cattle.

It was a little homestead fit to adorn an art calendar to be entitled Peace and Plenty—a veritable small farm from some softer little country far to the east. It looked strangely lost amid these bleaker holdings. There was a white little house and it sported nothing less than green blinds. There was a red barn, with toy outbuildings. There was a vegetable garden, an orchard of blossoming fruit trees, and, in front of the glistening little house, a gay garden of flowers. Even now I could detect the yellow of daffodils and the martial—at least it used to be martial—scarlet of tulips. The little place seemed to drowse here in the noontide, dreaming of its lost home and other little farms that once companioned it.

To my pleased surprise this unbelievable little farm proved to be our next stopping place. At its gate Ma Pettengill dismounted, eased the cinch of her saddle and tied her horse to the hitching rack. I did likewise by the one-time cinch binder.

"Now," I wondered, "what devastating bomb shall we hurl into this flower-spiced Arcady? What woe will she put upon its unsuspecting dwellers, even as she has ruined four other homes this day? This should be something really choice." But I said no word and followed where the avenger stalked.

We unlatched the white gate and went up a gravelled walk between the rows of daffodils and tulips and hyacinths. We did not ascend the spotless front porch to assault its innocent white door, but turned aside on a narrow-gauge branch of the gravelled pathway and came to a side porch, shaded by maples. And here, in stric conformity to the soundest behests of tradition, sat two entirely genuine Arcadians in wooden rocking-chairs The male was a smiling old thing with winter-appl cheeks and white hair, and the female was a smiling old thing with winter-apple cheeks and white hair; both had bright eyes of doll blue, and both wore, among other neat things, loose and lovely carpet slippers and white stockings.

And, of course, the male was named Uncle Henry and the other one was named Aunt Mollie, for I was now presented to them. They shyly greeted me as one returned to them after many years in which they had given me up. And again I wondered what particular iniquity we had come here to do.

Then Ma Pettengill eased my worry. She said in a few simple but affecting words, that we had stopped in for a bite to eat. No self-torturing stylist could have put the thing better. And results were sudden. Uncle Henry, the male one, went to take our horses round to the barn, and the other one said they had et an hour ago; but give her ten minutes and she'd have a couple of them young pullets skinned and on the fire.

Ma Pettengill said, with very questionable taste, I thought: "Oh, no; nothing like that!"—because we didn't want to make the least bit of trouble. The woman is dense at times. What else had we come there for? But Aunt Mollie said, then, how about some prime young pork tenderline? And Ma Pettengill said she guessed that would do, and I said I guessed that would do. And there we were! The ladies went to the kitchen, where they made quick and grateful noises.

Pretty soon Uncle Henry came round a lovely corner and said try a tumbler of this here grape wine, which he poured from a pressed-glass pitcher; so I tried it and gave him a town cigarette, which he tucked between his beautiful white moustache and his beautiful white whiskers. And I hoped he didn't use gasoline to get them so clean, because if he did something might happen when he lighted the cigarette; but nothing did, so probably he didn't. I tried the grape wine again; and dear old Uncle Henry said he was turning out quite a bit of it since the Gov'ment had shet down on regular dramshops, quite considerable of parties happening along from time to time to barter with him, getting it for dances or colds, or something.

A yellow cat, with blue eyes like Uncle Henry's, came and slept on his lap. A large fussy hen with a litter of chickens—or however a hen designates her assemblage of little ones—clucked her way to our feet. I could see three hives of bees, a grape arbour, and a row of milk pans drying in the sun, each leaning on its neighbour along a white bench. Uncle Henry said drink it up while it was cold. All Nature seemed to smile. The hen found a large and charming bug, and chuckled humorously while her cunning little ones tore it limb from limb. It was idyllic.

Then Aunt Mollie pushed open the screen door and said come in and set up; so I came in and set up quickly, having fried pork tenderloin and fried potatoes, and hot biscuit and pork gravy, and cucumber pickles, and cocoanut cake and pear preserves, peach preserves, apricot preserves, loganberry jelly, crab-apple jelly, and another kind of preserves I was unable to identify, though trying again and again.

Ma Pettengill ate somewhat, but talked also, keeping Uncle Henry and Aunt Mollie shiny with smiles. They both have polished white teeth of the most amazing regularity. I ate almost exclusively, affecting to be preoccupied about something. The time was urgent. I formed an entangling alliance with the pork tenderloin, which endured to a point where but one small fragment was left on the platter. I coolly left it there, so that Aunt Mollie might believe she had cooked more than enough.

I have never ceased to regret that hollow bit of chivalry. Was it honest, genuine, open? No! Why will men at critical junctures stoop to such trickery? Aunt Mollie said I might think that tenderline was fresh-killed; but not so—she had fried it last December and put it down in its own juice in a four-gallon crock, and now look how fresh it come out! She seemed as proud as if she had invented something. She had a right to be. It was a charming notion and I could have eaten the rest of the crock—but, no matter. Half a dozen biscuits copiously gummed up with preserves of one kind or another would do as well—almost.

So Aunt Mollie showed me objects of interest in the room, including her new carpet sweeper, a stuffed road runner, a ship built in a bottle, and the coloured crayon portraits of herself and Uncle Henry, wearing blue clothes and gold jewellery and white collars and ecru neckties. Also, the marriage certificate. This was no mere official certificate. It was the kind that costs three dollars flat, over and above what you give to the party that does it for you, being genuine steel-engraved, with a beautiful bridal couple under a floral bell, the groom in severe evening dress, and liberally spotted with cupids and pigeons. It is worth the money and an ornament to any wall, especially in the gilt frame.

Aunt Mollie seemed as proud of this document as she had been with the tenderloin. I scanned it word by word for her pleasure. I noticed especially the date. Aunt Mollie said that her and Henry were now in the fortieth year on this place, and it had changed in looks a whole lot since they came here. I again looked at the date of the certificate.

Ma Pettengill said, well, we must be getting on, and they must both come over to the Arrowhead for a day right soon. And Uncle Henry said here was a quart bottle of his peach brandy, going on eight year old, and would I take it along back with me and try it? Parties had told him it was good; but he didn't know——mebbe so, mebbe not. He'd like to know what I thought. It seemed little enough to do to bring a bit of gladness into this old gentleman's life, and I was not the man to wound him by refusal. It was as if Michelangelo had said "Come on round to the Sistine Chapel this afternoon and look over a little thing I've dashed off." If he had brought two bottles instead of one my answer would have been the same.

So we were out on our refreshed horses and heading home; and I said, without loss of time, that Aunt Mollie might have a good heart and a cunning way with pork interiors, and it was none of my business, anyway; but, nevertheless, she had mentioned forty long years with this amateur saloon keeper, whereas her marriage certificate was dated but one year previous, in figures all too shamefully legible. So what about it? I said I mind observing the underworld from time to time; but I like to be warned in advance, even when its denizens were such a charming, bright-eyed winter-apple-cheeked old couple as the two we were now leaving.

The sun was on our backs, a light breeze fanned us, the horses knew which way they were going, and work for the day was over; so Ma Pettengill spoke, in part, as follows:

"Oh, well, of course everyone knows about that. Simple enough! Aunt Mollie and her first husband trekked in here forty years ago. He was a consumptive and the first winter put him out. They had a hard time; no neighbours to speak of, harsh weather, hard work, poor shelter, and a dying man. Henry Mortimer happened by and stayed to help—nursed the invalid, kept the few head of stock together, nailed up holes in the shack, rustled grub and acted like a friend in need. At the last he nailed a coffin together; did the rest of that job; then stayed on to nurse Aunt Mollie, who was all in herself. After he got her to stepping again he put in a crop for her. Then he stayed to build a barn and do some fencing. Then he harvested the crop. And getting no wages! They was both living off the land. Pretty soon they got fond of each other and decided to marry. It's one of Aunt Mollie's jokes that she owed him two years' wages and had to marry him.

"Marriage was easier said than done. No preacher, or even a justice of the peace, was within ninety miles, which meant a four days' trip over the roads of that day, and four days back, providing high water or some other calamity didn't make it a month; and no one to leave on the place, which meant there wouldn't be a head of stock left when they got back, what with Indians and rustlers. Uncle Henry will tell you how it seemed too bad that just one of 'em wouldn't make the trip down and have the ceremony done, leaving the other to protect the place.

"Then along comes a horse trader, who stops over to rest his stock, and learns their trouble. He tells 'em to quit their worry; that he's a notary public and can perform a marriage as good as any Baptist preacher they ever saw. I never been able to make out whether he was crazy or just a witty, practical joker. Anyway, he married the pair with something like suitable words, wouldn't take a cent for it, and gave 'em a paper saying he had performed the deed. It had a seal on it showing he was a genuine notary public, though from back in Iowa somewhere. That made no difference to the new bride and groom. A notary public was a notary public to them, highly important and official.

"They had enough other things to worry about, anyway. They had to buckle down to the hard life that waits for any young couple without capital in a new country. They had years of hard sledding; but they must of had a good time somehow, because they never have any but pleasant things to tell of it. Whatever that notary public was, he seemed to of pulled off a marriage that took as well or better than a great many that may be more legal. So that's all there is to it— only, here about a year ago they was persuaded to have it done proper at last by a real preacher who makes Kulanche two Sundays a month. That's why the late date's on that certificate. The old lady is right kittenish about that; shows it to everyone, in spite of the fact that it makes her out of been leading an obliquitous life, or something, for about thirty-eight years.

"But then, she's a sentimental old mush-head, anyhow. Guess what she told me out in the kitchen! She's been reading what the Germans did to women and children in Belgium, and she says: 'Of course I hate Germans; and yet it don't seem as if I could ever hate 'em enough to want to kill a lot of German babies!' Wasn't that the confession of a weakling? I guess that's all you'd want to know about that woman. My sakes! Will you look at that mess of clouds? I bet it's falling weather over in Surprise Valley. A good moisting wouldn't hurt us any either."

That seemed to be about all. Yet I was loath to leave the topic. I still had a warm glow in my heart for the aged couple, and I could hear Uncle Henry's bottle of adolescent peach brandy laughing to itself from where it was lashed to the back of my saddle. I struck in the only weak spot in the wall.

"You say they were persuaded into this marriage. Well, who persuaded them? Isn't there something interesting about that?"

It had, indeed, been a shrewd stroke. Ma Pettengill's eyes lighted.

"Say, didn't I ever tell you about Mrs. Julia Wood Atkins, the well-known lady reformer?"

"You did not. We have eight miles yet."

"Oh, very well!"

So for eight miles of a road that led between green fields on our right and a rolling expanse of sagebrush on our left, I heard something like this:

"Well, this prominent club lady had been out on the Coast for some time heading movements and telling people how to do things, and she had got run down. She's a friend of Mrs. W. B. Hemingway, the well-known social leader and club president of Yonkers, who is an old friend of mine; and Mrs. W. B. writes that dear Julia is giving her life to the cause—I forget what cause it was right then—and how would it be for me to have her up here on the ranch for a vacation, where she could recover her spirits and be once more fitted to enter the arena. I say I'm only too glad to oblige, and the lady comes along.

"She seemed right human at first—kind of haggard and overtrained, but with plenty of fights left in her; a lady from forty-eight to fifty-four, with a fine hearty manner that must go well on a platform, and a kind of accusing face. That's the only word I can think of for it. She'd be pretty busy a good part of the day with pamphlets and papers that she or someone else had wrote, but I finally managed to get her out on a gentle old horse—that one you're riding—so she could liven up some; and we got along quite well together.

"The only thing that kind of went against me was,

she's one of them that thinks a kind word and a pleasant smile will get 'em anywhere, and she worked both on me a little too much like it was something professional.

"Still, I put it by and listened to her tell about the awful state the world is in, and how a few earnest women could set it right in a week if it wasn't for the police.

"Prison reform, for instance. That was the first topic on which she delivered addresses to me. I couldn't make much out of it, except that we don't rely enough on our convicts' rugged honour. It was only a side line with her; still, she didn't slight it. She could talk at length about the innate sterling goodness of the mis-understood burglar. I got tired of it. I told her one day that, if you come right down to it, I'd bet the men inside penitentiaries didn't average up one bit higher morally than the men outside. She said, with her pleasantest smile, that I didn't understand; so I never tried to after that.

"The lady had a prowling mind. Mebbe that ain't the right word, but it come to me soon after she got here. I think it was the day she begun about our drinking water. She wanted to know what the analysis showed it to contain. She was scared out of her pleasant smile for a minute when she found I'd never had the water analyzed. I thought, first, the poor thing had been reading these beer advertisements; you know—the kind they print asking if you are certain about the purity of your drinking water, telling of the fatal germs that will probably be swimming there, and intimating that probably the only dead-safe bet when you are thirsty is a pint of their pure, wholesome beer, which never yet gave typhoid fever to any one. But, no; Julia just thought all water ought to be analyzed on general principles, and wouldn't I have a sample of ours sent off at once? She'd filled a bottle with some and suggested it with her pleasantest platform smile.

"'Yes,' I says; 'and suppose the report comes back that this water is fatal to man and beast? And it's the only water round here. What then? I'd be in a hell of a fix—wouldn't I?'

"I don't deny I used to fall back on words now and then when her smile got to me. And we went right on using water that might or might not make spicy reading in a chemist's report; I only been here thirty years and it's too soon to tell. Anyway, it was then I see she was gifted with a prowling mind, which is all I can think of to call it. It went with her accusing face. She didn't think anything in this world was as near right as it could be made by some good woman.

"Of course she had other things besides the water to worry about. She was a writer, too. She would write about how friction in the home life may be avoided by one of the parties giving in to the other and letting the wife say how the money shall be spent, and pieces about what the young girl should do next, and what the young wife should do if necessary, and so on. For some reason she was paid money for these pieces.

"However, she was taking longer rides and getting her pep back, which was what she had come here for. And having failed to reform anything on the Arrowhead, she looked abroad for more plastic corruption as you might say. She rode in one night and said she was amazed that this here community didn't do something about Dave Pickens. That's the place we stopped this morning. She said his children were neglected and starving, his wife worked to the bone, and Dave doing nothing but play on a cheap fiddle! How did they get their bread from day to day?

"I told her no one in the wide world had ever been

able to answer this puzzle. There was Dave and his
wife and five children, all healthy, and eating somehow,
and Dave never doing a stroke of work he could side-
step. I told her it was such a familiar puzzle we'd
quit being puzzled by it.

"She said someone ought to smash his fiddle and
make him work. She said she would do something
about it. I applauded. I said we needed new blood
up here and she seemed to of fetched it.

"She come back the next day with a flush of triumph
on her severely simple face. And guess the first thing
she asked me to do! She asked me to take chances in
a raffle for Dave's fiddle. Yes, sir; with her kind words
and pleasant smile she had got Dave to consent to raffle
off his fiddle, and she was going to sell twenty-four
chances at fifty cents a chance, which would bring
twelve dollars cash to the squalid home. I had to respect the woman at that moment.

"'There they are, penniless,' says she, 'and in want
for the barest necessities; and this man fiddling his time
away! I had a struggle persuading him to give up his
wretched toy; but I've handled harder cases. You
should of seen the light in the mother's wan face when
he consented! The twelve dollars won't be much,
though it will do something for her and those starving
children; and then he will no longer have the instrument to tempt him.'

"I handed over a dollar for two chances right quick,
and Julia went out to the bunk-house and wormed two
dollars out of the boys there. And next day she was
out selling off the other chances. She didn't dislike
the work. It gave her a chance to enter our homes and
see if they needed reforming, and if the children was
subjected to refining influences, and so on. The first

day she scared parties into taking fifteen tickets, and the second day she got rid of the rest; and the next Sunday she held the drawing over at Dave's house. The fiddle was won by a nester from over in Surprise Valley, who had always believed he could play one if he only had a fair chance.

"So this good deed was now completed, there being no music, and twelve dollars in the Pickens home that night. And Mrs. Julia now felt that she was ready for the next big feat of uplift, which was a lot more important because it involved the very sanctity of the marriage tie. Yes, sir; she'd come back from her prowling one night and told me in a hushed voice, behind a closed door, about a couple that had been for years living in a state of open immorality.

"I didn't get her, at first, not thinking of Uncle Henry and Aunt Mollie. But she meant just them two. I gave her a good hearty laugh, at first; but it pained her so much I let her talk. It seems she'd gone there to sell raffle tickets, and they'd taken four, and cooked food for her, and give her some cherry cordial, which she took on account of being far from a strong woman; and then Aunt Mollie had told all her past life, with this horrid scandal about the notary public sticking innocently out of it.

"Mrs. Julia hadn't been able to see anything but the scandal, she being an expert in that line. So she had started in to persuade Aunt Mollie that it was her sacred duty to be married decently to her companion in crime for forty years. And Aunt Mollie had been right taken with the idea; in fact, she had entered into it with a social enthusiasm that didn't seem to Mrs. Julia to have quite enough womanly shame for her dark past in it. Still, anything to get the guilty couple lawful wedded:

and before she left it was all fixed. Uncle Henry was
to make an honest woman of Aunt Mollie as soon as she
could get her trousseau ready.

"Me? I didn't know whether to laugh or get mad.
I said the original marriage had satisfied the peace and
dignity of the state of Washington; and it had done
more—it had even satisfied the neighbours. So why
not let it rest? But, no, indeed! It had never been
a marriage in the sight of God and couldn't be one now.
Facts was facts! And she talked some more about Aunt
Mollie not taking her false position in the proper way.

"It had been Mrs. Julia's idea to have the preacher
come up and commit this ceremony quite furtively,
with mebbe a couple of legal witnesses, keeping everything quiet, so as not to have a public scandal. But
nothing like that for the guilty woman! She was going
to have a trousseau and a wedding, with guests and
gayety. She wasn't taking it the right way at all. It
seemed like she wanted all the scandal there was going.

"'Really, I can't understand the creature,' says Mrs.
Julia. 'She even speaks of a wedding breakfast! Can
you imagine her wishing to flaunt such a thing?'

"It was then I decided to laugh instead of telling
this lady a few things she couldn't of put in an article.
I said Aunt Mollie's taking it this way showed how depraved people could get after forty years of it; and we
must try to humour the old trollop, the main thing being
to get her and her debased old Don Juan into a legal
married state, even if they did insist on going in with a
brass band. Julia said she was glad I took it this way.

"She came back to my room again that night, after
her hair was down. The only really human thing this
lady ever did, so far as I could discover, was to put some
of this magic remedy on her hair that restores the natural colour if the natural colour happened to be what

this remedy restores it to. Any way, she now wanted to know if I thought it was right for Aunt Mollie to continue to reside there in that house between now and the time when they would be lawful man and wife. I said no; I didn't think it was right. I thought it was a monstrous infamy and an affront to public morals; but mebbe we better resolve to ignore it and plow a straight furrow, without stopping to pull weeds. She sadly said she supposed I was right.

"So Uncle Henry hitched up his fat white horse to the buggy, and him and Aunt Mollie drove round the country for three days, inviting folks to their wedding. Aunt Mollie had the time of her life. It seemed as if there wasn't no way whatever to get a sense of shame into that brazen old hussy. And when this job was done she got busy with her trousseau, which consisted of a bridge gown in blue organdie, and a pair of high white shoes. She didn't know what a bridge gown was for, but she liked the looks of one in a pattern book and sent down to Red Gap for Miss Gunslaugh to bring up the stuff and make it. And she'd always had this secret yearning for a pair of high white shoes; so they come up, too.

"Furthermore, Aunt Mollie had read the city paper for years and knew about wedding breakfasts; so she was bound to have one of those. It looked like a good time was going to be had by all present except the lady who started it. Mrs. Julia was more malignantly scandalized by these festal preparations than she had been by the original crime; but she had to go through with it now.

"The date had been set and we was within three days of it when Aunt Mollie postponed it three days more because Dave Pickens couldn't be there until this later day. Mrs. Julia made a violent protest, because she

had made her plans to leave for larger fields of crime
but Aunt Mollie was stubborn. She said Dave Picken
was one of the oldest neighbours and she wouldn't have
a wedding he couldn't attend; and besides, marriage was
a serious step and she wasn't going to be hurried into it.

"So Mrs Julia went to a lot of trouble about her
ticket and reservations, and stayed over. She was
game enough not to run out before Uncle Henry had
made Aunt Mollie a lady. I was a good deal puzzled
about this postponement. Dave Pickens was nothing
to postpone anything for. There never was any date
that he couldn't be anywhere—at least, unless he had
gone to work after losing his fiddle, which was highly
ridiculous.

"The date held this time. We get word the wedding
is to be held in the evening and that everyone must stay
there overnight. This was surprising, but simple after
Aunt Mollie explained it. The guests, of course, had
to stay over for the wedding breakfast. Aunt Mollie
had figured it all out. A breakfast is something you
eat in the morning, about six-thirty or seven; so a wedding breakfast must be held the morning after the wedding. You couldn't fool Aunt Mollie on social niceties.

"Anyway, there we all was at the wedding; Uncle
Henry in his black suit and his shiny new teeth, and
Aunt Mollie in her bridge gown and white shoes, and
this young minister that wore a puzzled look from start
to finish. I guess he never did know what kind of a
game he was helping out in. But he got through with
the ceremony. There proved to be not a soul present
knowing any reason why this pair shouldn't be joined
together in holy wedlock, though Mrs. Julia looked
more severe than usual at this part of the ceremony.
Uncle Henry and Aunt Mollie was firm in their re-
sponses and promised to cling to each other till death

did them part. They really sounded as if they meant it.

"Mrs. Julia looked highly noble and sweet when all was over, like she had rescued an erring sister from the depths. You could see she felt that the world would indeed be a better place if she could only give a little more time to it.

"We stood round and talked some after the ceremony; but not for long. Aunt Mollie wound the clock and set the mouse-trap, and hustled us all off to bed so we could be up bright and early for the wedding breakfast. You'd think she'd been handling these affairs in metropolitan society for years. The women slept on beds and sofas, and different places, and the men slept out in the barn and in a tent Uncle Henry had put up or took their blanket rolls and bunked under a tree.

"Then ho! for the merry wedding breakfast at six-thirty A. M.! The wedding breakfast consisted of ham and eggs and champagne. Yes, sir; don't think Aunt Mollie had overlooked the fashionable drink. Hadn't she been reading all her life about champagne being served at wedding breakfasts? So there it was in a new wash boiler, buried in cracked ice. And while the women was serving the ham and eggs and hot biscuits at the long table built out in the side yard, Uncle Henry exploded several bottles of this wine and passed it to one and all, and a toast was drunk to the legal bride and groom; after which eating was indulged in heartily.

"It was a merry feast, even without the lobster salad, which Aunt Mollie apologized for not having. She said she knew lobster salad went with a wedding breakfast, the same as champagne; but the canned lobster she had ordered hadn't come, so we'd have to make out with the home-cured ham and some pork sausage that now come along. Nobody seemed downhearted about the missing lobster salad. Uncle Henry passed up and down the table filling cups and glasses, and Aunt Mollie, in her wedding finery, kept the food coming with some buckwheat cakes at the finish.

"It was a very satisfactory wedding breakfast, if any one should ever make inquiries of you. By the time Uncle Henry had the ends out of half the champagne bottles I guess everyone there was glad he had decided to drag Aunt Mollie back from the primrose path.

"It all passed off beautifully, except for one tragedy. Oh, yes; there's always something to mar these affairs. But this hellish incident didn't come till the very last. After the guests had pretty well et themselves to a standstill, Dave Pickens got up and come back with a fiddle, and stood at the end of the grape arbour and played a piece.

"'Someone must have supplied that wretch with another fiddle!' says Mrs. Julia, who was kind of cross, anyway, having been bedded down on a short sofa and not liking champagne for breakfast—and, therefore, not liking to see others drink it.

"'Oh, he's probably borrowed one for your celebration,' I says.

"Dave played a couple more lively pieces; and pretty soon, when we got up from the table, he come over to Mrs. Julia and me.

"'It's a peach of a fiddle,' says Dave. 'It says in the catalogue it's a genuine Cremonika—looks like a Cremona and plays just as good. I bet it's the best fiddle in the world to be had for twelve dollars!'

"'What's that?' says Mrs. Julia, erecting herself like an alarmed rattlesnake.

"'Sure! It's a genuine twelve-dollar one,' says Dave proudly. 'My old one, that you so kindly raffled off, cost only five. I always wanted a better one, but I never had the money to spare till you come along. It's awful hard to save up money round here.'

" 'Do you mean to tell me———' says Mrs. Julia. She was so mad she couldn't get any farther. Dave thought she was merely enthusiastic about his new fiddle.

" 'Sure! Only twelve dollars for this beauty,' he says, fondling the instrument. 'We got down the mail-order catalogue the minute you left that money with us, and had a postal order on the way to Chicago that very night. I must say, lady, you brought a great pleasure into our life.'

" 'What about your poor wife?' snaps Mrs. Julia.

"His poor wife comes up just then and looks affectionately at Dave and the new fiddle.

" 'He spent that money for another fiddle!' says Mrs. Julia to her in low tones of horror.

" 'Sure! What did you think he was going to do with it?' says Mrs. Dave. 'I must say we had two mighty dull weeks while Dave was waiting for this new one. He just mopes round the house when he hain't got anything to play on. But this is a lot better than the old fiddle; it was worth waiting for. Did you thank the lady, Dave?'

"Mrs. Julia was now plump speechless and kind of weak. And on top of these blows up comes Aunt Mollie the new-wed, and beams fondly on her.

" 'There!' says she. 'Ain't that a fine new fiddle that Dave bought with his twelve dollars? And wasn't it worth postponing my wedding for, so we could have some music?'

" 'What's that?' says Mrs. Julia again. 'Why did you postpone it?'

" 'Because the fiddle didn't get here till last night,' says Aunt Mollie, 'and I wasn't going to have a wedding

without music. It wouldn't seem right. And don't
you think, yourself, it's a lot better fiddle than Dave's
old one?'

"So this poor Mrs. Julia woman was now stricken
for fair, thinking of all the trouble she'd been to about
her tickets, and all to see this new fiddle.

"She went weakly into the house and lay down, with
a headache, till I was ready to leave the gay throng.
And the next day she left us to our fate. Still, she'd
done us good. Dave has a new fiddle and Aunt Mollie
has her high white shoes. So now you know all about
it."

We neared the Arrowhead gate. Presently its bell
would peal a sweet message to those who laboured.
Ma Pettengill turned in her saddle to scan the western
horizon.

"A red sun has water in his eye," said she. "Well,
a good soak won't hurt us."

"Curious thing about reformers: They don't seem
to get a lot of pleasure out of their labours unless the
ones they reform resist and suffer, and show a proper
sense of their degradation. I bet a lot of reformers
would quit to-morrow if they knew their work wasn't
going to bother people any."

THE SKYLIGHT ROOM

BY O. HENRY

FIRST Mrs. Parker would show you the double parlors. You would not dare to interrupt her description of their advantages and of the merits of the gentleman who had occupied them for eight years. Then you would manage to stammer forth the confession that you were neither a doctor nor a dentist. Mrs. Parker's manner of receiving the admission was such that you could never afterward entertain the same feeling toward your parents, who had neglected to train you up in one of the professions that fitted Mrs. Parker's parlors.

Next you ascended one flight of stairs and looked at the second-floor-back at $8. Convinced by her second-floor manner that it was worth the $12 that Mr. Toosenberry always paid for it until he left to take charge of his brother's orange plantation in Florida near Palm Beach, where Mrs. McIntyre always spent the winters that had the double front room with private bath, you managed to babble that you wanted something still cheaper.

If you survived Mrs. Parker's scorn, you were taken to look at Mr. Skidder's large hall room on the third floor. Mr. Skidder's room was not vacant. He wrote plays and smoked cigarettes in it all day long. But every room-hunter was made to visit his room to admire the lambrequins. After each visit, Mr. Skidder, from the fright caused by possible eviction, would pay something on his rent.

Then—oh, then—if you still stood on one foot, with your hot hand clutching the three moist dollars in your pocket, and hoarsely proclaimed your hideous and culpable poverty, nevermore would Mrs. Parker be cicerone of yours. She would honk loudly the word "Clara," she would show you her back, and march downstairs. Then Clara, the colored maid, would escort you up the carpeted ladder that served for the fourth flight, and show you the Skylight Room. It occupied 7 x 8 feet of floor space in the middle of the hall. On each side of it was a dark lumber closet or storeroom.

In it was an iron cot, a washstand and a chair. A shelf was the dresser. Its four bare walls seemed to close in upon you like the sides of a coffin. Your hand crept to your throat, you gasped, you looked up as from a well—and breathed once more. Through the glass of the little skylight you saw a square of blue infinity.

"Two dollars, suh," Clara would say in her half-contemptuous, half-Tuskegeenial tones.

One day Miss Leeson came hunting for a room. She carried a typewriter made to be lugged around by a much larger lady. She was a very little girl, with eyes and hair that had kept on growing after she had stopped and that always looked as if they were saying: "Goodness me! Why didn't you keep up with us?"

Mrs. Parker showed her the double parlors. "In this closet," she said, "one could keep a skeleton or anæsthetic or coal——"

"But I am neither a doctor nor a dentist," said Miss Leeson, with a shiver.

Mrs. Parker gave her the incredulous, pitying, sneering, icy stare that she kept for those who failed to qualify as doctors or dentists, and led the way to the second-floor-back.

"Eight dollars?" said Miss Leeson. "Dear me! I'm not Hetty if I do look green. I'm just a poor little working girl. Show me something higher and lower."

Mr. Skidder jumped and strew the floor with cigarette stubs at the rap on his door.

"Excuse me, Mr. Skidder," said Mrs. Parker, with her demon's smile at his pale looks. "I didn't know you were in. I asked the lady to have a look at your lambrequins."

"They're too lovely for anything," said Miss Leeson, smiling in exactly the way the angels do.

After they had gone Mr. Skidder got very busy erasing the tall, black-haired heroine from his latest (unproduced) play and inserted a small, roguish one with heavy, bright hair and vivacious features.

"Anna Held'll jump at it," said Mr. Skidder to himself, putting his feet up against the lambrequins and disappearing in a cloud of smoke like an aërial cuttlefish.

Presently the tocsin call of "Clara!" sounded to the world the state of Miss Leeson's purse. A dark goblin seized her, mounted a Stygian stairway, thrust her into a vault with a glimmer of light in its top and muttered the menacing and cabalistic words "Two dollars!"

"I'll take it!" sighed Miss Leeson, sinking down upon the squeaky iron bed.

Every day Miss Leeson went out to work. At night she brought home papers with handwriting on them and made copies with her typewriter. Sometimes she had no work at night, and then she would sit on the steps of the high stoop with the other roomers. Miss Leeson was not intended for a skylight room when the plans were drawn for her creation. She was gay-hearted and full of tender, whimsical fancies. Once she let Mr. Skidder read to her three acts of his great (unpublished) comedy, "It's No Kid; or, The Heir of the Subway."

There was rejoicing among the gentlemen roomers whenever Miss Leeson had time to sit on the steps for an hour or two. But Miss Longnecker, the tall blonde who taught in a public school and said, "Well, really!" to everything you said, sat on the top step and sniffed. And Miss Dorn, who shot at the moving ducks at Coney every Sunday and worked in a department store, sat on the bottom step and sniffed. Miss Leeson sat on the middle step and the men would quickly group around her.

Especially Mr. Skidder, who had cast her in his mind for the star part in a private, romantic (unspoken) drama in real life. And especially Mr. Hoover, who was forty-five, fat, flush and foolish. And especially very young Mr. Evans, who set up a hollow cough to induce her to ask him to leave of cigarettes. The men voted her "the funniest and jolliest ever," but the sniffs on the top step and the lower step were implacable.

. . . .

I pray you let the drama halt while Chorus stalks to the footlights and drops an epicedian tear upon the fatness of Mr. Hoover. Tune the pipes to the tragedy of tallow, the bane of bulk, the calamity of corpulence. Tried out, Falstaff might have rendered more romance to the ton than would have Romeo's rickety ribs to the ounce. A lover may sigh, but he must not puff. To the train of Momus are the fat men remanded. In vain beats the faithfullest heart above a 52-inch belt. Avaunt, Hoover! Hoover, forty-five, flush and foolish, might carry off Helen herself; Hoover, forty-five, flush, foolish and fat is meat for perdition. There was never a chance for you, Hoover.

As Mrs. Parker's roomers sat thus one summer's evening, Miss Leeson looked up into the firmament and cried with her little gay laugh:

"Why, there's Billy Jackson! I can see him from down here, too."

All looked up—some at the windows of skyscrapers, some casting about for an airship, Jackson-guided.

"It's that star," explained Miss Leeson, pointing with a tiny finger. "Not the big one that twinkles—the steady blue one near it. I can see it every night through my skylight. I named it Billy Jackson."

"Well, really!" said Miss Longnecker. "I didn't know you were an astronomer, Miss Leeson."

"Oh, yes," said the small star gazer, "I know as much as any of them about the style of sleeves they're going to wear next fall in Mars."

"Well, really!" said Miss Longnecker. "The star you refer to is Gamma, of the constellation Cassiopeia. It is nearly of the second magnitude, and its meridian passage is——"

"Oh," said the very young Mr. Evans, "I think Billy Jackson is a much better name for it."

"Same here," said Mr. Hoover, loudly breathing defiance to Miss Longnecker. "I think Miss Leeson has just as much right to name stars as any of those old astrologers had."

"Well, really!" said Miss Longnecker.

"I wonder whether it's a shooting star," remarked Miss Dorn. "I hit nine ducks and a rabbit out of ten in the gallery at Coney Sunday."

"He doesn't show up very well from down here," said Miss Leeson. "You ought to see him from my room. You know you can see stars even in the daytime from the bottom of a well. At night my room is like the shaft of a coal mine, and it makes Billy Jackson look like the big diamond pin that Night fastens her kimono with."

There came a time after that when Miss Leeson brought no formidable papers home to copy. And when she went out in the morning, instead of working, she went from office to office and let her heart melt away in the drip of cold refusals transmitted through insolent office boys. This went on.

There came an evening when she wearily climbed Mrs. Parker's stoop at the hour when she always returned from her dinner at the restaurant. But she had had no dinner.

As she stepped into the hall Mr. Hoover met her and seized his chance. He asked her to marry him, and his fatness hovered above her like an avalanche. She dodged, and caught the balustrade. He tried for her hand, and she raised it and smote him weakly in the face. Step by step she went up, dragging herself by the railing. She passed Mr. Skidder's door as he was redinking a stage direction for Myrtle Delorme (Miss Leeson) in his (unaccepted) comedy, to "pirouette across stage from L to the side of the Count." Up the carpeted ladder she crawled at last and opened the door of the skylight room.

She was too weak to light the lamp or to undress. She fell upon the iron cot, her fragile body scarcely hollowing the worn springs. And in that Erebus of a room she slowly raised her heavy eyelids, and smiled.

For Billy Jackson was shining down on her, calm and bright and constant through the skylight. There was no world about her. She was sunk in a pit of blackness, with but that small square of pallid light framing the star that she had so whimsically and oh, so ineffectually, named. Miss Longnecker must be right: it was Gamma, of the constellation Cassiopeia, and not Billy Jackson. And yet she could not let it be Gamma.

As she lay on her back, she tried twice to raise her arm. The third time she got two thin fingers to her lips and blew a kiss out of the black pit to Billy Jackson. Her arm fell back limply.

"Good-bye, Billy," she murmured, faintly. "You're millions of miles away and you won't even twinkle once. But you kept where I could see you most of the time up there when there wasn't anything else but darkness to look at, didn't you? . . . Millions of miles. . . . Good-bye, Billy Jackson."

Clara, the coloured maid, found the door locked at 10 the next day, and they forced it open. Vinegar, and the slapping of wrists and burnt feathers proving of no avail, some one ran to 'phone for an ambulance.

In due time it backed up to the door with much gong-clanging, and the capable young medico, in his white linen coat, ready, active, confident, with his smooth face half debonair, half grim, danced up the steps.

"Ambulance call to 49," he said, briefly. "What's the trouble?"

"Oh, yes, doctor," sniffed Mrs. Parker, as though her trouble that there should be trouble in the house was the greater. "I can't think what can be the matter with her. Nothing we could do would bring her to. It's a young woman, a Miss Elsie—yes, a Miss Elsie Leeson. Never before in my house——"

"What room?" cried the doctor in a terrible voice, to which Mrs. Parker was a stranger.

"The skylight room. It——"

Evidently the ambulance doctor was familiar with the location of skylight rooms. He was gone up the stairs, four at a time. Mrs. Parker followed slowly, as her dignity demanded.

On the first landing she met him coming back bearing the astronomer in his arms. He stopped and let loose the practised scalpel of his tongue, not loudly. Gradually Mrs. Parker crumpled as a stiff garment that slips down from a nail. Ever afterwards there remained crumples in her mind and body. Sometimes her curious roomers would ask her what the doctor said to her.

"Let that be," she would answer. "If I can get forgiveness for having heard it I will be satisfied."

The ambulance physician strode with his burden through the pack of hounds that follow the curiosity chase, and even they fell back along the sidewalk abashed, for his face was that of one who bears his own dead.

They noticed that he did not lay down upon the bed prepared for it in the ambulance the form that he carried, and all that he said was: "Drive like h—l, Wilson," to the driver.

That is all. Is it a story? In the next morning's paper I saw a little news item, and the last sentence of it may help you (as it helped me) to weld the incidents together.

It recounted the reception into Bellevue Hospital of a young woman who had been removed from No. 49 East —— Street, suffering from debility induced by starvation. It concluded with these words:

"Dr. William Jackson, the ambulance physician who attended the case, says the patient will recover."

RUPE COLLINS

FROM *Penrod*

BY BOOTH TARKINGTON

FOR several days after this, Penrod thought of growing up to be a monk, and engaged in good works so far as to carry some kittens (that otherwise would have been drowned) and a pair of Margaret's outworn dancing-slippers to a poor, ungrateful old man sojourning in a shed up the alley. And although Mr. Robert Williams, after a very short interval, began to leave his guitar on the front porch again, exactly as if he thought nothing had happened, Penrod, with his younger vision of a father's mood, remained coldly distant from the Jones neighbourhood. With his own family his manner was gentle, proud and sad, but not for long enough to frighten them. The change came with mystifying abruptness at the end of the week.

It was Duke who brought it about.

Duke could chase a much bigger dog out of the Schofields' yard and far down the street. This might be thought to indicate unusual valour on the part of Duke and cowardice on that of the bigger dogs whom he undoubtedly put to rout. On the contrary, all such flights were founded in mere superstition, for dogs are even more superstitious than boys and coloured people; and the most firmly established of all dog superstitions is that any dog—be he the smallest and feeblest in the world—can whip any trespasser whatsoever.

A rat-terrier believes that on his home grounds he can

whip an elephant. It follows, of course, that a big dog, away from his own home, will run from a little dog in the little dog's neighbourhood. Otherwise, the big dog must face a charge of inconsistency and dogs are as consistent as they are superstitious. A dog believes in war, but he is convinced that there are times when it is moral to run; and the thoughtful physiognomist, seeing a big dog fleeing out of a little dog's yard, must observe that the expression of the big dog's face is more conscientious than alarmed: it is the expression of a person performing a duty to himself.

Penrod understood these matters perfectly; he knew that the gaunt brown hound Duke chased up the alley had fled only out of deference to a custom, yet Penrod could not refrain from bragging of Duke to the hound's owner, a fat-faced stranger of twelve or thirteen, who had wandered into the neighbourhood.

"You better keep that ole yellow dog o' yours back," said Penrod ominously, as he climbed the fence. "You better catch him and hold him till I get mine inside the yard again. Duke's chewed up some pretty bad bulldogs around here."

The fat-faced boy gave Penrod a fishy stare. "You'd oughta learn him not to do that," he said. "It'll make him sick."

"What will?"

The stranger laughed raspingly and gazed up the alley, where the hound, having come to a halt, now coolly sat down, and, with an expression of roguish benevolence, patronizingly watched the tempered fury of Duke, whose assaults and barkings were becoming perfunctory.

"What'll make Duke sick?" Penrod demanded.

"Eatin' dead bulldogs people leave around here."

This was not improvisation but formula, adapted

from other occasions to the present encounter; nevertheless, it was new to Penrod, and he was so taken with it that resentment lost itself in admiration. Hastily committing the gem to memory for use upon a dog-owning friend, he inquired in a sociable tone:

"What's your dog's name?"

"Dan. You better call your ole pup, 'cause Dan eats *live* dogs."

Dan's actions poorly supported his master's assertion, for, upon Duke's ceasing to bark, Dan rose and showed the most courteous interest in making the little, old dog's acquaintance. Dan had a great deal of manner, and it became plain that Duke was impressed favourably in spite of former prejudice, so that presently the two trotted amicably back to their masters and sat down with the harmonious but indifferent air of having known each other intimately for years.

They were received without comment, though both boys looked at them reflectively for a time. It was Penrod who spoke first.

"What number you go to?" (In an "oral lesson in English," Penrod had been instructed to put this question in another form: "May I ask which of our public schools you attend?")

"Me? What number do I go to?" said the stranger, contemptuously. "I don't go to *no* number in vacation!"

"I mean when it ain't."

"Third," returned the fat-faced boy. "I got 'em *all* scared in *that* school."

"What of?" innocently asked Penrod, to whom "the Third"—in a distant part of town—was undiscovered country.

"What of? I guess you'd soon see what of, if you ever was in that school about one day. You'd be lucky if you got out alive!"

"Are the teachers mean?"

The other boy frowned with bitter scorn. "Teachers! Teachers don't order *me* around, I can tell you! They're mighty careful how they try to run over Rupe Collins."

"Who's Rupe Collins?"

"Who is he?" echoed the fat-faced boy incredulously. "Say, ain't you got *any* sense?"

"What?"

"Say, wouldn't you be just as happy if you had *some* sense?"

"Ye-es." Penrod's answer, like the look he lifted to the impressive stranger, was meek and placative. "Rupe Collins is the principal at your school, I guess."

The other yelled with jeering laughter, and mocked Penrod's manner and voice. " 'Rupe Collins is the principal at your school, I guess!' " He laughed harshly again, then suddenly showed truculence. "Say, 'bo, whyn't you learn enough to go in the house when it rains? What's the matter of you, anyhow?"

"Well," urged Penrod timidly, "nobody ever *told* me who Rupe Collins is: I got a *right* to think he's the principal, haven't I?"

The fat-faced boy shook his head disgustedly. "Honest, you make me sick!"

Penrod's expression became one of despair. "Well, who *is* he?" he cried.

" 'Who *is* he?' " mocked the other, with a scorn that withered. " 'Who *is* he?' ME!"

"Oh!" Penrod was humiliated but relieved: he felt that he had proved himself criminally ignorant, yet a peril seemed to have passed. "Rupe Collins is *your* name, then, I guess. I kind of thought it was, all the time."

The fat-faced boy still appeared embittered, burlesquing this speech in a hateful falsetto. " 'Rupe Collins is *your* name, then, I guess!' Oh, you 'kind of thought it was, all the time,' did you?" Suddenly concentrating his brow into a histrionic scowl he thrust his face within an inch of Penrod's. "Yes, sonny, Rupe Collins is my name, and you better look out what you say when he's around or you'll get in big trouble! *You understand that, 'bo?*"

Penrod was cowed but fascinated: he felt that there was something dangerous and dashing about this newcomer.

"Yes," he said, feebly, drawing back. "My name's Penrod Schofield."

"Then I reckon your father and mother ain't got good sense," said Mr. Collins promptly, this also being formula.

"Why?"

" 'Cause if they had they'd of give you a good name!" And the agreeable youth instantly rewarded himself for the wit with another yell of rasping laughter, after which he pointed suddenly at Penrod's right hand.

"Where'd you get that wart on your finger?" he demanded severely.

"Which finger?" asked the mystified Penrod, extending his hand.

"The middle one."

"Where?"

"There!" exclaimed Rupe Collins, seizing and vigorously twisting the wartless finger naïvely offered for his inspection.

"Quit!" shouted Penrod in agony. "*Quee*-yut!"

"Say your prayers!" commanded Rupe, and continued to twist the luckless finger until Penrod writhed to his knees.

"*Ow!*" The victim, released, looked grievously upon the still painful finger.

At this Rupe's scornful expression altered to one of

contrition. "Well, I declare!" he exclaimed remorse-
fully. "I didn't s'pose it would hurt. Turn about's fair
play; so now you do that to me."

He extended the middle finger of his left hand and
Penrod promptly seized it, but did not twist it, for he
was instantly swung round with his back to his amiable
new acquaintance: Rupe's right hand operated upon the
back of Penrod's slender neck; Rupe's knee tortured the
small of Penrod's back.

"*Ow!*" Penrod bent far forward involuntarily and
went to his knees again.

"Lick dirt," commanded Rupe, forcing the captive's
face to the sidewalk; and the suffering Penrod completed this ceremony.

Mr. Collins evinced satisfaction by means of his
horse laugh. "You'd last jest about one day up at the
Third!" he said. "You'd come runnin' home, yellin'
'*Mom-muh, mom-*muh,' before recess was over!"

"No, I wouldn't," Penrod protested rather weakly,
dusting his knees.

"You would, too!"

"No, I w——"

"Looky here," said the fat-faced boy, darkly, "what
you mean, counterdicking me?"

He advanced a step and Penrod hastily qualified his
contradiction.

"I mean, I don't *think* I would. I——"

"You better look out!" Rupe moved closer, and unexpectedly grasped the back of Penrod's neck again.
"Say, 'I *would* run home yellin' "*Mom*-muh!" ' "

"Ow! I *would* run home yellin' 'Mom-muh.' "

"There!" said Rupe, giving the helpless nape a final
squeeze. "That's the way we do up at the Third."

Penrod rubbed his neck and asked meekly:

"Can you do that to any boy up at the Third?"

"See here now," said Rupe, in the tone of one goaded beyond all endurance, "*you* say if I can! You better say it quick, or——"

"I knew you could," Penrod interposed hastily, with the pathetic semblance of a laugh. "I only said that in fun."

"In 'fun'!" repeated Rupe stormily. "You better look out how you——"

"Well, I *said* I wasn't in earnest!" Penrod retreated a few steps. "*I* knew you could, all the time. I expect *I* could do it to some of the boys up at the Third, myself. Couldn't I?"

"No, you couldn't."

"Well, there must be *some* boy up there that I could——"

"No, they ain't! You better——"

"I expect not, then," said Penrod, quickly.

"You *better* 'expect not.' Didn't I tell you once you'd never get back alive if you ever tried to come up around the Third? You want me to *show* you how we do up there, 'bo?"

He began a slow and deadly advance, whereupon Penrod timidly offered a diversion:

"Say, Rupe, I got a box of rats in our stable under a glass cover, so you can watch 'em jump around when you hammer on the box. Come on and look at 'em."

"All right," said the fat-faced boy, slightly mollified. "We'll let Dan kill 'em."

"No, *sir*! I'm goin' to keep 'em. They're kind of pets; I've had 'em all summer—I got names for 'em, and——"

"Looky here, 'bo. Did you hear me say we'll let Dan kill 'em?"

"Yes, but I won't——"

"*What* won't you?" Rupe became sinister immediately. "It seems to me you're gettin' pretty fresh around here."

"Well, I don't want——"

Mr. Collins once more brought into play the dreadful eye-to-eye scowl as practised "up at the Third," and, sometimes, also by young leading men upon the stage. Frowning appallingly, and thrusting forward his under-lip, he placed his nose almost in contact with the nose of Penrod, whose eyes naturally became crossed.

"Dan kills the rats. See?" hissed the fat-faced boy, maintaining the horrible juxtaposition.

"Well, all right," said Penrod, swallowing, "*I* don't want 'em much." And when the pose had been relaxed, he stared at his new friend for a moment, almost with reverence. Then he brightened.

"Come on, Rupe!" he cried enthusiastically, as he climbed the fence. "We'll give our dogs a little live meat—'bo!"

At the dinner-table, that evening, Penrod surprised his family by remarking, in a voice they had never heard him attempt—a lawgiving voice of intentional gruffness:

"Any man that's makin' a hunderd dollars a month is makin' good money."

"What?" asked Mr. Schofield, staring, for the previous conversation had concerned the illness of an infant relative in Council Bluffs.

"Any man that's makin' a hunderd dollars a month is makin' good money."

"What *is* he talking about!" Margaret appealed to the invisible.

"Well," said Penrod, frowning, "that's what foremen at the ladder works get."

"How in the world do you know?" asked his mother.

"Well, I *know* it! A hunderd dollars a month is good money, I tell you!"

"Well, what of it?" said the father, impatiently.

"Nothin'. I only said it was good money."

Mr. Schofield shook his head, dismissing the subject; and here he made a mistake: he should have followed up his son's singular contribution to the conversation. That would have revealed the fact that there was a certain Rupe Collins whose father was a foreman at the ladder works. All clues are important when a boy makes his first remark in a new key.

" 'Good money'?" repeated Margaret, curiously. "What is 'good' money?"

Penrod turned upon her a stern glance. "Say, wouldn't you be just as happy if you had *some* sense?"

"Penrod!" shouted his father. But Penrod's mother gazed with dismay at her son: he had never before spoken like that to his sister.

Mrs. Schofield might have been more dismayed than she was, if she had realized that it was the beginning of an epoch. After dinner, Penrod was slightly scalded in the back as the result of telling Della, the cook, that there was a wart on the middle finger of her right hand. Della thus proving poor material for his new manner to work upon, he approached Duke, in the backyard, and, bending double, seized the lowly animal by the forepaws.

"I let you know my name's Penrod Schofield," hissed the boy. He protruded his underlip ferociously, scowled, and thrust forward his head until his nose touched the dog's. "And you better look out when Penrod Schofield's around, or you'll get in big trouble! *You understan' that, 'bo?*"

The next day, and the next, the increasing change in

Penrod puzzled and distressed his family, who had no idea of its source. How might they guess that hero-worship takes such forms? They were vaguely conscious that a rather shabby boy, not of the neighbourhood, came to "play" with Penrod several times; but they failed to connect this circumstance with the peculiar behaviour of the son of the house, whose ideals (his father remarked) seemed to have suddenly become identical with those of Gyp the Blood.

Meanwhile, for Penrod himself, "life had taken on new meaning, new richness." He had become a fighting man—in conversation at least. "Do you want to know how I do when they try to slip up on me from behind?" he asked Della. And he enacted for her unappreciative eye a scene of fistic manœuvres wherein he held an imaginary antagonist helpless in a net of stratagems.

Frequently, when he was alone, he would outwit and pummel this same enemy, and, after a cunning feint, land a dolorous stroke full upon a face of air. "There! I guess you'll know better next time. That's the way we do up at the Third!"

Sometimes, in solitary pantomime, he encountered more than one opponent at a time, for numbers were apt to come upon him treacherously, especially at a little after his rising hour, when he might be caught at a disadvantage—perhaps standing on one leg to encase the other in his knickerbockers. Like lightning, he would hurl the trapping garment from him, and, ducking and pivoting, deal great sweeping blows among the circle of sneaking devils. (That was how he broke the clock in his bedroom.) And while these battles were occupying his attention, it was a waste of voice to call him to breakfast, though if his mother, losing patience, came to his room, she would find him seated on the bed pulling at a stocking. "Well, ain't I coming fast as I can?"

At the table and about the house generally he was bumptious, loud with fatuous misinformation, and assumed a domineering tone, which neither satire nor reproof seemed able to reduce; but it was among his own intimates that his new superiority was most outrageous. He twisted the fingers and squeezed the necks of all the boys of the neighbourhood, meeting their indignation with a hoarse and rasping laugh he had acquired after short practice in the stable, where he jeered and taunted the lawn-mower, the garden-scythe and the wheelbarrow quite out of countenance.

Likewise he bragged to the other boys by the hour, Rupe Collins being the chief subject of encomium— next to Penrod himself. "That's the way we do up at the Third," became staple explanation of violence, for Penrod, like Tartarin, was plastic in the hands of his own imagination, and at times convinced himself that he really was one of those dark and murderous spirits exclusively of whom "the Third" was composed—according to Rupe Collins.

Then, when Penrod had exhausted himself repeating to nausea accounts of the prowess of himself and his great friend, he would turn to two other subjects for vainglory. These were his father and Duke.

Mothers must accept the fact that between babyhood and manhood their sons do not boast of them. The boy, with boys, is a Choctaw; and either the influence or the protection of women is shameful. "Your mother won't let you," is an insult. But, "My father won't let me," is a dignified explanation and cannot be hooted. A boy is ruined among his fellows if he talks much of his mother or sisters; and he must recognize it as his duty to offer at least the appearance of persecution to all things ranked as female, such as cats and every species of fowl. But he must champion his father and his dog, and, ever ready to pit either against any challenger, must picture both as ravening for battle and absolutely unconquerable.

Penrod, of course, had always talked by the code, but, under the new stimulus, Duke was represented virtually as a cross between Bob, Son of Battle, and a South American vampire; and this in spite of the fact that Duke himself often sat close by, a living lie, with the hope of peace in his heart. As for Penrod's father, that gladiator was painted as of sentiments and dimensions suitable to a super-demon composed of equal parts of Goliath, Jack Johnson and the Emperor Nero.

Even Penrod's walk was affected; he adopted a gait which was a kind of taunting swagger; and, when he passed other children on the street, he practised the habit of feinting a blow; then, as the victim dodged, he rasped the triumphant horse laugh which he gradually mastered to horrible perfection. He did this to Marjorie Jones—ay! this was their next meeting, and such is Eros, young! What was even worse, in Marjorie's opinion, he went on his way without explanation, and left her standing on the corner talking about it, long after he was out of hearing.

Within five days from his first encounter with Rupe Collins, Penrod had become unbearable. He even almost alienated Sam Williams, who for a time submitted to finger twisting and neck squeezing and the new style of conversation, but finally declared that Penrod made him "sick." He made the statement with fervour, one sultry afternoon, in Mr. Schofield's stable, in the presence of Herman and Verman.

"You better look out, 'bo," said Penrod, threateningly. "I'll show you a little how we do up at the Third."

"Up at the Third!" Sam repeated with scorn. "You haven't ever been up there."

"I haven't?" cried Penrod. "I *haven't?*"

"No, you haven't!"

"Looky here!" Penrod, darkly argumentative, prepared to perform the eye-to-eye business. "When haven't I been up there?"

"You haven't *never* been up there!" In spite of Penrod's closely approaching nose Sam maintained his ground, and appealed for confirmation. "Has he, Herman?"

"I don' reckon so," said Herman, laughing.

"*What!*" Penrod transferred his nose to the immediate vicinity of Herman's nose. "You don't reckon so, 'bo, don't you? You better look out how you reckon around here! *You understan' that, 'bo?*"

Herman bore the eye-to-eye very well; indeed, it seemed to please him, for he continued to laugh while Verman chuckled delightedly. The brothers had been in the country picking berries for a week, and it happened that this was their first experience of the new manifestation of Penrod.

"*Haven't* I been up at the Third?" the sinister Penrod demanded.

"I don' reckon so. How come you ast *me?*"

"Didn't you just hear me *say* I been up there?"

"Well," said Herman mischievously, "hearin' ain't believin'!"

Penrod clutched him by the back of the neck, but Herman, laughing loudly, ducked and released himself at once, retreating to the wall.

"You take that back!" Penrod shouted, striking out wildly.

"Don' git mad," begged the small darky, while a number of blows falling upon his warding arms failed to abate his amusement, and a sound one upon the cheek only made him laugh the more unrestrainedly. He behaved exactly as if Penrod were tickling him, and his brother, Verman, rolled with joy in a wheelbarrow. Penrod pummelled till he was tired, and produced no greater effect.

"There!" he panted, desisting finally. "*Now* I reckon you know whether I been up there or not!"

Herman rubbed his smitten cheek. "Pow!" he exclaimed. "Pow-ee! You cert'ny did lan' me good one *nat* time! Oo-ee! she *hurt!*"

"You'll get hurt worse'n that," Penrod assured him, "if you stay around here much. Rupe Collins is comin' this afternoon, he said. We're goin' to make some policemen's billies out of the rake handle."

"You go' spoil new rake you' pa bought?"

"What do *we* care? I and Rupe got to have billies, haven't we?"

"How you make 'em?"

"Melt lead and pour in a hole we're goin' to make in the end of 'em. Then we're goin' to carry 'em in our pockets, and if anybody says anything to us—*oh*, oh! look out! They won't get a crack on the head—*oh*, no!"

"When's Rupe Collins coming?" Sam Williams inquired rather uneasily. He had heard a great deal too much of this personage, but as yet the pleasure of actual acquaintance had been denied him.

"He's liable to be here any time," answered Penrod. "You better look out. You'll be lucky if you get home alive, if you stay till *he* comes."

"I ain't afraid of him," Sam returned, conventionally.

"You are, too!" (There was some truth in the retort.) "There ain't any boy in this part of town but me that wouldn't be afraid of him. You'd be afraid to talk to him. You wouldn't get a word out of your mouth before old Rupie'd have you where you'd wished you never come around *him*, lettin' on like you was so much! *You* wouldn't run home yellin' 'Mom-muh' or nothin'! *Oh, no!*"

"Who Rupe Collins?" asked Herman.

"'Who Rupe Collins?'" Penrod mocked, and used his rasping laugh, but, instead of showing fright, Herman appeared to think he was meant to laugh, too; and so he did, echoed by Verman. "You just hang around here a little while longer," Penrod added, grimly, "and you'll find out who Rupe Collins is, and I pity *you* when you do!"

"What he go' do?"

"You'll see; that's all! You just wait and——"

At this moment a brown hound ran into the stable through the alley door, wagged a greeting to Penrod, and fraternized with Duke. The fat-faced boy appeared upon the threshold and gazed coldly about the little company in the carriage-house, whereupon the coloured brethren, ceasing from merriment, were instantly impassive, and Sam Williams moved a little nearer the door leading into the yard.

Obviously, Sam regarded the newcomer as a redoubtable if not ominous figure. He was a head taller than either Sam or Penrod; head and shoulders taller than Herman, who was short for his age; and Verman could hardly be used for purposes of comparison at all, being a mere squat brown spot, not yet quite nine years on this planet. And to Sam's mind, the aspect of Mr. Collins realized Penrod's portentous foreshadowings. Upon the fat face there was an expression of truculent

intolerance which had been cultivated by careful habit
to such perfection that Sam's heart sank at sight of it.
A somewhat enfeebled twin to this expression had of
late often decorated the visage of Penrod, and appeared
upon that ingenuous surface now, as he advanced to
welcome the eminent visitor.

The host swaggered toward the door with a great
deal of shoulder movement, carelessly feinting a slap at
Verman in passing, and creating by various means the
atmosphere of a man who has contemptuously amused
himself with underlings while awaiting an equal.

"Hello, 'bo!" Penrod said in the deepest voice possible
to him.

"Who you callin' 'bo?" was the ungracious response,
accompanied by immediate action of a similar nature.
Rupe held Penrod's head in the crook of an elbow and
massaged his temples with a hard-pressing knuckle.

"I was only in fun, Rupie," pleaded the sufferer, and
then, being set free, "Come here, Sam," he said.

"What for?"

Penrod laughed pityingly. "Pshaw, I ain't goin' to
hurt you. Come on." Sam, maintaining his position near
the other door, Penrod went to him and caught him
round the neck.

"Watch me, Rupie!" Penrod called, and performed
upon Sam the knuckle operation which he had himself
just undergone, Sam submitting mechanically, his eyes
fixed with increasing uneasiness upon Rupe Collins. Sam
had a premonition that something even more painful
than Penrod's knuckle was going to be inflicted upon
him.

"*That* don' hurt," said Penrod, pushing him away.

"Yes, it does, too!" Sam rubbed his temple.

"Puh! It didn't hurt me, did it, Rupie? Come on in,

Rupe: show this baby where he's got a wart on his finger."

"*You* showed me that trick," Sam objected. "You already did that to me. You tried it twice this afternoon and I don't know how many times before, only you weren't strong enough after the first time. Anyway, I know what it is, and I don't——"

"Come on, Rupe," said Penrod. "Make the baby lick dirt."

At this bidding, Rupe approached, while Sam, still protesting, moved to the threshold of the outer door; but Penrod seized him by the shoulders and swung him indoors with a shout.

"Little baby wants to run home to its Mom-muh! Here he is, Rupie."

Thereupon was Penrod's treachery to an old comrade properly rewarded, for as the two struggled, Rupe caught each by the back of the neck, simultaneously, and, with creditable impartiality, forced both boys to their knees.

"Lick dirt!" he commanded, forcing them still forward, until their faces were close to the stable floor.

At this moment he received a real surprise. With a loud whack something struck the back of his head, and, turning, he beheld Verman in the act of lifting a piece of lath to strike again.

"Em moys ome!" said Verman, the Giant Killer.

"He tongue-tie'," Herman explained. "He say, let 'em boys alone."

Rupe addressed his host briefly:

"Chase them nigs out o' here!"

"Don' call me nig," said Herman. "I mine my own biznuss. You let 'em boys alone."

Rupe strode across the still prostrate Sam, stepped

upon Penrod, and, equipping his countenance with the
terrifying scowl and protruded jaw, lowered his head to
the level of Herman's.

"Nig, you'll be lucky if you leave here alive!" And
he leaned forward till his nose was within less than an
inch of Herman's nose.

It could be felt that something awful was about to
happen, and Penrod, as he rose from the floor, suffered
an unexpected twinge of apprehension and remorse: he
hoped that Rupe wouldn't *really* hurt Herman. A sudden dislike of Rupe and Rupe's ways rose within him,
as he looked at the big boy overwhelming the little darky
with that ferocious scowl. Penrod, all at once, felt sorry
about something indefinable; and, with equal vagueness,
he felt foolish. "Come on, Rupe," he suggested, feebly,
"let Herman go, and let's us make our billies out of the
rake handle."

The rake handle, however, was not available, if Rupe
had inclined to favour the suggestion. Verman had dis-
carded his lath for the rake, which he was at this moment lifting in the air.

"You ole black nigger," the fat-faced boy said
venomously to Herman, "I'm agoin' to——"

But he had allowed his nose to remain too long near
Herman's. Penrod's familiar nose had been as close with
only a ticklish spinal effect upon the not very remote
descendant of Congo man-eaters. The result produced
by the glare of Rupe's unfamiliar eyes, and by the dreadfully suggestive proximity of Rupe's unfamiliar nose, was
altogether different. Herman's and Verman's Bangala
great-grandfathers never considered people of their own
jungle neighbourhood proper material for a meal, but
they looked upon strangers—especially truculent strangers—as distinctly edible.

Penrod and Sam heard Rupe suddenly squawk and

bellow; saw him writhe and twist and fling out his arms like flails, though without removing his face from its juxtaposition; indeed, for a moment, the two heads seemed even closer.

Then they separated—and battle was on!

How neat and pure is the task of the chronicler who has the tale to tell of a "good rousing fight" between boys or men who fight in the "good old English way," according to a model set for fights in books long before Tom Brown went to Rugby. There are seconds and rounds and rules of fair-play, and always there is great good feeling in the end—though sometimes, to vary the model, "the Butcher" defeats the hero—and the chronicler who stencils this fine old pattern on his page is certain of applause as the stirrer of "red blood." There is no surer recipe.

But when Herman and Verman set to 't the record must be no more than a few fragments left by the expurgator. It has been perhaps sufficiently suggested that the altercation in Mr. Schofield's stable opened with mayhem in respect to the aggressor's nose. Expressing vocally his indignation and the extremity of his pained surprise, Mr. Collins stepped backward, holding his left hand over his nose, and striking at Herman with his right. Then Verman hit him with the rake.

Verman struck from behind. He struck as hard as he could. And he struck with the tines down. For, in his simple, direct African way he wished to kill his enemy, and he wished to kill him as soon as possible. That was his single, earnest purpose.

On this account, Rupe Collins was peculiarly unfortunate. He was plucky and he enjoyed conflict, but neither his ambitions nor his anticipations had ever included murder. He had not learned that an habitually aggressive person runs the danger of colliding with beings in

one of those lower stages of evolution wherein theories
about "hitting below the belt" have not yet made their
appearance.

The rake glanced from the back of Rupe's head to
his shoulder, but it felled him. Both darkies jumped full
upon him instantly, and the three rolled and twisted
upon the stable floor, unloosing upon the air sincere
maledictions closely connected with complaints of cruel
and unusual treatment; while certain expressions of
feeling presently emanating from Herman and Verman
indicated that Rupe Collins, in this extremity, was proving himself not too slavishly addicted to fighting by rule.
Dan and Duke, mistaking all for mirth, barked gayly.

From the panting, pounding, yelling heap issued
words and phrases hitherto quite unknown to Penrod
and Sam; also, a hoarse repetition in the voice of Rupe
concerning his ear left it not to be doubted that additional mayhem was taking place. Appalled, the two
spectators retreated to the doorway nearest the yard,
where they stood dumbly watching the cataclysm.

The struggle increased in primitive simplicity: time
and again the howling Rupe got to his knees only to
go down again as the earnest brothers, in their own way,
assisted him to a more reclining position. Primal forces
operated here, and the two blanched, slightly higher
products of evolution, Sam and Penrod, no more thought
of interfering than they would have thought of interfering with an earthquake.

At last, out of the ruck rose Verman, disfigured and
maniacal. With a wild eye he looked about him for his
trusty rake; but Penrod, in horror, had long since thrown
the rake out into the yard. Naturally, it had not seemed
necessary to remove the lawn-mower.

The frantic eye of Verman fell upon the lawn-mower,
and instantly he leaped to its handle. Shrilling a word-

less war-cry, he charged, propelling the whirling, deaf-
ening knives straight upon the prone legs of Rupe Collins. The lawn-mower was sincerely intended to pass
longitudinally over the body of Mr. Collins from heel to
head; and it was the time for a death-song. Black
Valkyrie hovered in the shrieking air.

"Cut his gizzud out!" shrieked Herman, urging on
the whirling knives.

They touched and lacerated the shin of Rupe, as, with
the supreme agony of effort a creature in mortal peril
puts forth before succumbing, he tore himself free of
Herman and got upon his feet.

Herman was up as quickly. He leaped to the wall and
seized the garden-scythe that hung there.

"I'm go to cut you' gizzud out," he announced defi-
nitely, "an' eat it!"

Rupe Collins had never run from anybody (except
his father) in his life; he was not a coward; but the
present situation was very, very unusual. He was already
in a badly dismantled condition, and yet Herman and
Verman seemed discontented with their work: Verman
was swinging the grass-cutter about for a new charge,
apparently still wishing to mow him, and Herman had
made a quite plausible statement about what he intended to do with the scythe.

Rupe paused but for an extremely condensed survey
of the horrible advance of the brothers, and then, utter-
ing a blood-curdled scream of fear, ran out of the stable
and up the alley at a speed he had never before attained, so that even Dan had hard work to keep within
barking distance. And a 'cross-shoulder glance, at the
corner, revealing Verman and Herman in pursuit, the
latter waving his scythe overhead, Mr. Collins slackened
not his gait, but, rather, out of great anguish, increased
it; the while a rapidly developing purpose became firm

in his mind—and ever after so remained—not only to refrain from visiting that neighbourhood again, but never by any chance to come within a mile of it.

From the alley door, Penrod and Sam watched the flight, and were without words. When the pursuit rounded the corner, the two looked wanly at each other, but neither spoke until the return of the brothers from the chase.

Herman and Verman came back, laughing and chuckling.

"Hiyi!" cackled Herman to Verman, as they came, "See 'at ole boy run!"

"Who-ee!" Verman shouted in ecstasy.

"Nev' did see boy run so fas'!" Herman continued, tossing the scythe into the wheelbarrow. "I bet he home in bed by viss time!"

Verman roared with delight, appearing to be wholly unconscious that the lids of his right eye were swollen shut and that his attire, not too finical before the struggle, now entitled him to unquestioned rank as a *sansculotte*. Herman was a similar ruin, and gave as little heed to his condition.

Penrod looked dazedly from Herman to Verman and back again. So did Sam Williams.

"Herman," said Penrod, in a weak voice, "you wouldn't *honest* of cut his gizzard out, would you?"

"Who? Me? I don' know. He mighty mean ole boy!" Herman shook his head gravely, and then, observing that Verman was again convulsed with unctuous merriment, joined laughter with his brother. "Sho'! I guess I uz dess *talkin'* whens I said 'at! Reckon he thought I meant it, f'm de way he tuck an' run. Hiyi! Reckon he thought ole Herman bad man! No, suh! I uz dess talkin', 'cause I nev' would cut *no*body! I ain' tryin' git in no jail—*no*, suh!"

Penrod looked at the scythe: he looked at Herman. He looked at the lawn-mower, and he looked at Verman. Then he looked out in the yard at the rake. So did Sam Williams.

"Come on, Verman," said Herman. "We ain' got 'at stove-wood f' supper yit."

Giggling reminiscently, the brothers disappeared, leaving silence behind them in the carriage-house. Penrod and Sam retired slowly into the shadowy interior, each glancing, now and then, with a preoccupied air, at the open, empty doorway where the late afternoon sunshine was growing ruddy. At intervals one or the other scraped the floor reflectively with the side of his shoe. Finally, still without either having made any effort at conversation, they went out into the yard and stood, continuing their silence.

"Well," said Sam, at last, "I guess it's time I better be gettin' home. So long, Penrod!"

"So long, Sam," said Penrod, feebly.

With a solemn gaze he watched his friend out of sight. Then he went slowly into the house, and after an interval occupied in a unique manner, appeared in the library, holding a pair of brilliantly gleaming shoes in his hand.

Mr. Schofield, reading the evening paper, glanced frowningly over it at his offspring.

"Look, papa," said Penrod. "I found your shoes where you'd taken 'em off in your room, to put on your slippers, and they were all dusty. So I took 'em out on the back porch and gave 'em a good blacking. They shine up fine, don't they?"

"Well, I'll be d-dud-dummed!" said the startled Mr. Schofield.

Penrod was zigzagging back to normal.

OUR NEW TELEPHONE

BY RUTH GORDON

I

"DAMN good magazine, *McClure's*," my father said one evening as he and my mother sat reading. He reached over and knocked the ashes out of his pipe into the Dresden china cuspidor that had been a bargain.

"I'm glad you got something to enjoy, Clinton. Lord knows you deserve it and I know if you say so it *must* be good because you don't like to read just any old thing. You know I been thinking, Clinton, that everybody else has got one and we ought to have a telephone."

"Wouldn't have one if you gave it to me," declared my father composedly and returned once more to *McClure's*.

"Why, Clinton?" asked my mother. "What have you got against it?"

My father sat still as a statue for a moment and then gave a loud sneeze. "Get that cat off the register," he demanded, blowing his nose with a groan. "Hot air coming up through cat fur'll give me back my old malaria. Get him off of there. I ain't goin' to have him lying around warming up all his germs."

"Here, Punk," said my mother kindly, lifting him off the register and settling him on her lap. "Punk's clean and healthy and hasn't any germs, Clinton. Please try not to be against a telephone."

"I ain't against it," said my father reasonably, "so long as we don't have to have one."

272

Punk stretched out across my mother's lap with such drowsy abandon that he very nearly rolled off. "Sit quiet, Punk," she counseled. "The kind of telephone we want, Clinton, won't cost a thing except just one old nickel a day, and Ruth's growing up, you know, into a young lady, and all the other girls have them, and it isn't as if we wanted to make outgoing calls to cost us money or anything. It's so the children—I mean the young people —can call up Ruth. So what we want is to get a coin-in-the-slot one that all you have to do is every day put a nickel in. Just one call a day is all the telephone company cares about, or of course two calls in one day and then skip tomorrow. And that way makes the bills be all paid, and you don't even have to waste so much as a stamp doing it because the telephone company comes themselves to collect its nickels and all *we* have to do is to just be at home that day, and if you're *not,* then they simply come another. And, Clinton, if you don't want to, you don't personally have to have a thing to do with it; it can just be Ruth's and mine."

"It can be Shem and Japeth's," said my father genially, "so long as I don't have to pay for it. But the way it'll turn out'll be, it *ain't* Shem and Japeth's but mine. And that I ain't goin' to have, and don't even put it in my name in the telephone book. I got no wish to call attention to myself."

"We won't use your name at all, Clinton. It can be in my name of Mrs. Clinton Jones and don't you trouble about the money end of it because that part is certainly all right. I can always get it from somewheres."

My father picked up his *McClure's Magazine* and hitched his chair a little closer to our green-shaded gasolier. "I ain't a wizard, either financial or fake, but I can tell you that the New England Telephone Company ain't goin' to care for *that* address for no source of its revenue. Tell me what good's a cat anyway. What about throwin' him away?"

My mother sighed and smoothed our cat's fur affectionately. "Clinton, you just like to hear yourself talk like that, but you don't fool even Punk. Punk likes you best of anyone, and well he might because you taught that cat just about every blessed thing he knows."

My father looked over at Punk coldly. "Jump over," he said and held up his foot. With perhaps just a little surreptitious assistance, Punk flopped down off my mother's lap, and when he found himself close to my father's foot, of his own free will he jumped over.

"There," exclaimed my mother happily. "A little faith is a wonderful thing. That cat loves and trusts you, Clinton, and it doesn't cost any more."

"A little faith," said my father judicially, "has to start with something a whole lot deeper than just a cat's true love and trust. And o' course the New England Telephone Company ain't had the splendid advantage of seeing how a little cat shall lead 'em, so when you get down to talkin' finance you can't give 'em turnip blood as security, sayin' it would be just as cheap for it to have some and for all you know, it really may."

My mother looked at my father admiringly. "Oh, Clinton," she sighed. "You're a wonderful talker. I wish more people could hear you though I don't know where you get your ideas from. How many people do we know that hasn't got a telephone, and I don't want Ruth to grow up feeling out of it. Why, I don't want to be out of it myself. Just think how'd you'd have felt that day President Cleveland died if you couldn't have called up Mrs. Litchfield to tell me to hang out our flag at half mast."

"Well," said my father plausibly, "how often do you think that occasion is likely to arise?"

"What was just a blessing, of course, was Eaton's ice man happening by. Otherwise I could never in this world have got out on that piazza roof, let alone finding how I was going to get that flag pulled up the pole. Of course I had to buy that 25-cent piece of ice extra, that I didn't want any more than a hen wants water, but with Ruth being named for Ruthie Cleveland, and the roof being so slanting, and you having telephoned, I just knew what had to be done *had* to be done, and so done it was."

"That feller lashed them ropes to the halyards like he'd took lessons from Corticelli's cat. Seemed like the only way to ever hope to get 'em untied again was to just let 'em rot off. I notice how people handle rope and strings is a lot of time pretty damn characteristic."

"Well now, Clinton," said my mother, gently reproving, "just because you happened to be a sailor doesn't mean everyone can knot a rope right."

My father favored her with a pitying glance. "People don't happen to be sailors," he said succinctly. "There's quite a knack to it."

II.

When our telephone was installed, my father ignored it unless he thought we were talking too long, and then he told us briefly to quit. Once it rang at nine o'clock, after we had gone to bed, and as I came upstairs again my father called out to me, "What's the matter? Is the house afire?"

"No," I said, "it was Richard DeNormandie."

"Oh," he said, "is DeNormandie's house afire?"

"No, Papa, nobody's house is afire," I said feeling grown-up and important. "He just simply asked me to go to a dance."

My father's bed creaked as he rolled over. "I knew it must have been something vital," he said. "Anything to prevent him askin' you in the daytime, or don't he get the power of speech before night?"

And then came the day when my father was troubled and used our telephone himself. There was word at the factory that Dan Weymouth, head of the shipping department, was going to retire on a pension, and it frightened my father, for he thought perhaps the retirement was compulsory. "Dan's only been there a little longer than me, you know," he reminded my mother. "Well, then, where's the axe going to fall next?"

"It's awful, Clinton," agreed my mother, "but couldn't you just try to eat supper."

My father pushed back his chair from the dining-room table and stood up. "No," he said, "I couldn't. I'm too troubled. I don't know *what* to think. See, if I knew Dan went and done it of his own free will, that would be all right. All right for *Dan*, I mean," he added hastily, "because o' course if they asked me to go and do like-wise, the only answer I got is to go over an' lay down on the New York, New Haven, and Hartford railroad tracks."

"Clinton!"

"O' course, with Dan it ain't so drastic. He owns his own house in Mather Street, and above that he's already got his G.A.R. pension—for *what*, o' course, no one seems to be clear. Far's I can make out, someone looked cross-eyed at him, so he went and lay down in an army hospital an' has been gettin' paid for it ever since. So it's just possible he *could* be quittin' an' *glad* to, but how'm I goin' to know for certain, if someone don't cough up some facts."

"What about the others, Clinton? Are any more men leaving, too?"

"Not's I know of. But see, now I ain't sure of anything any more, because two hours ago I didn't know nothin' about Dan Weymouth neither."

"Well, has anyone said anything to make you suspicious?"

"Where would I get time to be suspicious, standin' on my feet all day?"

"Well, Clinton, it's probably all your imagination, but if it's goin' to make you worry like this, won't you please, just to make me happy, call up Dan on the telephone and see what he has to say."

"Oh no," said my father miserably, "I guess it ain't as bad as all *that*."

"Think a minute, Clinton. Is your peace of mind worth a nickel? We can't eat our dinner tonight. Won't you even pay a nickel for that?"

My father looked moodily out the window. "What the hell consolation is it goin' to be? If it's good news it'll still be good news tomorrow, and if it's bad news, *that* ain't consolin', and we're payin' a nickel to get it quicker." My father pulled down the window shade. "No wonder they make fortunes out of poor people. All right, I'll telephone to him. You got to have money to have the heart to wait for bad news."

My mother did not stop to hear anything further but hurried to the telephone book hanging beside our telephone in the entry between the cellar stairs and our kitchen door.

My father sat down in his reading chair and looked at the back of his hands. "There's two things takes the gimp out of a man," he said dejectedly. "One's injustice and one is cancer."

"Oh, cancer—don't talk," agreed my mother, ruffling the pages until she came to W. "Some people used to say it came from tomatoes, but I for one never thought it did. You know my grandmother Beal died of it, and the saying is it's supposed to skip a generation. Well, right this minute I don't know what state of mind I'd be in if it wasn't for my Mental Science. I wish I could get you to try it, Clinton, even if you never got any further than to just read 'Unity.' Here's Dan's number, Clinton, just there in back of my thumb."

My father took a nickel out of the Clark's O.N.T. (Our New Thread) box, which stood by the phone for that purpose. He dropped it in the slot, listened to the little bell ring, and cleared his throat several times, so as to be ready. There was a click at the other end of the line and my father became as stiff as a ramrod. "Hello," he said distinctly, "is that you, Dan?" He paused. "Yes, I thought it was, it sounds like you. This is Jones and I'm telephoning to you. Can you hear me, or do you want me to be louder?" Results were apparently satisfactory at Mr. Weymouth's end and so my father continued, "I'm telephoning to you, Dan, about a matter that's give me a whole lot of concern, and what I'd like to do is find out about it without in no ways buttin' in. It's what's goin' on in the factory about you getting ready to leave."

A short pause followed, while my father listened absorbedly. Suddenly his whole expression brightened. "Just repeat that, Dan," he said eagerly, "so's I can make sure I got it correct. You done it because you wanted to. They didn't ask you to do it. In other words the whole idea came straight from your end." Relief was in my father's voice and face. "Well, Dan, I'm glad to hear you say so. I'm *damn* glad to hear you say it. Fixed as I am, it's a relief. Just one more thing: you can appreciate I ain't askin' you all this out of no idle curiosity and that's all I had in my mind to say. So you can start to hang up now same as me. I been telephonin' to you from Wollaston, so good-bye."

"What, Clinton?" asked my mother.

My father took off his glasses, held them to the light, and polished them. When he spoke it sounded as though his voice was being meted out a little at a time, "Why," he said carefully, "Dan give me to understand there weren't no call to be alarmed. There hasn't been no pressure brought to bear on him, no pressure whatsoever in any shape, form, or manner. The idea sprang only from himself."

"Oh, isn't that just a blessing!" exclaimed my mother jubilantly. "Dan's a real lovely man. Oh, isn't it lovely it's all straightened out. I declare I *love* a telephone."

"A telephone," said my father learnedly, "is a very remarkable invention. I never said it wasn't. I could hear Dan just now as clear, say, as if he was down in our cellar. As a scientific achievement it can't be beat. Of course, what effect it's going to have on the next generation's powers of hearing, with all that clickin' and bell ringin', still remains to be seen. But anyway, whoever ain't got their hearing *eventually*, I'm damn glad I got mine this evening, so's I could hear Dan Weymouth say he wasn't fired."

SOME LIKE THEM COLD

BY RING LARDNER

N. Y., Aug 3.

DEAR Miss Gillespie: How about our bet now as you bet me I would forget all about you the minute I hit the big town and would never write you a letter. Well girlie it looks like you lose so pay me. Seriously we will call all bets off as I am not the kind that bet on a sure thing and it sure was a sure thing that I would not forget a girlie like you and all that is worrying me is whether it may not be the other way round and you are wondering who this fresh guy is that is writeing you this letter. I bet you are so will try and refreshen your memory.

Well girlie I am the handsome young man that was wondering round the Lasalle st. station Monday and "happened" to sit down beside of a mighty pretty girlie who was waiting to meet her sister from Toledo and the train was late and I am glad of it because if it had not of been that little girlie and I would never of met. So for once I was a lucky guy but still I guess it was time I had some luck as it was certainly tough luck for you and I to both be liveing in Chi all that time and never get together till a half hour before I was leaveing town for good.

Still "better late than never" you know and maybe we can make up for lost time though it looks like we would have to do our makeing up at long distants unless you make good on your threat and come to N. Y. I wish you would do that little thing girlie as it looks like that was the only way we would get a chance to play round together as it looks like they was little or no chance of me comeing back to Chi as my whole future is in the big town. N. Y. is the only spot and specially for a man that expects to make my liveing in the song writeing game as here is the Mecca for that line of work and no matter how good a man may be they don't get no recognition unless they live in N. Y.

Well girlie you asked me to tell you all about my trip. Well I remember you saying that you would give anything to be makeing it yourself but as far as the trip itself was conserned you ought to be thankfull you did not have to make it as you would of sweat your head off. I know I did specially wile going through Ind. Monday P. M. but Monday night was the worst of all trying to sleep and finely I give it up and just layed there with the prespiration rolling off of me though I was laying on top of the covers and nothing on but my underwear.

Yesterday was not so bad as it rained most of the A. M. comeing through N. Y. state and in the P. M. we road along side of the Hudson all P. M. Some river girlie and just looking at it makes a man forget all about the heat and everything else except a certain girlie who I seen for the first time Monday and then only for a half hour but she is the kind of a girlie that a man don't need to see her only once and they would be no danger of forgetting her. There I guess I better lay off that subject or you will think I am a "fresh guy."

Well that is about all to tell you about the trip only they was one amuseing incidence that come off yesterday which I will tell you. Well they was a dame got on the train at Toledo Monday and had the birth opp. mine but I did not see nothing of her that night as I was out smoking till late and she hit the hay early but yesterday A. M. she come in the dinner and sit at the same table with me and tried to make me and it was so raw that the dinge waiter seen it and give me the wink and of course I paid no tension and I waited till she got through so as they would be no danger of her folling me out but she stopped on the way out to get a tooth pick and when I come out she was out on the platform with it so I tried to brush right by but she spoke up and asked me what time it was and I told her and she said she guessed her watch was slow so I said maybe it just seemed slow on acct. of the company it was in.

I don't know if she got what I was driveing at or not but any way she give up trying to make me and got off at Albany. She was a good looker but I have no time for gals that tries to make strangers on a train.

Well if I don't quit you will think I am writeing a book but will expect a long letter in answer to this letter and we will see if you can keep your promise like I have kept mine. Don't dissapoint me girlie as I am all alone in a large city and hearing from you will keep me from getting home sick for old Chi though I never thought so much of the old town till I found out you lived there. Don't think that is kidding girlie as I mean it.

You can address me at this hotel as it looks like I will be here right along as it is on 47th st. right off of old Broadway and handy to everything and am only paying $21 per wk. for my rm. and could of got one for $16 but without bath but am glad to pay the differents as am lost without my bath in the A. M. and sometimes at night too.

Tomorrow I expect to commence fighting the "battle of Broadway" and will let you know how I come out

that is if you answer this letter. In the mean wile girlie
au reservoir and don't do nothing I would not do.

Your new friend (?)

Chas. F. Lewis.

Chicago, Ill., Aug. 6.

My Dear Mr. Lewis: Well, that certainly was a "surprise party" getting your letter and you are certainly
a "wonder man" to keep your word as I am afraid
most men of your sex are gay deceivers but maybe you
are "different." Any way it sure was a surprise and
will gladly pay the bet if you will just tell me what it
was we bet. Hope it was not money as I am a "working
girl" but if it was not more than a dollar or two will
try to dig it up even if I have to "beg, borrow or
steal."

Suppose you will think me a "case" to make a bet
and then forget what it was, but you must remember,
Mr. Man, that I had just met you and was "dazzled."
Joking aside I was rather "fussed" and will tell you
why. Well, Mr. Lewis, I suppose you see lots of girls
like the one you told me about that you saw on the
train who tried to "get acquainted" but I want to
assure you that I am not one of those kind and sincerely
hope you will believe me when I tell you that you was
the first man I ever spoke to meeting them like that and
my friends and the people who know me would simply
faint if they knew I ever spoke to a man without a
proper introduction."

Believe me, Mr. Lewis, I am not that kind and I don't
now now why I did it only that you was so "different"
looking if you know what I mean and not at all like
the kind of men that usually try to force their atten-
ions on every pretty girl they see. Lots of times I act

on impulse and let my feelings run away from me and
sometimes I do things on the impulse of the moment
which I regret them later on, and that is what I did
this time, but hope you won't give me cause to regret
it and I know you won't as I know you are not that
kind of a man a specially after what you told me about
the girl on the train. But any way as I say, I was in
a "daze" so can't remember what it was we bet, but
will try and pay it if it does not "break" me.

Sis's train got in about ten minutes after yours had
gone and when she saw me what do you think was the
first thing she said? Well, Mr. Lewis, she said: "Why
Mibs (That is a pet name some of my friends have
given me) what has happened to you? I never seen you
have as much color." So I passed it off with some remark about the heat and changed the subject as I certainly was not going to tell her that I had just been
talking to a man who I had never met or she would
have dropped dead from the shock. Either that or she
would not of believed me as it would be hard for a
person who knows me well to imagine me doing a
thing like that as I have quite a reputation for "squelch-
ing" men who try to act fresh. I don't mean anything
personal by that, Mr. Lewis, as am a good judge of
character and could tell without you telling me that
you are not that kind.

Well, Sis and I have been on the "go" ever since she
arrived as I took yesterday and today off so I could
show her the "sights" though she says she would be
perfectly satisfied to just sit in the apartment and listen
to me "rattle on." Am afraid I am a great talker, Mr.
Lewis, but Sis says it is as good as a show to hear me
talk as I tell things in such a different way as I cannot
help from seeing the humorous side of everything and
she says she never gets tired of listening to me, but of

course she is my sister and thinks the world of me, but she really does laugh like she enjoyed my craziness.

Maybe I told you that I have a tiny little apartment which a girl friend of mine and I have together and it is hardly big enough to turn round in, but still it is "home" and I am a great home girl and hardly ever care to go out evenings except occasionally to the theater or dance. But even if our "nest" is small we are proud of it and Sis complimented us on how cozy it is and how "homey" it looks and she said she did not see how we could afford to have everything so nice and Edith (my girl friend) said: "Mibs deserves all the credit for that. I never knew a girl who could make a little money go a long ways like she can." Well, of course she is my best friend and always saying nice things about me, but I do try and I hope I get results. Have always said that good taste and being careful is a whole lot more important than lots of money though it is nice to have it.

You must write and tell me how you are getting along in the "battle of Broadway" (I laughed when I read that) and whether the publishers like your songs though I know they will. Am crazy to hear them and hear you play the piano as I love good jazz music even better than classical, though I suppose it is terrible to say such a thing. But I usually say just what I think though sometimes I wish afterwards I had not of. But still I believe it is better for a girl to be her own self and natural instead of always acting. But am afraid I will never have a chance to hear you play unless you come back to Chi and pay us a visit as my "threat" to come to New York was just a "threat" and I don't see any hope of ever getting there unless some rich New Yorker should fall in love with me and take me there to live. Fine chance for poor little me, eh Mr. Lewis?

Well, I guess I have "rattled on" long enough and

you will think I am writing a book unless I quit an
besides, Sis has asked me as a special favor to make he
a pie for dinner. Maybe you don't know it, Mr. Mar
but I am quite famous for my pie and pastry, but I don
suppose a "genius" is interested in common things lik
that.

Well, be sure and write soon and tell me what N. Y
is like and all about it and don't forget the little girli
who was "bad" and spoke to a strange man in the statio
and have been blushing over it ever since.

Your friend (?)
Mabelle Gillespie.

N. Y., Aug. 10.

Dear Girlie: I bet you will think I am a fresh gu
commencing that way but Miss Gillespie is too cold an
a man can not do nothing cold in this kind of weathe
specially in this man's town which is the hottest plac
I ever been in and I guess maybe the reason why Nev
Yorkers is so bad is because they think they are all read
in H—— and can not go no worse place no matter hov
they behave themselves. Honest girlie I certainly env
you being where there is a breeze off the old Lake an
Chi may be dirty but I never heard of nobody dyin
because they was dirty but four people died here yes
terday on acct. of the heat and I seen two differen
women flop right on Broadway and had to be taker
away in the ambulance and it could not of been becaus
they was dressed too warm because it would be impos
sible for the women here to leave off any more cloths.

Well have not had much luck yet in the battle o
Broadway as all the heads of the big music publishers i
out of town on their vacation and the big boys is th
only ones I will do business with as it would be silly fo
a man with the stuff I have got to waste my time or

somebody that is just on the staff and have not got the final say. But I did play a couple of my numbers for the people up to Levy's and Goebel's and they went crazy over them in both places. So it looks like all I have to do is wait for the big boys to get back and then play my numbers for them and I will be all set. What I want is to get taken on the staff of one of the big firms as that gives a man the inside and they will plug your numbers more if you are on the staff. In the mean wile have not got nothing to worry me but am just seeing the sights of the big town as have saved up enough money to play round for a while and any way a man that can play piano like I can don't never have to worry about starveing. Can certainly make the old music box talk girlie and am always good for a $75 or $100 job.

Well have been here a week now and on the go every minute and I thought I would be lonesome down here but no chance of that as I have been treated fine by the people I have met and have sure met a bunch of them. One of the boys liveing in the hotel is a vaudeville actor and he is a member of the Friars club and took me over there to dinner the other night and some way another the bunch got wise that I could play piano so of course I had to sit down and give them some of my numbers and everybody went crazy over them. One of the boys I met there was Paul Sears the song writer but he just writes the lyrics and has wrote a bunch of hits and when he heard some of my melodies he called me over to one side and said he would like to work with me on some numbers. How is that girlie as he is one of the biggest hit writers in N. Y.

N. Y. has got some mighty pretty girlies and I guess it would not be hard to get acquainted with them and in fact several of them has tried to make me since I been here but I always figure that a girl must be something

wrong with her if she tries to make a man that she don'
know nothing about so I pass them all up. But I dic
meet a couple of pips that a man here in the hotel wen
up on Riverside Drive to see them and insisted on me
going along and they got on some way that I coulc
make a piano talk so they was nothing but I must play
for them so I sit down and played some of my own stuf
and they went crazy over it.

One of the girls wanted I should come up and see her
again, and I said I might but I think I better keep away
as she acted like she wanted to vamp me and I am no
the kind that likes to play round with a gal just fo
their company and dance with them etc. but when I see
the right gal that will be a different thing and she won'
have to beg me to come and see her as I will camp right
on her trail till she says yes. And it won't be none of
these N. Y. fly by nights neither. They are all right to
look at but a man would be a sucker to get serious with
them as they might take you up and next thing you
know you would have a wife on your hands that don't
know a dish rag from a waffle iron.

Well girlie will quit and call it a day as it is too hot
to write any more and I guess I will turn on the cold
water and lay in the tub a wile and then turn in. Don't
forget to write to

Your friend,
Chas. F. Lewis.

Chicago, Ill., Aug. 13.

Dear Mr. Man: Hope you won't think me a "silly
Billy" for starting my letter that way but "Mr. Lewis"
is so formal and "Charles" is too much the other way
and any way I would not dare to call a man by their
first name after only knowing them only two weeks.
Though I may as well confess that Charles is my favor-

ite name for a man and have always been crazy about
it as it was my father's name. Poor old dad, he died of
cancer three years ago, but left enough insurance so
that mother and we girls were well provided for and do
not have to do anything to support ourselves though I
have been earning my own living for two years to make
things easier for mother and also because I simply can't
bear to be doing nothing as I feel like a "drone.' So I
flew away from the "home nest" though mother felt bad
about it as I was her favorite and she always said I was
such a comfort to her as when I was in the house she
never had to worry about how things would go.

But there I go gossiping about my domestic affairs
just like you would be interested in them though I don't
see how you could be though personly I always like to
know all about my friends, but I know men are different so will try and not bore you any longer. Poor Man,
I certainly feel sorry for you if New York is as hot as
all that. I guess it has been very hot in Chi, too, at least
everybody has been complaining about how terrible it
is. Suppose you will wonder why I say "I guess" and
you will think I ought to know if it is hot. Well, sir, the
reason I say "I guess" is because I don't feel the heat
like others do or at least I don't let myself feel it. That
sounds crazy I know, but don't you think there is a good
deal in mental suggestion and not letting yourself feel
things? I believe that if a person simply won't allow
themselves to be affected by disagreeable things, why
such things won't bother them near as much. I know it
works with me and that is the reason why I am never
cross when things go wrong and "keep smiling" no matter what happens and as far as the heat is concerned,
why I just don't let myself feel it and my friends say I
don't even look hot no matter if the weather is boiling
and Edith, my girl friend, often says that I am like a

breeze and it cools her off just to have me come in the room. Poor Edie suffers terribly during the hot weather and says it almost makes me mad at me to see how cool and unruffled I look when everybody else is perspiring and have red faces etc.

I laughed when I read what you said about New York being so hot that people thought it was the "other place." I can appreciate a joke, Mr. Man, and that one did not go "over my head." Am still laughing at some of the things you said in the station though they probably struck me funnier than they would most girls as I always see the funny side and sometimes something is said and I laugh and the others wonder what I am laughing at as they cannot see anything in it themselves, but it is just the way I look at things so of course I cannot explain to them why I laughed and they think I am crazy. But I had rather part with almost anything rather than my sense of humor as it helps me over a great many rough spots.

Sis has gone back home though I would of liked to of kept her here much longer, but she had to go though she said she would of liked nothing better than to stay with me and just listen to me "rattle on." She always says it is just like a show to hear me talk as I always put things in such a funny way and for weeks after she has been visiting me she thinks of some of the things I said and laughs over them. Since she left Edith and I have been pretty quiet though poor Edie wants to be on the "go" all the time and tries to make me go out with her every evening to the pictures and scolds me when I say I had rather stay home and read and calls me a "book worm." Well, it is true that I had rather stay home with a good book than go to some crazy old picture and the last two nights I have been reading myself to sleep with

Robert W. Service's poems. Don't you love Service or don't you care for "highbrow" writings?

Personly there is nothing I love more than to just sit and read a good book or sit and listen to somebody play the piano, I mean if they can really play and I really believe I like popular music better than the classical though I suppose that is a terrible thing to confess, but I love all kinds of music but a specially the piano when it is played by somebody who can really play.

Am glad you have not "fallen" for the "ladies" who have tried to make your acquaintance in New York. You are right in thinking there must be something wrong with girls who try to "pick up" strange men as no girl with self respect would do such a thing and when I say that, Mr. Man, I know you will think it is a funny thing for me to say on account of the way our friendship started, but I mean it and I assure you that was the first time I ever done such a thing in my life and would never of thought of doing it had I not known you were the right kind of a man as I flatter myself that I am a good judge of character and can tell pretty well what a person is like by just looking at them and I assure you I had made up my mind what kind of a man you were before I allowed myself to answer your opening remark. Otherwise I am the last girl in the world that would allow myself to speak to a person without being introduced to them.

When you write again you must tell me all about the girl on Riverside Drive and what she looks like and if you went to see her again and all about her. Suppose you will think I am a little old "curiosity shop" for asking all those questions and will wonder why I want to know. Well, sir, I won't tell you why, so there, but I insist on you answering all questions and will scold you if you don't. Maybe you will think that the reason why I am so curious is because I am "jealous" of the lady in question. Well, sir, I won't tell you whether I am or not, but will keep you "guessing." Now, don't you wish you knew?

Must close or you will think I am going to "rattle on" forever or maybe you have all ready become disgusted and torn my letter up. If so all I can say is poor little me—she was a nice little girl and meant well, but the man did not appreciate her.

There! Will stop or you will think I am crazy if you do not all ready.

Yours (?)

Mabelle.

N. Y., Aug. 20.

Dear Girlie: Well girlie I suppose you thought I was never going to answer your letter but have been busier than a one armed paper hanger the last week as have been working on a number with Paul Sears who is one of the best lyric writers in N. Y. and has turned out as many hits as Berlin or Davis or any of them. And believe me girlie he has turned out another hit this time that is he and I have done it together. It is all done now and we are just waiting for the best chance to place it but will not place it nowheres unless we get the right kind of a deal but maybe will publish it ourselves.

The song is bound to go over big as Sears has wrote a great lyric and I have give it a great tune or at least every body that has heard it goes crazy over it and it looks like it would go over bigger than any song since Mammy and would not be surprised to see it come out the hit of the year. If it is handled right we will make a bbl. of money and Sears says it is a cinch we will clean up as much as $25000 apiece which is pretty fair for

one song but this one is not like the most of them but
has got a great lyric and I have wrote a melody that will
knock them out of their seats. I only wish you could
hear it girlie and hear it the way I play it. I had to play
it over and over about 50 times at the Friars last night.

I will copy down the lyric of the chorus so you can
see what it is like and get the idea of the song though
of course you can't tell much about it unless you hear
it played and sang. The title of the song is When
They're Like You and here is the chorus:

"Some like them hot, some like them cold.
Some like them when they're not too darn old.
Some like them fat, some like them lean.
Some like them only at sweet sixteen.
Some like them dark, some like them light.
Some like them in the park, late at night.
Some like them fickle, some like them true,
But the time I like them is when they're like you."

How is that for a lyric and I only wish I could play
my melody for you as you would go nuts over it but
will send you a copy as soon as the song is published
and you can get some of your friends to play it over for
you and I know you will like it though it is a different
melody when I play it or when somebody else plays it.

Well girlie you will see how busy I have been and am
libel to keep right on being busy as we are not going to
let the grass grow under our feet but as soon as we have
got this number placed we will get busy on another one
as a couple like that will put me on Easy st. even if they
don't go as big as we expect but even 25 grand is a big
bunch of money and if a man could only turn out one
hit a year and make that much out of it I would be on
Easy st. and no more hammering on the old music box
in some cabaret.

Who ever we take the song to we will make them come across with one grand for advance royaltys and that will keep me going till I can turn out another one. So the future looks bright and rosey to yours truly and I am certainly glad I come to the big town though sorry I did not do it a whole lot quicker.

This is a great old town girlie and when you have lived here a wile you wonder how you ever stood for a burg like Chi which is just a hick town along side of this besides being dirty etc. and a man is a sucker to stay there all their life specially a man in my line of work as N. Y. is the Mecca for a man that has got the musical gift. I figure that all the time I spent in Chi was just wasteing my time and never really started to live till I come down here and I have to laugh when I think of the boys out there that is trying to make a liveing in the song writeing game and most of them starve to death all their life and the first week I am down here I meet a man like Sears and the next thing you know we have turned out a song that will make us a fortune.

Well girlie you asked me to tell you about the girlie up on the Drive that tried to make me and asked me to come and see her again. Well I can assure you you have no reasons to be jealous in that quarter as I have not been back to see her as I figure it is wasteing my time to play round with a dame like she that wants to go out somewheres every night and if you married her she would want a house on 5th ave. with a dozen servants so I have passed her up as that is not my idea of home.

What I want when I get married is a real home where a man can stay home and work and maybe have a few of his friends in once in a wile and entertain them or go to a good musical show once in a wile and have a wife that is in sympathy with you and not nag at you all the wile but be a real help mate. The girlie up on the Drive would run me ragged and have me in the poor house inside of a year even if I was makeing 25 grand out of one song. Besides she wears a make up that you would have to blast to find out what her face looks like. So I have not been back there and don't intend to see her again so what is the use of me telling you about her. And the only other girlie I have met is a sister of Paul Sears who I met up to his house wile we was working on the song but she don't hardly count as she has not got no use for the boys but treats them like dirt and Paul says she is the coldest proposition he ever seen.

Well I don't know no more to write and besides have got a date to go out to Paul's place for dinner and play some of my stuff for him so as he can see if he wants to set words to some more of my melodies. Well don't do nothing I would not do and have as good a time as you can in old Chi and will let you know how we come along with the song.

Chas. F. Lewis.

Chicago, Ill., Aug. 23.

Dear Mr. Man: I am thrilled to death over the song and think the words awfully pretty and am crazy to hear the music which I know must be great. It must be wonderful to have the gift of writing songs and then hear people play and sing them and just think of making $25,000 in such a short time. My, how rich you will be and I certainly congratulate you though am afraid when you are rich and famous you will have no time for insignificant little me or will you be an exception and remember your "old" friends even when you are up in the world? I sincerely hope so.

Will look forward to receiving a copy of the song and

will you be sure and put your name on it? I am all ready
very conceited just to think that I know a man that
writes songs and makes all that money.

Seriously I wish you success with your next song and
I laughed when I read your remark about being busier
than a one armed paper hanger. I don't see how you
think up all those comparisons and crazy things to say.
The next time one of the girls asks me to go out with
them I am going to tell them I can't go because I am
busier than a one armed paper hanger and then they
will think I made it up and say: "The girl is clever."

Seriously I am glad you did not go back to see the girl
on the Drive and am also glad you don't like girls who
makes themselves up so much as I think it is disgusting
and would rather go round looking like a ghost than
put artificial color on my face. Fortunately I have a
complexion that does not need "fixing" but even if my
coloring was not what it is I would never think of lowering myself to "fix" it. But I must tell you a joke that
happened just the other day when Edith and I were out
at lunch and there was another girl in the restaurant
whom Edie knew and she introduced her to me and I
noticed how this girl kept staring at me and finally she
begged my pardon and asked if she could ask me a personal question and I said yes and she asked me if my
complexion was really "mine." I assured her it was and
she said: "Well, I thought so because I did not think
anybody could put it on so artistically. I certainly envy
you." Edie and I both laughed.

Well, if that girl envies me my complexion, why I
envy you living in New York. Chicago is rather dirty
though I don't let that part of it bother me as I bathe
and change my clothing so often that the dirt does not
have time to "settle." Edie often says she cannot see
how I always keep so clean looking and says I always

look like I had just stepped out of a band box. She also calls me a fish (jokingly) because I spend so much time in the water. But seriously I do love to bathe and never feel so happy as when I have just "cleaned up" and put on fresh clothing.

Edie has just gone out to see a picture and was cross at me because I would not go with her. I told her I was going to write a letter and she wanted to know to whom and I told her and she said: "You write to him so often that a person would almost think you was in love with him." I just laughed and turned it off, but she does says the most embarrassing things and I would be angry if it was anybody but she that said them.

Seriously I had much rather sit here and write letters or read or just sit and dream than go out to some crazy old picture show except once in awhile I do like to go to the theater and see a good play and a specially a musical play if the music is catchy. But as a rule I am contented to just stay home and feel cozy and lots of evenings Edie and I sit here without saying hardly a word to each other though she would love to talk but she knows I had rather be quiet and she often says it is just like living with a deaf and dumb mute to live with me because I make so little noise round the apartment. I guess I was born to be a home body as I so seldom care to go "gadding."

Though I do love to have company once in awhile, just a few congenial friends whom I can talk to and feel at home with and play cards or have some music. My friends love to drop in here, too, as they say Edie and I always give them such nice things to eat. Though poor Edie has not much to do with it, I am afraid, as she hates anything connected with cooking which is one of the things I love best of anything and I often say that when I begin keeping house in my own home I will insist on doing most of my own work as I would take so much more interest in it than a servant, though I would want somebody to help me a little if I could afford it as I often think a woman that does all her own work is liable to get so tired that she loses interest in the bigger things of life like books and music. Though after all what bigger thing is there than home making a specially for a woman?

I am sitting in the dearest old chair that I bought yesterday at a little store on the North Side. That is my one extravagance, buying furniture and things for the house, but I always say it is economy in the long run as I will always have them and have use for them and when I can pick them up at a bargain I would be silly not to. Though heaven knows I will never be "poor" in regards to furniture and rugs and things like that as mother's house in Toledo is full of lovely things which she says she is going to give to Sis and myself as soon as we have real homes of our own. She is going to give me the first choice as I am her favorite. She has the loveliest old things that you could not buy now for love or money including lovely old rugs and a piano which Sis wanted to have a player attachment put on it but I said it would be an insult to the piano so we did not get one. I am funny about things like that, a specially old furniture and feel towards them like people whom I love.

Poor mother, I am afraid she won't live much longer to enjoy her lovely old things as she has been suffering for years from stomach trouble and the doctor says it has been worse lately instead of better and her heart is weak besides. I am going home to see her a few days this fall as it may be the last time. She is very cheerful and always says she is ready to go now as she has had enough joy out of life and all she would like would be to see her girls settled down in their own homes before she goes.

There I go, talking about my domestic affairs again and I will bet you are bored to death though personly I am never bored when my friends tell me about themselves. But I won't "rattle on" any longer, but will say good night and don't forget to write and tell me how you come out with the song and thanks for sending me the words to it. Will you write a song about me some time? I would be thrilled to death! But I am afraid I am not the kind of girl that inspires men to write songs about them, but am just a quiet "mouse" that loves home and am not giddy enough to be the heroine of a song.

Well, Mr. Man, good night and don't wait so long before writing again to

Yours (?)
Mabelle.

N. Y., Sept. 8.

Dear Girlie: Well girlie have not got your last letter with me so cannot answer what was in it as I have forgotten if there was anything I was supposed to answer and besides have only a little time to write as I have a date to go out on a party with the Sears. We are going to the Georgie White show and afterwards somewheres for supper. Sears is the boy who wrote the lyric to my song and it is him and his sister I am going on the party with. The sister is a cold fish that has no use for men but she is show crazy and insists on Paul taking her to 3 or 4 of them a week.

Paul wants me to give up my room here and come and live with them as they have plenty of room and I am running a little low on money but don't know if I will do it or not as am afraid I would freeze to death in the same house with a girl like the sister as she is ice cold but she don't hang round the house much as she is always takeing trips or going to shows or somewheres.

So far we have not had no luck with the song. All the publishers we have showed it to has went crazy over it but they won't make the right kind of a deal with us and if they don't loosen up and give us a decent royalty rate we are libel to put the song out ourselves and show them up. The man up to Goebel's told us the song was O. K. and he liked it but it was more of a production number than anything else and ought to go in a show like the Follies but they won't be in N. Y. much longer and what we ought to do is hold it till next spring.

Mean wile I am working on some new numbers and also have taken a position with the orchestra at the Wilton and am going to work there starting next week. They pay good money $60 and it will keep me going.

Well girlie that is about all the news. I believe you said your father was sick and hope he is better and also hope you are getting along O. K. and take care of yourself. When you have nothing else to do write to your friend,

Chas. F. Lewis.

Chicago, Ill., Sept. 11.

Dear Mr. Lewis: Your short note reached me yesterday and must say I was puzzled when I read it. It sounded like you was mad at me though I cannot think of any reason why you should be. If there was something I said in my last letter that offended you I wish you would tell me what it was and I will ask your pardon though I cannot remember anything I could of said that you could take offense at. But if there was something, why I assure you, Mr. Lewis, that I did not mean anything by it. I certainly did not intend to offend you in any way.

Perhaps it is nothing I wrote you, but you are worried on account of the publishers not treating you fair in regards to your song and that is why your letter sounded so distant. If that is the case I hope that by this time matters have rectified themselves and the future looks brighter. But any way, Mr. Lewis, don't allow yourself to worry over business cares as they will all come right in the end and I always think it is silly for people to worry themselves sick over temporary troubles, but the best way is to "keep smiling" and look for the "silver lining" in the cloud. That is the way I always do and no matter what happens, I manage to smile and my girl friend, Edie, calls me Sunny because I always look on the bright side.

Remember also, Mr. Lewis, that $60 is a salary that a great many men would like to be getting and are living on less than that and supporting a wife and family on it. I always say that a person can get along on whatever amount they make if they manage things in the right way.

So if it is business troubles, Mr. Lewis, I say don't worry, but look on the bright side. But if it is something I wrote in my last letter that offended you I wish you would tell me what it was so I can apologize as I assure you I meant nothing and would not say anything to hurt you for the world.

Please let me hear from you soon as I will not feel comfortable until I know I am not to blame for the sudden change.

Sincerely,
Mabelle Gillespie.

N. Y., Sept. 24.

Dear Miss Gillespie: Just a few lines to tell you the big news or at least it is big news to me. I am engaged

to be married to Paul Sears' sister and we are going to
be married early next month and live in Atlantic City
where the orchestra I have been playing with has got
an engagement in one of the big cabarets.

I know this will be a surprise to you as it was even
a surprise to me as I did not think I would ever have
the nerve to ask the girlie the big question as she was
always so cold and acted like I was just in the way.
But she said she supposed she would have to marry
somebody some time and she did not dislike me as
much as most of the other men her brother brought
round and she would marry me with the understanding
that she would not have to be a slave and work round
the house and also I would have to take her to a show
or somewheres every night and if I could not take her
myself she would "run wild" alone. Atlantic City will
be O. K. for that as a lot of new shows opens down
there and she will be able to see them before they get to
the big town. As for her being a slave, I would hate to
think of marrying a girl and then have them spend
their lives in druggery round the house. We are going
to live in a hotel till we find something better but will
be in no hurry to start house keeping as we will have
to buy all new furniture.

Betsy is some doll when she is all fixed up and believe
me she knows how to fix herself up. I don't know what
she uses but it is weather proof and I have been out in
a rain storm with her and we both got drowned but her
face stayed on. I would almost think it was real only
she tells me different.

Well girlie I may write to you again once in a wile as
Betsy says she don't give a damn if I write to all the
girls in the world just so I don't make her read the answers but that is all I can think of to say now except
good bye and good luck and may the right man come

along soon and he will be a lucky man getting a girl that is such a good cook and got all that furniture etc.

But just let me give you a word of advice before I close and that is don't never speak to strange men who you don't know nothing about as they may get you wrong and think you are trying to make them. It just happened that I knew better so you was lucky in my case but the luck might not last.

Your friend,
Chas. F. Lewis.

Chicago, Ill., Sept. 27.

My Dear Mr. Lewis: Thanks for your advice and also thank your fiance for her generosity in allowing you to continue your correspondence with her "rivals," but personly I have no desire to take advantage of that generosity as I have something better to do than read letters from a man like you, a specially as I have a man friend who is not so generous as Miss Sears and would strongly object to my continuing a correspondence with another man. It is at his request I am writing this note to tell you not to expect to hear from me again.

Allow me to congratulate you on your engagement to Miss Sears and I am sure she is to be congratulated too, though if I met the lady I would be tempted to ask her to tell me her secret, namely how she is going to "run wild" on $60.

Sincerely,
Mabelle Gillespie.

AT THE END OF THE
CAR LINE

BY BEN HUR LAMPMAN

These sketches were first published separately in the
Portland Oregonian.

I.

SHE was redding-up her back yard, as she would
have said—there is such a sight of work around
her place at this time of year—and the old gray cat was
now at her heels and now underfoot. The little old lady
who lives at the end of the car line, soul alone with the
old gray cat, sometimes asks herself how she ever en-
dures him—with a catch at her throat in quick fear that
one day he may not answer. Get away with you! Land
o' Goshen, but you are a nuisance!

Then the old gray cat, he gave her such a look in
return, he did—real wicked—and he arched his tail,
that looks so moth-eaten, and he humped his back, and
ran to the apple tree and up it like a kitten. And there
he peered down at her, taunting her with great golden
eyes of mockery. He knows well enough, the old rap-
scallion, that a body cannot climb trees.

These stalks that are withered and dead are a little
bit too coarse for the compost, and she will heap them
here in the central garden and let them dry in the wind,
and then put match to them on some day that is suitable.
She said the phrase over again in her mind, quite primly,
and then aloud to the old gray cat. "On some day that
is suitable," she said. He sprang high into air at a flut-
tering moth, and it wasn't his fault that he missed it.

The little old lady, with her arms full of hollyhock stalks, stood there and admired him.

Well-a-day! With so much to redd-up there was no time for this. And here at the lip of the field, where the wild land comes down to her delphiniums, the joyous green-leaved briar of the creeping blackberry has crept. The little old lady set her lips firmly and shook her gray head so vigorously that wisps escaped this way and wisps flew that, and she was put to some trouble to tuck them back again. She had meant only to indicate to the almost apologetic little invader that it must be thrust from her province again. The vine is real pretty, like she always told Henry, and the little-small berries it has are the best of all blackberries for pies—but once you turn your back on it, bless you, it'll take the place in a season. She would have to be using her trowel.

In the fall of the year, so she always says, a body can get half their spring work done if they've a mind to. You redd-up the whole place, front yard to back, and where the ground's right for it who could resist spading a bit? If she turns the soil now, rebuking the grass and the weeds, it'll be in fine shape for spring gardening—while if she doesn't, land sakes, a body might as well try to garden one of those wild lots.

Maybe the ground is a mite too wet, but it turns well enough, and better than it will have ever a chance to be spaded again this fall, she will venture. Some of the neighbors have told her that she shouldn't be doing her own spading, but that's half the pleasure of gardening. Even when Henry—when Henry—well, when Henry was here she had insisted on saving some of the best ground to spade for herself and without help. There wasn't a lazy bone in his body, but Henry never had patience with a spade. Give him room to turn the bay team around and Henry would be in there with a plow,

Henry wasn't a gardener—so ran her thought, and it pleased her—though he was a farmer like all his folks before him. A good farmer. But lots of folks that can farm aren't gardeners. Some few gardeners are men, she reflected, though not many of them, but all women are gardeners whether they have gardens or haven't. A body can understand that readily enough, old gray cat. She had always been a gardener, she reflected, and to witness the spear of a plant coming through, so eagerly into sunshine out of darkness, into life out of dream, is as dear to her now as when she was a girl and came west from Peoria.

She believed, as she snipped the last mildewed stalk from the delphinium bed, that it would be better, not only to spade the patch well, and to give it lime, but even to lift the plants, and divide them before she replaced them. For though it was here that the hencoop stood, a body is apt to be forgetting that that was twenty years ago, or such a matter, and that this china doorknob, for example, must once have been used as a nest egg. Where was she, old gray cat? Yes. Well, yes. This patch needs a good working over.

She felt the spade slither and grate again in the deep black soil of the delphinium bed where the chicken yard used to be—for the children must have their fresh eggs, and Henry was the great hand for them, too, but it doesn't pay any longer in town so everybody says. It would be a spike, she supposed, from the time they tore down the chicken house. There. No. Well, there, then. She brushed the moist earth from it with her fingers. It looked like it might be a jackknife—and it was one—or rather it had been one.

Go away from her now, old gray cat, go away! She has to see what it is, doesn't she? And you rubbing against her ankles all the while, and fit to drive her distracted. Go away, now! Her fingers trembled as they brushed at the clinging earth. Yes, there it was. It said "I O O F," and the letters scarcely were tarnished, once she had rubbed them a bit. Well, it was Henry's all right, and she remembered the day when he lost it. The peddler took it, Henry always said, but the peddler hadn't. It must have fallen in the straw when they were cutting the twine on the red hen's legs.

And you are here, old gray cat, and so is she, but the children are grown-up and gone away—and there is Henry's lodge knife, as he always called it, and so the peddler didn't take it, after all. Come here, old gray cat; she is sorry she scolded. The wind has an edge to it now, and some stray drops are falling. It is time you and she went indoors.

II.

The china bowl of the Dresden Shepherdess with the blue ribbon, hidden away on the topmost shelf of the cupboard, so that she must stand on a chair to reach it, came west with her folks from Peoria, old gray cat— and what if a body should break it! Get away from her now. It isn't so easy to get up and down any more, but that's the safest place she can think of; and that is what the Dresden shepherdess always was used for, as far back as when the children were little. The little old lady who lives at the end of the car line got stiffly down from the chair, clasping the china bowl.

It keeps a body busy all the time, and even then the place never really is dusted as it should be—it was only a week ago that the shepherdess came down from the top shelf the last time, and there's a film of dust on her bonnet. Will you, gray cat, get out from under her feet? You seem to think you can help, with your ridiculous purring and tail-waving. As she stepped to the floor the china bowl gave out a slurred, musical tinkle.

What Henry always said was that money makes the pot boil, and that a man who wants a new scythe will mow with an old one unless he is thrifty. And how many a time have the two of them together, as now she does soul alone, found the friendship of the Dresden shepherdess to stand them in good stead. They made a game of it then, when the children were little, and when something was needed for the house—something extra —Henry used to laugh and say that they must ask the shepherdess for it. And they would take down the bowl —it stood where it does even then—well knowing how much it held in trust for them, but delighting to pour out the treasure and count.

If it were not enough—like the time they wanted the new clock for the parlor—Henry would say that the Dresden shepherdess said no, and told them they must wait until they could afford it. For a man that is helped to money, Henry always said, may help himself to whatever he chooses. And the Dresden shepherdess helped them to money. But Henry was the most impulsive man, like all his mother's people, and he wouldn't always wait. Here on the rim of the bowl is the chip where he cast the dollar, to make up enough for the clock. And sudden and strangely, for a body never hears it usually, the still house was filled with its deliberate ticking.

The little old lady who lives at the end of the car line tipped the china bowl, and respectfully, so that the coins slipped and slithered to the blue tablecloth—the quarters, dimes, nickels and pennies. When they had fallen there she caught some of them up in her hand and let them escape through her fingers. If the neighbors could see her now they would think, she supposed, that she was a miser—and goodness, the minister!

Dear Lord, if it is miserly to hoard one's money in a china bowl, and avarice to feel this eagerness for more, may it not be said for her that the old lawnmower will not cut any longer? For the camel cannot pass through the eye of the needle, it is true, but this is a very different matter, Lord, and she does need a new lawnmower. My gracious! The old one was new, they bought it at Mr. Pilkington's, when the lawn was first planted. It is all wore out, and it rattles, and there's no use sharpening it any more. The old lawnmower is all wore out. Amen.

You are watching her with a cynical eye, old gray cat; mind your business and go on washing your face.

She marshalled them all in piles by themselves, according to their rank and degree, and in a company of lesser coins the twenty-five cent piece is royalty, and even the dimes are dukes and duchesses—but there weren't many quarters. You have to be careful as can be, and walk a chalk line, and scrimp a little on this, and save a little on that, but still it isn't often a body comes by a whole entire quarter at one time and can put it safely away. Then, too, though she supposes this is an advantage, sometimes a body runs short and must go to the Dresden shepherdess for her assistance—and that sets the new lawnmower back quite a ways, like the time she broke her glasses last summer. But for that—. Money in orderly piles looked so neat and pleasing. Will you get down off the table!

The first time the little old lady reckoned it, quarters, dimes, nickels and pennies, setting it down with a stub pencil, it came out $7.86, and she frowned, but when she counted it again to make sure, and was extra careful, seemed like it was only $7.74. Some of it surely was gone. Now she simply mustn't get nervous, or she never would know. This time she checked each pile twice as she counted, and, with a sigh of relief, there was a whole dollar more. There was $8.86, and that was what she remembered from last week. If she could spare a dime and four pennies—here she searched through her purse —that would make just $9. Nine dollars! And that left only three more dollars, and seventy-five cents, to save. If she is real careful, old gray cat, she won't have to mow the lawn more than once more with the old one before the new one comes out on delivery.

It takes a body a long while to save as much as will buy a new lawnmower, and you have to give up a few things to help get it, but much never cost little, Henry always said; and money makes the mare go, Henry always said. But there is something else about it, surely there is, that it is hard to find words for. To get things this way, as Henry and she well knew, is—is—and she sought for the word. Well, nicer, she said, but what she meant was that it was adventure.

Go back to your shelf again, little shepherdess with the blue ribbon, who watches over the china bowl wherein the new lawnmower is shaping. It doesn't lack any more than the rubber-tired wheels now, and by the second cutting there ought to be money enough. Can she afford it? The Dresden shepherdess will answer yes. And maybe, old gray cat, for a big order like that they will send it out special delivery.

III.

She considered, as she paused on the back steps a moment, that already there was a touch of fall in the air, and she shook her head at the thought, and said aloud, "Mercy!" Yet she was smiling. Though fleet as the swallows that used to nest in the eaves of the barn, when Henry and she were farming, so fleet are the seasons. They fly past a body, they do. They are gone. The old gray cat looked up at her from the walk, and his eyes were widely golden with interest. His disreputable tail, the old rascal, was waving.

"Come," said the little old lady who lives at the end of the car line, "and we shall pick the sweetpeas." He leaned on her ankles. Go away with you now! She vowed that she never had known such a cat, for he is a caution. And together they went into the garden.

But she paused again at the trellis of knotted twine and old broomsticks and such, and stood there to look. It was as though she was thirsty and must drink. It was like that. Like the time, of a summer long gone, they came over the hills by a deer trail, and so down to the valley, and found a blue spring by a brown rock. There isn't another flower that's quite equal to sweetpeas in blossom. No'm, there isn't another.

The scissors are those that she keeps for cutting sweetpeas, and they wobble. Now Henry was the great hand for fixing such things as scissors. He had the knack of it. But these wobble. Why stare at her so, old gray cat? They've surely a right for to wobble a little, for they are the scissors she used when the children were small and she did all her own sewing, though sometimes Mrs. Johnson, who was real good at it, helped with the fitting. The only scissors that do not wobble, that's true, are the scissors that snip away at the years. Land of goodness!

Then, pursing her mouth as she does when she is cutting sweetpeas, the little old lady who lives at the end of the car line began the harvest of beauty. She does not bunch them at first, blossom by blossom, as some will, but drops them all in a brown wicker basket. Snip. Snip. You will find in the end it is tidier so. Yes, a basket. Time was, old gray cat, when you were a kitten, that Martha carried you in it—oh, often—with your tail hanging over. But even then the children had learned to call it "the sweetpea basket." It really was meant to take eggs to the grocery, but you know how it is. Things change. Eggs were ten cents a dozen. Get away from that basket! Sometimes she doesn't know what she ever will do with him.

Yes, sweetpeas. Now Henry, he never was partial to flowers, seemed like, though he'd never get tired of watching the grain. He just didn't have any fancy for flowers. Excepting sweetpeas. Come early spring, for they do best when they are in the ground early, seemed he always remembered it was time to plant the sweet-peas, and come fall he believed in saving the seed of them. You grow your own seed, Henry used always to say, and you'll know what you have. Seemed like he favored the blue sugar bowl, that was his grandmother's, filled with sweetpeas on the sitting room table. Yes, gray cat, sweetpeas were his flowers.

And snipping, she began to think of the generations of them, the begats and begats, without ever a break, until she was back in the time they bought the new washing machine, the first one, when the children were little. Snip. Slowly. Snip. More slowly still. Yes, that was the year. Mercy sakes! It didn't seem possible, so it didn't, that these were the same flowers. Yet they were. And swiftly she turned, but there was only the sunshine on the steps, and the old gray cat drowsing. Only these. Snip. Snip.

Nobody ever imagined such colors as these, nobody did, for such colors never have been save only in sweet-peas, they haven't. A waist of this one, perhaps, or maybe a dress, if there was money, to wear to a dance at the corners, with a brooch of rhinestones at the throat, and full sleeves, and a touch of lace, maybe. But in those times there weren't such dresses, and nobody dreamed of having them, not anybody. Ah, did they not! She reflected that dreams are often unguessed at the time, and after remembered, as we remember them from sleep, long after. This misty softness of blue, had she not dreamed it many the time? It is dream. Snip.

This was foolishness, as she well knew, and she shook it away with decision, until her head tossed. Now then, resolutely—snip, snip—this much is certain as can be, that nobody she knows ever manages somehow to grow such sweetpeas as hers. And they have fertilizers, too, that they buy at the seed store, and they have seed that costs more than she could ever afford. But they haven't such sweetpeas as hers. You take the stems of them. In all your born days did ever you see such stems on sweetpeas? When stems are as long as these are there is never a mite of trouble in fixing them so they look real nice in a bowl or a vase. But when the stems are stingy, as hers never are, people have dreadful times. Snip. So they do.

She came to the end of the row, where she helped a tendril to grip the twine, and the task was at an end then. The sweetpeas were all picked. For if a body picks them, they bloom the longer, and that is part of the secret. You simply must keep them picked. Yet here and there on the vines she had left a stray blossom, crimson, or purple, or white, to leave something of color. For if she should take quite the last of them, her heart would misgive her. It wouldn't seem right, so it wouldn't. Then she bent her face to the basket, heaped with the soft sweetness of them, and breathed of their fullness. It took her back quite a ways, like always. Land of goodness!

They went into the kitchen together, out at the end of the car line, and the old gray cat almost tripped her. He's a caution. She doesn't know how she abides him. And she took down the blue sugar bowl from the cupboard, and hummed "Beulah Land" while she fixed them. Now. Fluff them out a mite. Straighten this one. There. There isn't anything quite so satisfactory as a blue bowl of sweetpeas.

THE JAPANESE

BY *OGDEN NASH*

How courteous is the Japanese;
He always says, "Excuse it, please."
He climbs into his neighbor's garden,
And smiles, and says, "I beg your pardon";
He bows and grins a friendly grin,
And calls his hungry family in;
He grins, and bows a friendly bow;
"So sorry, this my garden now."

FIFTY GRAND

BY ERNEST HEMINGWAY

Here is an early story by the man who wrote A Farewell to Arms and For Whom the Bell Tolls. It was written in Paris and made the disconsolate rounds of the American magazines. Cosmopolitan, The Saturday Evening Post, Collier's, Scribner's—they one and all turned it down. But The Atlantic Monthly, which had also been the first to publish another little item in this collection called "The Battle Hymn of the Republic," clasped the despised and rejected of editors to its withered bosom. Such anecdotes comfort all authors who relish confirmation of their chronic suspicion that most editors are not quite bright.

"HOW are you going yourself, Jack?" I asked him.

"You seen this, Walcott?" he says.

"Just in the gym."

"Well," Jack says, "I'm going to need a lot of luck with that boy."

"He can't hit you, Jack," Soldier said.

"I wish to hell he couldn't."

"He couldn't hit you with a handful of bird-shot."

"Bird-shot'd be all right," Jack says. "I wouldn't mind bird-shot any."

"He looks easy to hit," I said.

"Sure," Jack says, "he ain't going to last long. He ain't going to last like you and me, Jerry. But right now he's got everything."

"You'll left-hand him to death."

"Maybe," Jack says. "Sure. I got a chance to."

"Handle him like you handled Kid Lewis."

"Kid Lewis," Jack said. "That kike!"

315

The three of us, Jack Brennan, Soldier Bartlett, and I were in Hanley's. There were a couple of broads sitting at the next table to us. They had been drinking.

"What do you mean, kike?" one of the broads says. "What do you mean, kike, you big Irish bum?"

"Sure," Jack says. "That's it."

"Kikes," this broad goes on. "They're always talking about kikes, these big Irishmen. What do you mean, kikes?"

"Come on. Let's get out of here."

"Kikes," this broad goes on. "Whoever saw you ever buy a drink? Your wife sews your pockets up every morning. These Irishmen and their kikes! Ted Lewis could lick you too."

"Sure," Jack says. "And you give away a lot of things free too, don't you?"

We went out. That was Jack. He could say what he wanted to when he wanted to say it.

Jack started training out at Danny Hogan's health farm over in Jersey. It was nice out there but Jack didn't like it much. He didn't like being away from his wife and the kids, and he was sore and grouchy most of the time. He liked me and we got along fine together; and he liked Hogan, but after a while Soldier Bartlett commenced to get on his nerves. A kidder gets to be an awful thing around a camp if his stuff goes sort of sour. Soldier was always kidding Jack, just sort of kidding him all the time. It wasn't very funny and it wasn't very good, and it began to get to Jack. It was sort of stuff like this. Jack would finish up with the weights and the bag and pull on the gloves.

"You want to work?" he'd say to Soldier.

"Sure. How you want me to work?" Soldier would ask. "Want me to treat you rough like Walcott? Want me to knock you down a few times?"

"That's it," Jack would say. He didn't like it any, though.

One morning we were all out on the road. We'd been out quite a way and now we were coming back. We'd go along fast for three minutes and then walk a minute, and then go fast for three minutes again. Jack wasn't ever what you would call a sprinter. He'd move around fast enough in the ring if he had to, but he wasn't any too fast on the road. All the time we were walking Soldier was kidding him. We came up the hill to the farmhouse.

"Well," says Jack, "you better go back to town, Soldier."

"What do you mean?"

"You better go back to town and stay there."

"What's the matter?"

"I'm sick of hearing you talk."

"Yes?" says Soldier.

"Yes," says Jack.

"You'll be a damn sight sicker when Walcott gets through with you."

"Sure," says Jack, "maybe I will. But I know I'm sick of you."

So Soldier went off on the train to town that same morning. I went down with him to the train. He was good and sore.

"I was just kidding him," he said. We were waiting on the platform. "He can't pull that stuff with me, Jerry."

"He's nervous and crabby," I said. "He's a good fellow, Soldier."

"The hell he is. The hell he's ever been a good fellow."

"Well," I said, "so long, Soldier."

The train had come in. He climbed up with his bag.

"So long, Jerry," he says. "You be in town before the fight?"

"I don't think so."

"See you then."

He went in and the conductor swung up and the train went out. I rode back to the farm in the cart. Jack was on the porch writing a letter to his wife. The mail had come and I got the papers and went over on the other side of the porch and sat down to read. Hogan came out the door and walked over to me.

"Did he have a jam with Soldier?"

"Not a jam," I said. "He just told him to go back to town."

"I could see it coming," Hogan said. "He never liked Soldier much."

"No. He don't like many people."

"He's a pretty cold one," Hogan said.

"Well, he's always been fine to me."

"Me too," Hogan said. "I got no kick on him. He's a cold one, though."

Hogan went in through the screen door and I sat there on the porch and read the papers. It was just starting to get fall weather and it's nice country there in Jersey, up in the hills, and after I read the paper through I sat there and looked out at the country and the road down below against the woods with cars going along it, lifting the dust up. It was fine weather and pretty nice-looking country. Hogan came to the door and I said, "Say, Hogan, haven't you got anything to shoot out here?"

"No," Hogan said. "Only sparrows."

"Seen the paper?" I said to Hogan.

"What's in it?"

"Sande booted three of them in yesterday."

"I got that on the telephone last night."

"You follow them pretty close, Hogan?" I asked.

"Oh, I keep in touch with them," Hogan said.

"How about Jack?" I says. "Does he still play them?"

"Him?" said Hogan. "Can you see him doing it?"

Just then Jack came around the corner with the letter in his hand. He's wearing a sweater and an old pair of pants and boxing shoes.

"Got a stamp, Hogan?" he asks.

"Give me the letter," Hogan said. "I'll mail it for you."

"Say, Jack," I said, "didn't you used to play the ponies?"

"Sure."

"I knew you did. I knew I used to see you out at Sheepshead."

"What did you lay off them for?" Hogan asked.

"Lost money."

Jack sat down on the porch by me. He leaned back against a post. He shut his eyes in the sun.

"Want a chair?" Hogan asked.

"No," said Jack. "This is fine."

"It's a nice day," I said. "It's pretty nice out in the country."

"I'd a damn sight rather be in town with the wife."

"Well, you only got another week."

"Yes," Jack says. "That's so."

We sat there on the porch. Hogan was inside at the office.

"What do you think about the shape I'm in?" Jack asked me.

"Well, you can't tell," I said. "You got a week to get around into form."

"Don't stall me."

"Well," I said, "you're not right."

"I'm not sleeping," Jack said.

"You'll be all right in a couple of days."

"No," says Jack, "I got the insomnia."

"What's on your mind?"

"I miss the wife."

"Have her come out."

"No. I'm too old for that."

"We'll take a long walk before you turn in and get you good and tired."

"Tired!" Jack says. "I'm tired all the time."

He was that way all week. He wouldn't sleep at night and he'd get up in the morning feeling that way, you know, when you can't shut your hands.

"He's stale as poorhouse cake," Hogan said. "He's nothing."

"I never seen Walcott," I said.

"He'll kill him," said Hogan. "He'll tear him in two."

"Well," I said, "everybody's got to get it sometime."

"Not like this, though," Hogan said. "They'll think he never trained. It gives the farm a black eye."

"You hear what the reporters said about him?"

"Didn't I! They said he was awful. They said they oughtn't to let him fight."

"Well," I said, "they're always wrong, ain't they?"

"Yes," said Hogan. "But this time they're right."

"What the hell do they know about whether a man's right or not?"

"Well," said Hogan, "they're not such fools."

"All they did was pick Willard at Toledo. This Lardner, he's so wise now, ask him about when he picked Willard at Toledo."

"Aw, he wasn't out," Hogan said. "He only writes the big fights."

"I don't care who they are," I said. "What the hell do they know? They can write maybe, but what the hell do they know?"

"You don't think Jack's in any shape, do you?" Hogan asked.

"No. He's through. All he needs is to have Corbett pick him to win for it to be all over."

"Well, Corbett'll pick him," Hogan says.

"Sure. He'll pick him."

That night Jack didn't sleep any either. The next morning was the last day before the fight. After breakfast we were out on the porch again.

"What do you think about, Jack, when you can't sleep?" I said.

"Oh, I worry," Jack says. "I worry about property I got up in the Bronx, I worry about property I got in Florida. I worry about the kids. I worry about the wife. Sometimes I think about fights. I think about that kike Ted Lewis and I get sore. I got some stocks and I worry about them. What the hell don't I think about?"

"Well," I said, "tomorrow night it'll all be over."

"Sure," said Jack. "That always helps a lot, don't it? That just fixes everything all up, I suppose. Sure."

He was sore all day. We didn't do any work. Jack just moved around a little to loosen up. He shadowboxed a few rounds. He didn't even look good doing that. He skipped the rope a little while. He couldn't sweat.

"He'd be better not to do any work at all," Hogan said. We were standing watching him skip rope. "Don't he ever sweat at all any more?"

"He can't sweat."

"Do you suppose he's got the con? He never had any trouble making weight, did he?"

"No, he hasn't got any con. He just hasn't got anything inside any more."

"He ought to sweat," said Hogan.

Jack came over, skipping the rope. He was skipping up and down in front of us, forward and back, crossing his arms every third time.

"Well," he says. "What are you buzzards talking about?"

"I don't think you ought to work any more," Hogan says. "You'll be stale."

"Wouldn't that be awful?" Jack says and skips away down the floor, slapping the rope hard.

That afternoon John Collins showed up out at the farm. Jack was up in his room. John came out in a car from town. He had a couple of friends with him. The car stopped and they all got out.

"Where's Jack?" John asked me.

"Up in his room, lying down."

"Lying down?"

"Yes," I said.

"How is he?"

I looked at the two fellows that were with John.

"They're friends of his," John said.

"He's pretty bad," I said.

"What's the matter with him?"

"He don't sleep."

"Hell," said John. "That Irishman could never sleep."

"He isn't right," I said.

"Hell," John said. "He's never right. I've had him for ten years and he's never been right yet."

The fellows who were with him laughed.

"I want you to shake hands with Mr. Morgan an Mr. Steinfelt," John said. "This is Mr. Doyle. He's bee training Jack."

"Glad to meet you," I said.

"Let's go up and see the boy," the fellow called Mor gan said.

"Let's have a look at him," Steinfelt said.

We all went upstairs.

"Where's Hogan?" John asked.

"He's out in the barn with a couple of his customers," I said.

"He got many people out here now?" John asked.

"Just two."

"Pretty quiet, ain't it?" Morgan said.

"Yes," I said. "It's pretty quiet."

We were outside Jack's room. John knocked on the door. There wasn't any answer.

"Maybe he's asleep," I said.

"What the hell's he sleeping in the daytime for?" John turned the handle and we all went in. Jack was lying asleep on the bed. He was face down and his face was in the pillow. Both his arms were around the pillow.

"Hey, Jack!" John said to him.

Jack's head moved a little on the pillow. "Jack!" John says, leaning over him. Jack just dug a little deeper in the pillow. John touched him on the shoulder. Jack sat up and looked at us. He hadn't shaved and he was wearing an old sweater.

"Christ! Why can't you let me sleep?" he says to John.

"Don't be sore," John says. "I didn't mean to wake you up."

"Oh no," Jack says. "Of course not."

"You know Morgan and Steinfelt," John said.

"Glad to see you," Jack says.

"How do you feel, Jack," Morgan asks him.

"Fine," Jack says. "How the hell would I feel?"

"You look fine," Steinfelt says.

"Yes, don't I," says Jack. "Say," he says to John. "You're my manager. You get a big enough cut. Why the hell don't you come out here when the reporters was out! You want Jerry and me to talk to them?"

"I had Lew fighting in Philadelphia," John said.

"What the hell's that to me?" Jack says. "You're my manager. You get a big enough cut, don't you? You aren't making me any money in Philadelphia, are you? Why the hell aren't you out here when I ought to have you?"

"Hogan was here."

"Hogan," Jack says. "Hogan's as dumb as I am."

"Soldier Bahtlett was out here wukking with you for a while, wasn't he?" Steinfelt said to change the subject.

"Yes, he was out here," Jack says. "He was out here all right."

"Say, Jerry," John said to me. "Would you go and find Hogan and tell him we want to see him in about half an hour?"

"Sure," I said.

"Why the hell can't he stick around?" Jack says. "Stick around, Jerry."

Morgan and Steinfelt looked at each other.

"Quiet down, Jack," John said to him.

"I better go find Hogan," I said.

"All right, if you want to go," Jack says. "None of these guys are going to send you away, though."

"I'll go find Hogan," I said.

Hogan was out in the gym in the barn. He had a couple of his health-farm patients with the gloves on. They neither one wanted to hit the other, for fear the other would come back and hit him.

"That'll do," Hogan said when he saw me come in. "You can stop the slaughter. You gentlemen take a shower and Bruce will rub you down."

They climbed out through the ropes and Hogan came over to me.

"John Collins is out with a couple of friends to see Jack," I said.

"I saw them come up in the car."

"Who are the two fellows with John?"

"They're what you call wise boys," Hogan said. "Don't you know them two?"

"No," I said.

"That's Happy Steinfelt and Lew Morgan. They got a poolroom."

"I been away a long time," I said.

"Sure," said Hogan. "That Happy Steinfelt's a big operator."

"I've heard his name," I said.

"He's a pretty smooth boy," Hogan said. "They're a couple of sharpshooters."

"Well," I said. "They want to see us in half an hour."

"You mean they don't want to see us until a half an hour?"

"That's it."

"Come on in the office," Hogan said. "To hell with those sharpshooters."

After about thirty minutes or so Hogan and I went upstairs. We knocked on Jack's door. They were talking inside the room.

"Wait a minute," somebody said.

"To hell with that stuff," Hogan said. "When you want to see me I'm down in the office."

We heard the door unlock. Steinfelt opened it.

"Come on in, Hogan," he says. "We're all going to have a drink."

"Well," says Hogan. "That's something."

We went in. Jack was sitting on the bed. John and Morgan were sitting on a couple of chairs. Steinfelt was standing up.

"You're a pretty mysterious lot of boys," Hogan said.

"Hello, Danny," John says.

"Hello, Danny," Morgan says and shakes hands.

Jack doesn't say anything. He just sits there on the bed. He ain't with the others. He's all by himself. He was wearing an old blue jersey and pants and had on boxing shoes. He needed a shave. Steinfelt and Morgan were dressers. John was quite a dresser too. Jack sat there looking Irish and tough.

Steinfelt brought out a bottle and Hogan brought in some glasses and everybody had a drink. Jack and I took one and the rest of them went on and had two or three each.

"Better save some for your ride back," Hogan said.

"Don't you worry. We got plenty," Morgan said.

Jack hadn't drunk anything since the one drink. He was standing up and looking at them. Morgan was sitting on the bed where Jack had sat.

"Have a drink, Jack," John said and handed him the glass and the bottle.

"No," Jack said, "I never liked to go to these wakes."

They all laughed. Jack didn't laugh.

They were all feeling pretty good when they left. Jack stood on the porch when they got into the car. They waved to him.

"So long," Jack said.

We had supper. Jack didn't say anything all during the meal except, "Will you pass me this?" or "Will you pass me that?" The two health-farm patients ate at the same table with us. They were pretty nice fellows. After we finished eating we went out on the porch. It was dark early.

"Like to take a walk, Jerry?" Jack asked.

"Sure," I said.

We put on our coats and started out. It was quite a way down to the main road and then we walked along the main road about a mile and a half. Cars kept going by and we would pull out to the side until they were past. Jack didn't say anything. After we had stepped out into the bushes to let a big car go by Jack said, "To hell with this walking. Come on back to Hogan's."

We went along a side road that cut up over the hill and cut across the fields back to Hogan's. We could see the lights of the house up on the hill. We came around to the front of the house and there standing in the doorway was Hogan.

"Have a good walk?" Hogan asked.

"Oh, fine," Jack said. "Listen, Hogan. Have you got any liquor?"

"Sure," says Hogan. "What's the idea?"

"Send it up to the room," Jack says. "I'm going to sleep tonight."

"You're the doctor," Hogan says.

"Come on up to the room, Jerry," Jack says.

Upstairs Jack sat on the bed with his head in his hands.

"Ain't it a life?" Jack says.

Hogan brought in a quart of liquor and two glasses. "Want some ginger ale?"

"What do you think I want to do, get sick?"

"I just asked you," said Hogan.

"Have a drink?" said Jack.

"No, thanks," said Hogan. He went out.

"How about you, Jerry?"

"I'll have one with you," I said.

Jack poured out a couple of drinks. "Now," he said, "I want to take it slow and easy."

"Put some water in it," I said.

"Yes," Jack said. "I guess that's better."

We had a couple of drinks without saying anything. Jack started to pour me another.

"No," I said, "that's all I want."

"All right," Jack said. He poured himself out another

big shot and put water in it. He was lighting up a little.

"That was a fine bunch out here this afternoon," he said. "They don't take any chances, those two."

Then a little later, "Well," he says, "they're right. What the hell's the good in taking chances?"

"Don't you want another, Jerry?" he said. "Come on, drink along with me."

"I don't need it, Jack," I said. "I feel all right."

"Just have one more," Jack said. It was softening him up.

"All right," I said.

Jack poured one for me and another big one for himself.

"You know," he said, "I like liquor pretty well. If I hadn't been boxing I would have drunk quite a lot."

"Sure," I said.

"You know," he said, "I missed a lot, boxing."

"You made plenty of money."

"Sure, that's what I'm after. You know I miss a lot, Jerry."

"How do you mean?"

"Well," he says, "like about the wife. And being away from home so much. It don't do my girls any good. 'Who's your old man?' some of those society kids 'll say to them. 'My old man's Jack Brennan.' That don't do them any good."

"Hell," I said, "all that makes a difference is if they got dough."

"Well," says Jack, "I got the dough for them all right."

He poured out another drink. The bottle was about empty.

"Put some water in it," I said. Jack poured in some water.

"You know," he says, "you ain't got any idea how I miss the wife."

"Sure."

"You ain't got any idea. You can't have an idea what it's like."

"It ought to be better out in the country than in town."

"With me now," Jack said, "it don't make any difference where I am. You can't have an idea what it's like."

"Have another drink."

"Am I getting soused? Do I talk funny?"

"You're coming on all right."

"You can't have an idea what it's like. They ain't anybody can have an idea what it's like."

"Except the wife," I said.

"She knows," Jack said. "She knows all right. She knows. You bet she knows."

"Put some water in that," I said.

"Jerry," says Jack, "you can't have an idea what it gets to be like."

He was good and drunk. He was looking at me steady. His eyes were sort of too steady.

"You'll sleep all right," I said.

"Listen, Jerry," Jack says. "You want to make some money? Get some money down on Walcott."

"Yes?"

"Listen, Jerry," Jack put down the glass. "I'm not drunk now, see? You know what I'm betting on him? Fifty grand."

"That's a lot of dough."

"Fifty grand," Jack says, "at two to one. I'll get twenty-five thousand bucks. Get some money on him, Jerry."

"It sounds good," I said.

"How can I beat him?" Jack says. "It ain't crooked. How can I beat him? Why not make money on it?"

"Put some water in that," I said.

"I'm through after this fight," Jack says. "I'm through with it. I got to take a beating. Why shouldn't I make money on it?"

"Sure."

"I ain't slept for a week," Jack says. "All night I lay awake and worry my can off. I can't sleep, Jerry. You ain't got an idea what it's like when you can't sleep."

"Sure."

"I can't sleep. That's all. I just can't sleep. What's the use of taking care of yourself all these years when you can't sleep?"

"It's bad."

"You ain't got an idea what it's like, Jerry, when you can't sleep."

"Put some water in that," I said.

Well, about eleven o'clock Jack passes out and I put him to bed. Finally he's so he can't keep from sleeping. I helped him get his clothes off and got him into bed.

"You'll sleep all right, Jack," I said.

"Sure," Jack says, "I'll sleep now."

"Good night, Jack," I said.

"Good night, Jerry," Jack says. "You're the only friend I got."

"Oh, hell," I said.

"You're the only friend I got," Jack says, "the only friend I got."

"Go to sleep," I said.

"I'll sleep," Jack says.

Downstairs Hogan was sitting at the desk in the office reading the papers. He looked up. "Well, you get your boy friend to sleep?" he asks.

"He's off."

"It's better for him than not sleeping," Hogan said.

"Sure."

"You'd have a hell of a time explaining that to these sport writers though," Hogan said.

"Well, I'm going to bed myself," I said.

"Good night," said Hogan.

In the morning I came downstairs about eight o'clock and got some breakfast. Hogan had his two customers out in the barn doing exercises. I went out and watched them.

"One! Two! Three! Four!" Hogan was counting for them. "Hello, Jerry," he said. "Is Jack up yet?"

"No. He's still sleeping."

I went back to my room and packed up to go in to town. About nine-thirty I heard Jack getting up in the next room. When I heard him go downstairs I went down after him. Jack was sitting at the breakfast table. Hogan had come in and was standing beside the table.

"How do you feel, Jack?" I asked him.

"Not so bad."

"Sleep well?" Hogan asked.

"I slept all right," Jack said. "I got a thick tongue but I ain't got a head."

"Good," said Hogan. "That was good liquor."

"Put it on the bill," Jack says.

"What time you want to go into town?" Hogan asked.

"Before lunch," Jack says. "The eleven o'clock train."

"Sit down, Jerry," Jack said. Hogan went out.

I sat down at the table. Jack was eating a grapefruit. When he'd find a seed he'd spit it out in the spoon and dump it on the plate.

"I guess I was pretty stewed last night," he started.

"You drank some liquor."

"I guess I said a lot of fool things."

"You weren't bad."

"Where's Hogan?" he asked. He was through with the grapefruit.

"He's out in front in the office."

"What did I say about betting on the fight?" Jack asked. He was holding the spoon and sort of poking at the grapefruit with it.

The girl came in with some ham and eggs and took away the grapefruit.

"Bring me another glass of milk," Jack said to her. She went out.

"You said you had fifty grand on Walcott," I said.

"That's right," Jack said.

"That's a lot of money."

"I don't feel too good about it," Jack said.

"Something might happen."

"No," Jack said. "He wants the title bad. They'll be shooting with him all right."

"You can't ever tell."

"No. He wants the title. It's worth a lot of money to him."

"Fifty grand is a lot of money," I said.

"It's business," said Jack. "I can't win. You know I can't win anyway."

"As long as you're in there you got a chance."

"No," Jack says. "I'm all through. It's just business."

"How do you feel?"

"Pretty good," Jack said. "The sleep was what I needed."

"You might go good."

"I'll give them a good show," Jack said.

After breakfast Jack called up his wife on the long-distance. He was inside the booth telephoning.

"That's the first time he's called her up since he's out here," Hogan said.

"He writes her every day."

"Sure," Hogan says, "a letter only costs two cents."

Hogan said good-by to us and Bruce, the nigger rubber, drove us down to the train in the cart.

"Good-by, Mr. Brennan," Bruce said at the train, "I sure hope you knock his can off."

"So long," Jack said. He gave Bruce two dollars. Bruce had worked on him a lot. He looked kind of disappointed. Jack saw me looking at Bruce holding the two dollars.

"It's all in the bill," he said. "Hogan charged me for the rubbing."

On the train going into town Jack didn't talk. He sat in the corner of the seat with his ticket in his hat-band and looked out of the window. Once he turned and spoke to me.

"I told the wife I'd take a room at the Shelby tonight," he said. "It's just around the corner from the Garden. I can go up to the house tomorrow morning."

"That's a good idea," I said. "Your wife ever see you fight, Jack?"

"No," Jack says. "She never seen me fight."

I thought he must be figuring on taking an awful beating if he doesn't want to go home afterward. In town we took a taxi up to the Shelby. A boy came out and took our bags and we went in to the desk.

"How much are the rooms?" Jack asked.

"We only have double rooms," the clerk says. "I can give you a nice double room for ten dollars."

"That's too steep."

"I can give you a double room for seven dollars."

"With a bath?"

"Certainly."

"You might as well bunk with me, Jerry," Jack says.

"Oh," I said, "I'll sleep down at my brother-in-law's."

"I don't mean for you to pay it," Jack says. "I just want to get my money's worth."

"Will you register, please?" the clerk says. He looked at the names. "Number 238, Mister Brennan."

We went up in the elevator. It was a nice big room with two beds and a door opening into a bath-room.

"This is pretty good," Jack says.

The boy who brought us up pulled up the curtains and brought in our bags. Jack didn't make any move, so I gave the boy a quarter. We washed up and Jack said we better go out and get something to eat.

We ate a lunch at Jimmy Hanley's place. Quite a lot of the boys were there. When we were about half through eating, John came in and sat down with us. Jack didn't talk much.

"How are you on the weight, Jack?" John asked him. Jack was putting away a pretty good lunch.

"I could make it with my clothes on," Jack said. He never had to worry about taking off weight. He was a natural welterweight and he'd never gotten fat. He'd lost weight out at Hogan's.

"Well, that's one thing you never had to worry about," John said.

"That's one thing," Jack says.

We went around to the Garden to weigh in after lunch. The match was made at a hundred forty-seven pounds at three o'clock. Jack stepped on the scales with a towel around him. The bar didn't move. Walcott had just weighed and was standing with a lot of people around him.

"Let's see what you weigh, Jack," Freedman, Walcott's manager said.

"All right, weigh *him* then," Jack jerked his head toward Walcott.

"Drop the towel," Freedman said.

"What do you make it?" Jack asked the fellows who were weighing.

"One hundred and forty-three pounds," the fat man who was weighing said.

"You're down fine, Jack," Freedman says.

"Weigh *him*," Jack says.

Walcott came over. He was a blond with wide shoulders and arms like a heavyweight. He didn't have much legs. Jack stood about half a head taller than he did.

"Hello, Jack," he said. His face was plenty marked up.

"Hello," said Jack. "How you feel?"

"Good," Walcott says. He dropped the towel from around his waist and stood on the scales. He had the widest shoulders and back you ever saw.

"One hundred and forty-six pounds and twelve ounces."

Walcott stepped off and grinned at Jack.

"Well," John says to him, "Jack's spotting you about four pounds."

"More than that when I come in, kid," Walcott says. "I'm going to go and eat now."

We went back and Jack got dressed. "He's a pretty tough-looking boy," Jack says to me.

"He looks as though he'd been hit plenty of times."

"Oh, yes," Jack says. "He ain't hard to hit."

"Where are you going?" John asked when Jack was dressed.

"Back to the hotel," Jack says. "You looked after everything?"

"Yes," John says. "It's all looked after."

"I'm going to lie down a while," Jack says.

"I'll come around for you about a quarter to seven and we'll go and eat."

"All right."

Up at the hotel Jack took off his shoes and his coat

and lay down for a while. I wrote a letter. I looked over
a couple of times and Jack wasn't sleeping. He was lying
perfectly still but every once in a while his eyes would
open. Finally he sits up.

"Want to play some cribbage, Jerry?" he says.

"Sure," I said.

He went over to his suitcase and got out the cards
and the cribbage board. We played cribbage and he
won three dollars off me. John knocked at the door and
came in.

"Want to play some cribbage, John?" Jack asked him.

John put his hat down on the table. It was all wet.
His coat was wet too.

"Is it raining?" Jack asks.

"It's pouring," John says. "The taxi I had got tied up
in the traffic and I got out and walked."

"Come on, play some cribbage," Jack says.

"You ought to go and eat."

"No," says Jack. "I don't want to eat yet."

So they played cribbage for about half an hour and
Jack won a dollar and a half off him.

"Well, I suppose we got to go eat," Jack says. He
went to the window and looked out.

"Is it still raining?"

"Yes."

"Let's eat in the hotel," John says.

"All right," Jack says, "I'll play you once more to see
who pays for the meal."

After a little while Jack gets up and says, "You buy
the meal, John," and we went downstairs and ate in the
big dining-room.

After we ate we went upstairs and Jack played cribbage with John again and won two dollars and a half
off him. Jack was feeling pretty good. John had a bag
with him with all his stuff in it. Jack took off his shirt

and collar and put on a jersey and a sweater, so he wouldn't catch cold when he came out, and put his ring clothes and his bathrobe in a bag.

"You all ready?" John asks him. "I'll call up and have them get a taxi."

Pretty soon the telephone rang and they said the taxi was waiting.

We rode down in the elevator and went out through the lobby, and got in a taxi and rode around to the Garden. It was raining hard but there was a lot of people outside on the streets. The Garden was sold out. As we came in on our way to the dressing-room I saw how full it was. It looked like half a mile down to the ring. It was all dark. Just the lights over the ring.

"It's a good thing, with this rain, they didn't try and pull this fight in the ball park," John said.

"They got a good crowd," Jack says.

"This is a fight that would draw a lot more than the Garden could hold."

"You can't tell about the weather," Jack says.

John came to the door of the dressing-room and poked his head in. Jack was sitting there with his bathrobe on, he had his arms folded and was looking at the floor. John had a couple of handlers with him. They looked over his shoulder. Jack looked up.

"Is he in?" he asked.

"He's just gone down," John said.

We started down. Walcott was just getting into the ring. The crowd gave him a big hand. He climbed through between the ropes and put his two fists together and smiled, and shook them at the crowd, first at one side of the ring, then at the other, and then sat down. Jack got a good hand coming down through the crowd. Jack is Irish and the Irish always get a pretty good hand. An Irishman don't draw in New York like a Jew or an Italian but they always get a good hand. Jack climbed up and bent down to go through the ropes and Walcott came over from his corner and pushed the rope down for Jack to go through. The crowd thought that was wonderful. Walcott put his hand on Jack's shoulder and they stood there just for a second.

"So you're going to be one of these popular champions," Jack says to him. "Take your goddam hand off my shoulder."

"Be yourself," Walcott says.

This is all great for the crowd. How gentlemanly the boys are before the fight. How they wish each other luck.

Solly Freedman came over to our corner while Jack is bandaging his hands and John is over in Walcott's corner. Jack puts his thumb through the slit in the bandage and then wrapped his hand nice and smooth. I taped it around the wrist and twice across the knuckles.

"Hey," Freedman says. "Where do you get all that tape?"

"Feel of it," Jack says. "It's soft, ain't it? Don't be a hick."

Freedman stands there all the time while Jack bandages the other hand, and one of the boys that's going to handle him brings the gloves and I pull them on and work them around.

"Say, Freedman," Jack asks, "what nationality is this Walcott?"

"I don't know," Solly says. "He's some sort of a Dane."

"He's a Bohemian," the lad who brought the gloves said.

The referee called them out to the center of the ring and Jack walks out. Walcott comes out smiling. They met and the referee put his arm on each of their shoulders.

"Hello, popularity," Jack says to Walcott.

"Be yourself."

"What do you call yourself 'Walcott' for?" Jack says. "Didn't you know he was a nigger?"

"Listen—" says the referee, and he gives them the same old line. Once Walcott interrupts him. He grabs Jack's arm and says, "Can I hit when he's got me like this?"

"Keep your hands off me," Jack says. "There ain't no moving-pictures of this."

They went back to their corners. I lifted the bathrobe off Jack and he leaned on the ropes and flexed his knees a couple of times and scuffed his shoes in the rosin. The gong rang and Jack turned quick and went out. Walcott came toward him and they touched gloves and as soon as Walcott dropped his hands Jack jumped his left into his face twice. There wasn't anybody ever boxed better than Jack. Walcott was after him, going forward all the time with his chin on his chest. He's a hooker and he carries his hands pretty low. All he knows is to get in there and sock. But every time he gets in there close, Jack has the left hand in his face. It's just as though it's automatic. Jack just raises the left hand up and it's in Walcott's face. Three or four times Jack brings the right over but Walcott gets it on the shoulder or high up on the head. He's just like all these hookers. The only thing he's afraid of is another one of the same kind. He's covered everywhere you can hurt him. He don't care about a left-hand in his face.

After about four rounds Jack has him bleeding bad and his face all cut up, but every time Walcott's got in close he's socked so hard he's got two big red patches on both sides just below Jack's ribs. Every time he gets in close, Jack ties him up, then gets one hand loose and uppercuts him, but when Walcott gets his hands loose he socks Jack in the body so they can hear it outside in the street. He's a socker.

It goes along like that for three rounds more. They don't talk any. They're working all the time. We worked over Jack plenty too, in between the rounds. He don't look good at all but he never does much work in the ring. He don't move around much and that left-hand is just automatic. It's just like it was connected with Walcott's face and Jack just had to wish it in every time. Jack is always calm in close and he doesn't waste any juice. He knows everything about working in close too and he's getting away with a lot of stuff. While they were in our corner I watched him tie Walcott up, get his right hand loose, turn it and come up with an uppercut that got Walcott's nose with the heel of the glove. Walcott was bleeding bad and leaned his nose on Jack's shoulder so as to give Jack some of it too, and Jack sort of lifted his shoulder sharp and caught him against the nose, and then brought down the right hand and did the same thing again.

Walcott was sore as hell. By the time they'd gone five rounds he hated Jack's guts. Jack wasn't sore; that is, he wasn't any sorer than he always was. He certainly did used to make the fellows he fought hate boxing. That was why he hated Kid Lewis so. He never got the Kid's goat. Kid Lewis always had about three new dirty things Jack couldn't do. Jack was as safe as a church all the time he was in there, as long as he was strong. He certainly was treating Walcott rough. The funny thing was it looked as though Jack was an open classic boxer. That was because he had all that stuff too.

After the seventh round Jack says, "My left's getting heavy."

From then he started to take a beating. It didn't show

at first. But instead of him running the fight it was Walcott was running it, instead of being safe all the time now he was in trouble. He couldn't keep him out with the left hand now. It looked as though it was the same as ever, only now instead of Walcott's punches just missing him they were just hitting him. He took an awful beating in the body.

"What's the round?" Jack asked.

"The eleventh."

"I can't stay," Jack says. "My legs are going bad."

Walcott had been just hitting him for a long time. It was like a baseball catcher pulls the ball and takes some of the shock off. From now on Walcott commenced to land solid. He certainly was a socking-machine. Jack was just trying to block everything now. It didn't show what an awful beating he was taking. In between the rounds I worked on his legs. The muscles would flutter under my hands all the time I was rubbing them. He was sick as hell.

"How's it go?" he asked John, turning around, his face all swollen.

"It's his fight."

"I think I can last," Jack says. "I don't want this bohunk to stop me."

It was going just the way he thought it would. He knew he couldn't beat Walcott. He wasn't strong any more. He was all right though. His money was all right and now he wanted to finish it off right to please himself. He didn't want to be knocked out.

The gong rang and we pushed him out. He went out slow. Walcott came right out after him. Jack put the left in his face and Walcott took it, came in under it and started working on Jack's body. Jack tried to tie him up and it was just like trying to hold on to a buzz-saw.

Jack broke away from it and missed with the right. Walcott clipped him with a left-hook and Jack went down. He went down on his hands and knees and looked at us. The referee started counting. Jack was watching us and shaking his head. At eight John motioned to him. You couldn't hear on account of the crowd. Jack got up. The referee had been holding Walcott back with one arm while he counted.

When Jack was on his feet Walcott started toward him.

"Watch yourself, Jimmy," I heard Solly Freedman yell to him.

Walcott came up to Jack looking at him. Jack stuck the left hand at him. Walcott just shook his head. He backed Jack up against the ropes, measured him and then hooked the left very light to the side of Jack's head and socked the right into the body as hard as he could sock, just as low as he could get it. He must have hit him five inches below the belt. I thought the eyes would come out of Jack's head. They stuck way out. His mouth come open.

The referee grabbed Walcott. Jack stepped forward. If he went down there went fifty thousand bucks. He walked as though all his insides were going to fall out.

"It wasn't low," he said. "It was a accident."

The crowd were yelling so you couldn't hear anything.

"I'm all right," Jack says. They were right in front of us. The referee looks at John and then he shakes his head.

"Come on, you polak son-of-a-bitch," Jack says to Walcott.

John was hanging onto the ropes. He had the towel ready to chuck in. Jack was standing just a little way out from the ropes. He took a step forward. I saw the sweat come out on his face like somebody had squeezed it and a big drop went down his nose.

"Come on and fight," Jack says to Walcott.

The referee looked at John and waved Walcott on.

"Go in there, you slob," he says.

Walcott went in. He didn't know what to do either. He never thought Jack could have stood it. Jack put the left in his face. There was such a hell of a lot of yelling going on. They were right in front of us. Walcott hit him twice. Jack's face was the worst thing I ever saw —the look on it! He was holding himself and all his body together and it all showed on his face. All the time he was thinking and holding his body in where it was busted.

Then he started to sock. His face looked awful all the time. He started to sock with his hands low down by his side, swinging at Walcott. Walcott covered up and Jack was swinging wild at Walcott's head. Then he swung the left and it hit Walcott in the groin and the right hit Walcott right bang where he'd hit Jack. Way low below the belt. Walcott went down and grabbed himself there and rolled and twisted around.

The referee grabbed Jack and pushed him toward his corner. John jumps into the ring. There was all this yelling going on. The referee was talking with the judges and then the announcer got into the ring with the megaphone and says, "Walcott on a foul."

The referee is talking to John and he says, "What could I do? Jack wouldn't take the foul. Then when he's groggy he fouls him."

"He'd lost it anyway," John says.

Jack's sitting on the chair. I've got his gloves off and he's holding himself in down there with both hands. When he's got something supporting it his face doesn't look so bad.

"Go over and say you're sorry," John says into his ear. "It'll look good."

Jack stands up and the sweat comes out all over his face. I put the bathrobe around him and he holds himself in with one hand under the bathrobe and goes across the ring. They've picked Walcott up and they're working on him. There're a lot of people in Walcott's corner. Nobody speaks to Jack. He leans over Walcott.

"I'm sorry," Jack says. "I didn't mean to foul you."

Walcott doesn't say anything. He looks too damned sick.

"Well, you're the champion now," Jack says to him. "I hope you get a hell of a lot of fun out of it."

"Leave the kid alone," Solly Freedman says.

"Hello, Solly," Jack says. "I'm sorry I fouled your boy."

Freedman just looks at him.

Jack went to his corner walking that funny jerky way and we got him down through the ropes and through the reporters' tables and out down the aisle. A lot of people want to slap Jack on the back. He goes out through all that mob in his bathrobe to the dressing-room. It's a popular win for Walcott. That's the way the money was bet in the Garden.

Once we got inside the dressing-room Jack lay down and shut his eyes.

"We want to get to the hotel and get a doctor," John says.

"I'm all busted inside," Jack says.

"I'm sorry as hell, Jack," John says.

"It's all right," Jack says.

He lies there with his eyes shut.

"They certainly tried a nice double-cross," John said.

"Your friends Morgan and Steinfelt," Jack said. "You got nice friends."

He lies there, his eyes are open now. His face has still got that awful drawn look.

"It's funny how fast you can think when it means that much money," Jack says.

"You're some boy, Jack," John says.

"No," Jack says. "It was nothing."

THE WALTZ

BY DOROTHY PARKER

WHY, *thank you so much. I'd adore to.*

I don't want to dance with him. I don't want to dance with anybody. And even if I did, it wouldn't be him. He'd be well down among the last ten. I've seen the way he dances; it looks like something you do on St. Walpurgis Night. Just think, not a quarter of an hour ago, here I was sitting, feeling so sorry for the poor girl he was dancing with. And now *I'm* going to be the poor girl. Well, well. Isn't it a small world?

And a peach of a world, too. A true little corker. Its events are so fascinatingly unpredictable, are not they? Here I was, minding my own business, not doing a stitch of harm to any living soul. And then he comes into my life, all smiles and city manners, to sue me for the favor of one memorable mazurka. Why, he scarcely knows my name, let alone what it stands for. It stands for Despair, Bewilderment, Futility, Degradation, and Premeditated Murder, but little does he wot. I don't wot his name, either; I haven't any idea what it is. Jukes, would be my guess from the look in his eyes. How do you do, Mr. Jukes? And how is that dear little brother of yours, with the two heads?

Ah, now why did he have to come around me, with his low requests? Why can't he let me lead my own life? I ask so little—just to be left alone in my quiet corner of the table, to do my evening brooding over all my sorrows. And he must come, with his bows and his scrapes and his may-I-have-this-ones. And I had to go and tell

346

him that I'd adore to dance with him. I cannot understand why I wasn't struck right down dead. Yes, and being struck dead would look like a day in the country, compared to struggling out a dance with this boy. But what could I do? Everyone else at the table had got up to dance, except him and me. There I was, trapped. Trapped like a trap in a trap.

What can you say, when a man asks you to dance with him? I most certainly will *not* dance with you, I'll see you in hell first. Why, thank you, I'd like to awfully, but I'm having labor pains. Oh, yes, *do* let's dance together—it's so nice to meet a man who isn't a scaredy-cat about catching my beri-beri. No. There was nothing for me to do, but say I'd adore to. Well, we might as well get it over with. All right, Cannonball, let's run out on the field. You won the toss; you can lead.

Why, I think it's more of a waltz, really. Isn't it? We might just listen to the music a second. Shall we? Oh, yes, it's a waltz. Mind? Why, I'm simply thrilled. I'd love to waltz with you.

I'd love to waltz with you. I'd love to waltz with you, I'd love to have my tonsils out, I'd love to be in a midnight fire at sea. Well, it's too late now. We're getting under way. *Oh.* Oh, dear. Oh, dear, dear, dear. Oh, this is even worse than I thought it would be. I suppose that's the one dependable law of life—everything is always worse than you thought it was going to be. Oh, if I had had any real grasp of what this dance would be like, I'd have held out for sitting it out. Well, it will probably amount to the same thing in the end. We'll be sitting it out on the floor in a minute, if he keeps this up.

I'm so glad I brought it to his attention that this is a waltz they're playing. Heaven knows what might have happened, if he had thought it was something fast; we'd have blown the sides right out of the building.

Why does he always want to be somewhere that he isn't? Why can't we stay in one place just long enough to get acclimated? It's this constant rush, rush, rush, that's the curse of American life. That's the reason that we're all of us so—— *Ow!* For God's sake, don't *kick*, you idiot; this is only second down. Oh, my shin. My poor, poor shin, that I've had ever since I was a little girl!

Oh, no, no, no. Goodness, no. It didn't hurt the least little bit. And anyway it was my fault. Really it was. Truly. Well, you're just being sweet, to say that. It really was all my fault.

I wonder what I'd better do—kill him this instant, with my naked hands, or wait and let him drop in his traces. Maybe it's best not to make a scene. I guess I'll just lie low, and watch the pace get him. He can't keep this up indefinitely—he's only flesh and blood. Die he must, and die he shall, for what he did to me. I don't want to be of the over-sensitive type, but you can't tell me that kick was unpremeditated. Freud says there are no accidents. I've led no cloistered life, I've known dancing partners who have spoiled my slippers and torn my dress; but when it comes to kicking, I am Outraged Womanhood. When you kick me in the shin, *smile*.

Maybe he didn't do it maliciously. Maybe it's just his way of showing his high spirits. I suppose I ought to be glad that one of us is having such a good time. I suppose I ought to think myself lucky if he brings me back alive. Maybe it's captious to demand of a practically strange man that he leave your shins as he found them. After all, the poor boy's doing the best he can. Probably he grew up in the hill country, and never had no larnin'. I bet they had to throw him on his back to get shoes on him.

Yes, it's lovely, isn't it? It's simply lovely. It's the loveliest waltz. Isn't it? Oh, I think it's lovely, too.

Why, I'm getting positively drawn to the Triple Threat here. He's my hero. He has the heart of a lion, and the sinews of a buffalo. Look at him—never a thought of the consequences, never afraid of his face, hurling himself into every scrimmage, eyes shining, cheeks ablaze. And shall it be said that I hung back? No, a thousand times no. What's it to me if I have to spend the next couple of years in a plaster cast? Come on, Butch, right through them! Who wants to live forever?

Oh. Oh, dear. Oh, he's all right, thank goodness. For a while I thought they'd have to carry him off the field. Ah, I couldn't bear to have anything happen to him. I love him. I love him better than anybody in the world. Look at the spirit he gets into a dreary, commonplace waltz; how effete the other dancers seem, beside him. He is youth and vigor and courage, he is strength and gaiety and— *Ow!* Get off my instep, you hulking peasant! What do you think I am, anyway—a gangplank? *Ow!*

No, of course it didn't hurt. Why, it didn't a bit. Honestly. And it was all my fault. You see, that little step of yours—well, it's perfectly lovely, but it's just a tiny bit tricky to follow at first. Oh, did you work it up yourself? You really did? Well, aren't you amazing! Oh, now I think I've got it. Oh, I think it's lovely. I was watching you do it when you were dancing before. It's awfully effective when you look at it.

It's awfully effective when you look at it. I bet I'm awfully effective when you look at me. My hair is hanging along my cheeks, my skirt is swaddled about me, I can feel the cold damp of my brow. I must look like something out of the Fall of the House of Usher. This sort of thing takes a fearful toll of a woman my age. And he worked up his little step himself, he with his degenerate cunning. And it was just a tiny bit tricky at first, but now I think I've got it. Two stumbles, slip, and a twenty-yard dash; yes, I've got it. I've got several other things, too, including a split shin and a bitter heart. I hate this creature I'm chained to. I hated him the moment I saw his leering, bestial face. And here I've been locked in his noxious embrace for the thirty-five years this waltz has lasted. Is that orchestra never going to stop playing? Or must this obscene travesty of a dance go on until hell burns out?

Oh, they're going to play another encore. Oh, goody. Oh, that's lovely. Tired? I should say I'm not tired. I'd like to go on like this forever.

I should say I'm not tired. I'm dead, that's all I am. Dead, and in what a cause! And the music is never going to stop playing, and we're going on like this, Double-Time Charlie and I, throughout eternity. I suppose I won't care any more, after the first hundred thousand years. I suppose nothing will matter then, not heat nor pain nor broken heart nor cruel, aching weariness. Well. It can't come too soon for me.

I wonder why I didn't tell him I was tired. I wonder why I didn't suggest going back to the table. I could have said let's just listen to the music. Yes, and if he would, that would be the first bit of attention he has given it all evening. George Jean Nathan said that the lovely rhythms of the waltz should be listened to in stillness and not be accompanied by strange gyrations of the human body. I think that's what he said. I think it was George Jean Nathan. Anyhow, whatever he said and whoever he was and whatever he's doing now, he's better off than I am. That's safe. Anybody who isn't waltzing with this Mrs. O'Leary's cow I've got here is having a good time.

Still, if we were back at the table, I'd probably have

to talk to him. Look at him—what could you say to a thing like that! Did you go to the circus this year, what's your favorite kind of ice cream, how do you spell cat? I guess I'm as well off here. As well off as if I were in a cement mixer in full action.

I'm past all feeling now. The only way I can tell when he steps on me is that I can hear the splintering of bones. And all the events of my life are passing before my eyes. There was the time I was in a hurricane in the West Indies, there was the day I got my head cut open in the taxi smash, there was the night the drunken lady threw a bronze ash-tray at her own true love and got me instead, there was that summer that the sailboat kept capsizing. Ah, what an easy, peaceful time was mine, until I fell in with Swifty, here. I didn't know what trouble was, before I got drawn into this *danse macabre*. I think my mind is beginning to wander. It almost seems to me as if the orchestra were stopping. It couldn't be, of course; it could never, never be. And yet in my ears there is a silence like the sound of angel voices. . . .

Oh, they've stopped, the mean things. They're not going to play any more. Oh, darn. Oh, do you think they would? Do you really think so, if you gave them fifty dollars? Oh, that would be lovely. And look, do tell them to play this same thing. I'd simply adore to go on waltzing.

YOU MEAN COMMON

BY ARTHUR KOBER

BELLA had sent her parents off to the movies so that she could be alone with Mr. Kaplan. Now, seated with him in the parlor, she knew that the efforts spent on an elaborate toilette had not been in vain: Mr. Kaplan was scanning her with an expression of intense admiration.

"Say," he said, as his eyes swept over her, "I din know we had a regella Greeta Gobbo in the awfice. If I'd of known we had a regella Greeta Gobbo in the awfice, I woulda tumbled a long time ago. But you know how it is," he elaborated. "When you're lookin' fa somethin' it's awways right unna your nose. The same is true here. I guess I din know how good-lookin' you was because you was right unna my nose."

"Listen," said Bella, deeply interested. "What do you mean you woulda tumbled a long time ago?"

"I mean, I woulda tried to take you out. That's what I mean."

"It seemsta me if I'm a regella Greeta Gobbo like you said," and here Bella looked at him coquettishly, "you woulda noticed me a long time ago."

"I did notice you a long time ago," declared Mr. Kaplan vehemently. "Din I awways smile at you? Fa you I awways had a 'Good mornin'!' any time of the day."

"Go on. God knows what you thought of me. You musta had a very funny impression of me, I bet."

"Say, I had a good impression of you." Mr. Kaplan

was quite emphatic about this. "The impression you made, may my best friends awways make such a good impression. But I dunno," he amended. "You was awways so serious. I mean, bringin' in books and talkin' over the phone about concerts. You gave me the impression—well, I dunno if I should say it."

"Go on," urged Bella. "We might as well be frank. After all, if we can't be frank—well, I mean, what'sa use?" she finished weakly.

"Oh, this ain't nothin' bad," he hastened to assure her. "This is oney that I thought you was—well, kinda highbrow."

"Oh, I'm not highbrow," said Bella, flattered at this estimate of her. "Just because I like to read books, just because I think it's silly not to keep developing your mind while you're working, is no reason to think I'm highbrow. After all, there are people just like me inclined along the lines of reading books who aren't highbrow. And I like music. I like good jazz and I like classical music. You can leave me in a room with classical music, and still and all I'd have a fine time. But that don't mean I'm highbrow."

"Guess you think I'm an awful dumbbell or something," said Mr. Kaplan, hoping Bella would express an opinion of him. He wasn't disappointed.

"Oh, no. I useta think you was a high-liver, you know—overdoing the night-club part of yesself. I mean, it's awright having a good time, but having a good time too much isn't healthy fa a person no matta who he or she may be."

"Yeah, I guess I kinda overdid the night-club life at that," said Mr. Kaplan, secretly pleased at this and feeling very much the rake. He rose, took an apple from the fruit bowl resting on the table, polished it with the palm of his hand, and then dug into it with his teeth.

"Yeah," said Bella, "if you din overdo the night-club part of yesself, you'd be much better off. At lease, that's my opinion."

"I guess you're right," he said swallowing. The apple was soon a core resting in his hand. He looked around for something in which to place it. Bella jumped to her feet.

"Here," she said, "gimme that."

Mr. Kaplan handed her the apple core. As he did so, his hand squeezed hers, and he clung to it.

"Say, Bella," he said softly, "that's certainey some soft hand you got there."

"It's not so soft," she said. "I just put lemon cream on my hands and arms before I go to bed evvey night. But it's not really soft."

"That's what you say."

"That's what I say." Her eyes met his.

"But I say your hand is soft. Nice 'n soft," he added insinuatingly. They faced each other, tense and expectant.

"What beyoodyful skin," said Mr. Kaplan in a voice that was almost a whisper now. "You must use up a coupla jars a night of that there cream because your skin, it's certainey beeyoodyful."

"It's not so beyoodyful." Her voice was hardly audible.

"It's soft 'n beyoodyful."

He placed his hands on her bare arms. Both looked at each other and didn't move. It was Bella who broke the silence.

"Please, Howard," she said, "don't."

This was Mr. Kaplan's cue, and he acted on it. He embraced her violently. She made a perfunctory movement to keep him off but soon relaxed. After a fervent kiss they separated. There was an embarrassed silence.

Suddenly Bella became active. She noticed that the apple core was still in her hand, and she now looked around for a place to deposit it. There was an ashtray on the table, and she placed it there.

Mr. Kaplan, puffing heavily, came toward her.

"Gee, Bella," he said, "you certainey are one sweet kid."

"No, I'm not," she said. "I'm just—well, I'm just a girl."

"Yeah," he said enthusiastically, "but what a girl!" With that he seized her, and again they embraced and kissed.

Suddenly voices were heard at the front door, and they quickly parted. Ma and Pa Gross came into the room.

"Hello, Mr. Kaplan," said Mrs. Gross, turning to greet the guest. "Look, company we got, and Bella don't tell her own mother even."

"Hello, Mr. Kaplan." It was Mr. Gross's turn to greet him. "How you filling, Mr. Kaplan? Good?" Then, without waiting for a reply, he added, "By me is a headick worse like a fecktree."

"How was the movie?" Bella asked.

"A fine moom pickcha we seen," replied Mrs. Gross. "Such moom pickchas my worst enemies should oney see."

"Look who's talking!" said Pa Gross, glaring at his wife. "In the first place you din see no moom pickcha, and in the secont place next time you can go alone."

"Now, Father," remonstrated Bella, "that's no way to talk."

"Talk-shmalk, who wantsta go with her to the movies?"

"What happened?" inquired Bella.

"So what should happen?" replied her father, still scowling at Ma Gross. "She falls aslipp in the middle the pickcha, and with all the people listening, she snores like a huss."

"So awright, Mr. Boss, what should I do? Maybe I should slipp in the theayter, Mr. Boss, and snore maybe here in the house, Mr. Boss. This you would like?"

"Fa my pott you can snore in the middle the stritt," said Mr. Gross. "Next time I want to spend a couple minutes bime movies, I can go by myself."

"Now, Father, is that nice?" asked Bella. "Mother just happened to be tired, that's all."

"Tired-shmired," said Mrs. Gross. "Fomm the pickchas I'm tired. All the movies, the same thing. So a boy sees awready a girl, so right away he kisses the girl bime face. So what should the girl do? So she kissed him back bime face. Nothing but kissing here and kissing there. *Feh!* This monkey business I don't like. Kissing all the time, that's common. I got right, Mr. Kaplan?" she asked, appealing to him.

He didn't want to reply, but said "Certainey," because he felt he had to. He caught Bella's eye and looked away, embarrassed.

"Well," he then said, "I think I better be goin'. Gotta lotta work to do in the mornin'."

"Maybe you'd like a gless tea?" asked Mrs. Gross.

"No, thanks," he said. "I gotta be goin'."

"Maybe a piece fruit you'd like?"

It was her husband who replied. "So he don't want a drop food. He has to go. Maybe you can't hear good bime ears?"

"Hold betta the tongue," said Mrs. Gross. "I'm talking to you?"

Bella saw Mr. Kaplan to the door. "See you at the awfice," she said.

"Sure," he replied. He seemed anxious to get away. "Thanks for a nice time."

"You don't mean nice," said Bella quickly. "You mean common."

She shut the door.

ADDRESS UNKNOWN

BY KRESSMANN TAYLOR

SCHULSE-EISENSTEIN GALLERIES
SAN FRANCISCO, CALIFORNIA, U. S. A.
NOVEMBER 12, 1932

Herrn Martin Schulse
Schloss Rantzenburg
Munich, Germany

MY DEAR MARTIN:

Back in Germany! How I envy you! Although I have
not seen it since my school days, the spell of *Unter den
Linden* is still strong upon me—the breadth of intellectual freedom, the discussions, the music, the lighthearted
comradeship. And now the old Junker spirit, the Prus-
sian arrogance and militarism are gone. You go to a
democratic Germany, a land with a deep culture and the
beginnings of a fine political freedom. It will be a good
life. Your new address is impressive and I rejoice that
the crossing was so pleasant for Elsa and the young
sprouts.

As for me, I am not so happy. Sunday morning finds
me a lonely bachelor without aim. My Sunday home is
now transported over the wide seas. The big old house
on the hill—your welcome that said the day was not
complete until we were together again! And our dear
jolly Elsa, coming out beaming, grasping my hand and
shouting "Max, Max!" and hurrying indoors to open my
favorite *Schnapps*. The fine boys, too, especially your

358

handsome young Heinrich; he will be a grown man before I set eyes upon him again.

And dinner—shall I evermore hope to eat as I have eaten? Now I go to a restaurant and over my lonely roast beef comes visions of *Gebackener Schinken* steaming in its Burgundy sauce, of *Spätzle*, ah! of *Spätzle* and *Spargel*. No, I shall never again become reconciled to my American diet. And the wines, so carefully slipped ashore from the German boats, and the pledges we made as the glasses brimmed for the fourth and fifth and sixth times.

Of course you are right to go. You have never become American despite your success here, and now that the business is so well established you must take your sturdy German boys back to the homeland to be educated. Elsa too has missed her family through the long years and they will be glad to see you as well. The impecunious young artist has now become the family benefactor, and that too will give you a quiet little triumph.

The business continues to go well. Mrs. Levine has bought the small Picasso at our price, for which I congratulate myself, and I have old Mrs. Fleshman playing with the notion of the hideous Madonna. No one ever bothers to tell her that any particular piece of hers is bad, because they are all so bad. However I lack your fine touch in selling to the old Jewish matrons. I can persuade them of the excellence of the investment, but you alone had the fine spiritual approach to a piece of art that unarmed them. Besides they probably never entirely trust another Jew.

A delightful letter came yesterday from Griselle. She writes that she is about to make me proud of my little sister. She has the lead in a new play in Vienna and the notices are excellent—her discouraging years with the small companies are beginning to bear fruit. Poor child, it has not been easy for her, but she has never complained. She has a fine spirit, as well as beauty, and I hope the talent as well. She asked about you, Martin, in a very friendly way. There is no bitterness left there, for that passes quickly when one is young as she is. A few years and there is only a memory of the hurt, and of course neither of you was to be blamed. Those things are like quick storms, for a moment you are drenched and blasted, and you are so wholly helpless before them. But then the sun comes, and although you have neither quite forgotten, there remains only gentleness and no sorrow. You would not have had it otherwise, nor would I. I have not written Griselle that you are in Europe but perhaps I shall if you think it wise, for she does not make friends easily and I know she would be glad to feel that friends are not far away.

Fourteen years since the war! Did you mark the date? What a long way we have traveled, as peoples, from that bitterness! Again, my dear Martin, let me embrace you in spirit, and with the most affectionate remembrances to Elsa and the boys, believe me,

Your ever most faithful,

MAX

SCHLOSS RANTZENBURG
MUNICH, GERMANY
DECEMBER 10, 1932

Mr. Max Eisenstein
Schulse-Eisenstein Galleries
San Francisco, California, U. S. A.

MAX, DEAR OLD FELLOW:

The check and accounts came through promptly, for

which my thanks. You need not send me such details of the business. You know how I am in accord with your methods, and here at Munich I am in a rush of new activities. We are established, but what a turmoil! The house, as you know, I had long in mind. And I got it at an amazing bargain. Thirty rooms and about ten acres of park, you would never believe it. But then, you could not appreciate how poor is now this sad land of mine. The servants' quarters, stables and outbuildings are most extensive, and would you believe it, we employ now ten servants for the same wages of our two in the San Francisco home.

The tapestries and pieces we shipped make a rich show, and some other fine furnishings I have been able to secure, so that we are much admired, I was almost to say envied. Four full services in the finest china I have bought and much crystal, as well as a full service of silver for which Elsa is in ecstasies.

And for Elsa—such a joke! You will, I know, laugh with me. I have purchased for her a huge bed. Such a size as never was before, twice the bigness of a double bed, and with great posters in carved wood. The sheets I must have made to order, for there are no sheets made that could fit it. And they are of linen, the finest linen sheets. Elsa laughs and laughs, and her old *Grossmutter* stands shaking her head and grumbles, "*Nein*, Martin, *nein*. You have made it so and now you must take care or she will grow to match it."

"*Ja*," says Elsa, "five more boys and I will fit it just nice and snug." And she will, Max.

For the boys there are three ponies (little Karl and Wolfgang are not big enough to ride yet) and a tutor. Their German is very bad, being too much mixed with English.

Elsa's family do not find things so easy now. The

brothers are in the professions and, while much respected, must live together in one house. To the family we seem American millionaires and while we are far from that yet our American income places us among the wealthy here. The better foods are high in price and there is much political unrest even now under the presidency of Hindenburg, a fine liberal whom I much admire.

Already old acquaintances urge me that I interest myself in administrative matters in the town. This I take under consideration. It may be somewhat to our benefit locally if I become an official.

As for you, my good Max, we have left you alone, but you must not become a misanthrope. Get yourself at once a nice fat little wife who will busy herself with all your cares and feed you into a good humor. That is my advice and it is good, although I smile as I write it.

You write of Griselle. So she wins her success, the lovely one! I rejoice with you, although even now I resent it that she must struggle to win her way, a girl alone. She was made, as any man can see, for luxury and for devotion and the charming and beautiful life where ease allows much play of the sensibilities. A gentle, grave soul is in her dark eyes, but there is something strong as iron and very daring too. She is a woman who does nothing and gives nothing lightly. Alas, dear Max, as always, I betray myself. But although you were silent during our stormy affair, you know that the decision was not easy for me. You never reproached me, your friend, while the little sister suffered, and I have always felt you knew that I suffered too, most gravely. What could I do? There was Elsa and my little sons. No other decision was possible to make. Yet for Griselle I keep a tenderness that will last long after she has taken a much younger man for husband or lover. The old wound has healed but the scar throbs at times, my friend.

I wish that you will give her our address. We are such a short distance from Vienna that she can feel there is for her a home close at hand. Elsa, too, knows nothing of the old feeling between us and you know with what warmth she would welcome your sister, as she would welcome you. Yes, you must tell her that we are here and urge her to soon make a contact with us. Give her our most warm congratulations for the fine success that she is making.

Elsa asks that I send to you her love, and Heinrich would also say "hello" to Uncle Max. We do not forget you, Maxel.

My heartiest greetings to you,

MARTIN

SCHULSE-EISENSTEIN GALLERIES
SAN FRANCISCO, CALIFORNIA, U. S. A.
JANUARY 21, 1933

Herrn Martin Schulse
Schloss Rantzenburg
Munich, Germany

MY DEAR MARTIN:

I was glad to forward your address to Griselle. She should have it shortly, if she has not already received it. What jollification there will be when she sees you all! I shall be with you in spirit as heartily as if I also could rejoin you in person.

You speak of the poverty there. Conditions have been bad here this winter, but of course we have known nothing of the privations you see in Germany.

Personally, you and I are lucky that we have such a sound following for the gallery. Of course our own clientele are cutting their purchases but if they buy only half as much as before we shall be comfortable, not extravagantly so, but very comfortable. The oils you sent are excellent, and the prices amazing. I shall dispose of them at an appalling profit almost at once. And the ugly Madonna is gone! Yes, to old Mrs. Fleshman. How I gasped at her perspicacity in recognizing its worth, hesitating to set a price! She suspected me of having another client, and I named an indecent figure. She pounced on it, grinning slyly as she wrote her check. How I exulted as she bore the horror off with her, you alone will know.

Alas, Martin, I often am ashamed of myself for the delight I take in such meaningless little triumphs. You in Germany, with your country house and your affluence displayed before Elsa's relatives, and I in America, gloating because I have tricked a giddy old woman into buying a monstrosity. What a fine climax for two men of forty! Is it for this we spend our lives, to scheme for money and then to strut it publicly? I am always castigating myself, but I continue to do as before. Alas, we are all caught in the same mill. We are vain and we are dishonest because it is necessary to triumph over other vain and dishonest persons. If I do not sell Mrs. Fleshman our horror, somebody else will sell her a worse one. We must accept these necessities.

But there is another realm where we can always find something true, the fireside of a friend, where we shed our little conceits and find warmth and understanding, where small selfishnesses are impossible and where wine and books and talk give a different meaning to existence. There we have made something that no falseness can touch. We are at home.

Who is this Adolph Hitler who seems rising toward power in Germany? I do not like what I read of him.

Embrace all the young fry and our abundant Elsa for

Your ever affectionate,

MAX

SCHLOSS RANTZENBURG
MUNICH, GERMANY
MARCH 25, 1933

Mr. Max Eisenstein
Schulse-Eisenstein Galleries
San Francisco, California, U. S. A.

DEAR OLD MAX:

You have heard of course of the new events in Germany, and you will want to know how it appears to us here on the inside. I tell you truly, Max, I think in many ways Hitler is good for Germany, but I am not sure. He is now the active head of the government. I doubt much that even Hindenburg could now remove him from power, as he was truly forced to place him there. The man is like an electric shock, strong as only a great orator and a zealot can be. But I ask myself, is he quite sane? His brown shirt troops are of the rabble. They pillage and have started a bad Jew-baiting. But these may be minor things, the little surface scum when a big movement boils up. For I tell you, my friend, there is a surge—a surge. The people everywhere have had a quickening. You feel it in the streets and shops. The old despair has been thrown aside like a forgotten coat. No longer the people wrap themselves in shame;

they hope again. Perhaps there may be found an end to this poverty. Something, I do not know what will happen. A leader is found! Yet cautiously to myself I ask, a leader to where? Despair overthrown often turns us in mad directions.

Publicly, as is natural, I express no doubt. I am now an official and a worker in the new regime and I exult very loud indeed. All of us officials who cherish whole skins are quick to join the National Socialists. That is the name for Herr Hitler's party. But also it is not only expedient, there is something more, a feeling that we of Germany have found our destiny and that the future sweeps toward us in an overwhelming wave. We too must move. We must go with it. Even now there are being wrongs done. The storm troopers are having their moment of victory, and there are bloody heads and sad hearts to show for it. But these things pass; if the end in view is right they pass and are forgotten. History writes a clean new page.

All I now ask myself, and I can say to you what I cannot say to any here is: Is the end right? Do we make for a better goal? For you know, Max, I have seen these people of my race since I came here, and I have learned what agonies they have suffered, what years of less and less bread, of leaner bodies, of the end of hope. The quicksand of despair held them, it was at their chins. Then just before they died a man came and pulled them out. All they now know is, they will not die. They are in hysteria of deliverance, almost they worship him. But whoever the savior was, they would have done the same. God grant it is a true leader and no black angel they follow so joyously. To you alone, Max, I say I do not know. I do not know. Yet I hope.

So much for politics. Ourselves, we delight in our new home and have done much entertaining. Tonight the mayor is our guest, at a dinner for twenty-eight. We spread ourselves a little, maybe, but that is to be forgiven. Elsa has a new gown of blue velvet, and is in terror for fear it will not be big enough. She is with child again. There is the way to keep a wife contented, Max. Keep her so busy with babies she has no time to fret.

Our Heinrich has made a social conquest. He goes out on his pony and gets himself thrown off, and who picks him up but the Baron von Freische. They have a long conversation about America, and one day the baron calls and we have coffee. Heinrich will go there to lunch next week. What a boy! It is too bad his German is not better but he delights everyone.

So we go, my friend, perhaps to become part of great events, perhaps only to pursue our simple family way, but never abandoning that trueness of friendship of which you speak so movingly. Our hearts go out to you across the wide sea, and when the glasses are filled we toast "Uncle Max."

Yours in affectionate regard,

MARTIN

SCHULSE-EISENSTEIN GALLERIES
SAN FRANCISCO, CALIFORNIA, U. S. A.
MAY 18, 1933

Herrn Martin Schulse
Schloss Rantzenburg
Munich, Germany

DEAR MARTIN:

I am in distress at the press reports that come pouring in to us from the Fatherland. Thus it is natural that I turn to you for light while there are only conflicting stories to be had here. I am sure things cannot be as bad as they are pictured. A terrible pogrom, that is the consensus of our American papers.

I know your liberal mind and warm heart will tolerate no viciousness and that from you I can have the truth. Aaron Silberman's son has just returned from Berlin and had, I hear, a narrow escape. The tales he tells of what he has seen, floggings, the forcing of quarts of castor oil through clenched teeth and the consequent hours of dying through the slow agony of bursting guts, are not pretty ones. These things may be true, and they may, as you have said, be but the brutal surface froth of human revolution. Alas, to us Jews they are a sad story familiar through centuries of repetition, and it is almost unbelievable that the old martyrdom must be endured in a civilized nation today. Write me, my friend, and set my mind at ease.

Griselle's play will come to a close about the end of June after a great success. She writes that she has an offer for another role in Vienna and also for a very fine one in Berlin for the autumn. She is talking most of the latter one, but I have written her to wait until the anti-Jewish feeling has abated. Of course she uses another name which is not Jewish (Eisenstein would be impossible for the stage anyway), but it is not her name that would betray her origin. Her features, her gestures, her emotional voice proclaim her a Jewess no matter what she calls herself, and if this feeling has any real strength she had best not venture into Germany just at present.

Forgive me, my friend, for so distrait and brief a letter but I cannot rest until you have reassured me. You will, I know, write in all fairness. Pray do so at once.

With the warmest protestations of faith and friendship for you and yours, I am ever your faithful

MAX

Deutsch=Völkische Bank und Handelsgesellschaft
München

JULY 9, 1933

Mr. Max Eisenstein
Schulse-Eisenstein Galleries
San Francisco, California, U. S. A.

DEAR MAX:

You will see that I write upon the stationery of my
bank. This is necessary because I have a request to
make of you and I wish to avoid the new censorship
which is most strict. We must for the present discon-
tinue writing each other. It is impossible for me to be in
correspondence with a Jew even if it were not that I
have an official position to maintain. If a communica-
tion becomes necessary you must enclose it with the
bank draft and not write to me at my house again.

As for the stern measures that so distress you, I myself did not like them at first, but I have come to see
their painful necessity. The Jewish race is a sore spot to
any nation that harbors it. I have never hated the individual Jew—yourself I have always cherished as a
friend, but you will know that I speak in all honesty
when I say I have loved you, not because of your race
but in spite of it.

The Jew is the universal scapegoat. This does not
happen without reason, and it is not the old superstition
about "Christ-killers" that makes them distrusted. But
this Jew trouble is only an incident. Something bigger
is happening.

If I could show you, if I could make you see—the re-
birth of this new Germany under our Gentle Leader!
Not for always can the world grind a great people

down in subjugation. In defeat for fourteen years we bowed our heads. We ate the bitter bread of shame and drank the thin gruel of poverty. But now we are free men. We rise in our might and hold our heads up before the nations. We purge our bloodstream of its baser elements. We go singing through our valleys with strong muscles tingling for a new work—and from the mountains ring the voices of Wodan and Thor, the old, strong gods of the German race.

But no. I am sure as I write, as with the new vision my own enthusiasm burns, that you will not see how necessary is all this for Germany. You will see only that your own people are troubled. You will not see that a few must suffer for the millions to be saved. You will be a Jew first and wail for your people. This I understand. It is the Semitic character. You lament but you are never brave enough to fight back. That is why there are pogroms.

Alas, Max, this will pain you, I know, but you must realize the truth. There are movements far bigger than the men who make them up. As for me, I am a part of the movement. Heinrich is an officer in the boys' corps which is headed by Baron von Freische whose rank is now shedding a luster upon our house, for he comes often to visit with Heinrich and Elsa, whom he much admires. Myself, I am up to the ears in work. Elsa concerns herself little with politics except to adore our Gentle Leader. She gets tired too easily this last month. Perhaps the babies come too fast. It will be better for her when this one is born.

I regret our correspondence must close this way, Max. Perhaps we can someday meet again on a field of better understanding.

As ever your,
MARTIN SCHULSE

Herrn Martin Schulse
(kindness of J. Lederer)
Schloss Rantzenburg
Munich, Germany

MARTIN, MY OLD FRIEND:

I am sending this by the hand of Jimmy Lederer, who will shortly pass through Munich on a European vacation. I cannot rest after the letter you last sent me. It is so unlike you I can only attribute its contents to your fear of the censorship. The man I have loved as a brother, whose heart has ever been brimming with sympathy and friendship, cannot possibly partake of even a passive partnership in the butchery of innocent people. I trust and pray that it may be so, that you will write me no exposition, which might be dangerous for you,—only a simple "yes." That will tell me that you play the part of expediency but that your heart has not changed, and that I was not deluded in believing you to be always a man of fine and liberal spirit to whom wrongs are wrongs in whosoever's name they may be committed.

This censorship, this persecution of all men of liberal thought, the burning of libraries and corruption of the Universities would arouse your antagonism if there had been no finger laid on one of my race in Germany. You are a liberal, Martin. You have always taken the long view. I know that you cannot be swept away from sanity by a popular movement which has so much that is bad about it, no matter how strong it may be.

I can see why the Germans acclaim Hitler. They react against the very real wrongs which have been laid on them since the disaster of the war. But you, Martin, have been almost an American since the war. I know that it is not my friend who has written to me, that it will prove to have been only the voice of caution and expediency.

Eagerly I await the one word that will set my heart at peace. Write your "Yes" quickly.

My love to you all,

MAX

Deutsch-Völkische Bank und Handelsgesellschaft, München

AUGUST 18, 1933

Mr. Max Eisenstein
Schulse-Eisenstein Galleries
San Francisco, California, U. S. A.

DEAR MAX:

I have your letter. The word is "no." You are a sentimentalist. You do not know that all men are not cut to your pattern. You put nice little tags on them, like "liberal" and expect them to act so-and-so. But you are wrong. So, I am an American liberal? No! I am a German patriot.

A liberal is a man who does not believe in doing anything. He is a talker about the rights of man, but just a talker. He likes to make a big noise about freedom of speech, and what is freedom of speech? Just the chance to sit firmly on the backside and say that whatever is being done by the active men is wrong. What is so futile as the liberal? I know him well because I have been one. He condemns the passive government because it makes no change. But let a powerful man arise, let an active man start to make a change, then where is your liberal? He is against it. To the liberal any change is the wrong one.

He calls this the "long view," but it is merely a bad scare that he will have to do something himself. He loves words and high-sounding precepts but he is useless to the men who make the world what it is. These are the only important men, the doers. And here in Germany a doer has risen. A vital man is changing things. The whole tide of a people's life changes in a minute because the man of action has come. And I join him. I am not just swept along by a current. The useless life that was all talk and no accomplishment I drop. I put my back and shoulders behind the great new movement. I am a man because I act. Before that I am just a voice. I do not question the ends of our action. It is not necessary. I know it is good because it is so vital. Men are not drawn into bad things with so much joy and eagerness.

You say we persecute men of liberal thought, we destroy libraries. You should wake from your musty sentimentalizing. Does the surgeon spare the cancer because he must cut to remove it? We are cruel. Of course we are cruel. As all birth is brutal, so is this new birth of ours. But we rejoice. Germany lifts high her head among the nations of the world. She follows her glorious Leader to triumph. What can you know of this, you who only sit and dream? You have never known a Hitler. He is a drawn sword. He is a white light, but hot as the sun of a new day.

I must insist that you write no further. We are no longer in sympathy, as now we must both realize.

MARTIN SCHULSE

EISENSTEIN GALLERIES

SAN FRANCISCO, CALIFORNIA, U. S. A.

SEPTEMBER 5, 1933

Herrn Martin Schulse
c/o Deutsch-Voelkische Bank
und Handelsgesellschaft
Munich, Germany

DEAR MARTIN:

Enclosed are your draft and the month's accounts. It is of necessity that I send a brief message. Griselle has gone to Berlin. She is too daring. But she has waited so long for success she will not relinquish it, and laughs at my fears. She will be at the Koenig Theater. You are an official. For old friendship's sake, I beg of you watch over her. Go to Berlin if you can and see whether she is in danger.

It will distress you to observe that I have been obliged to remove your name from the firm's name. You know who our principal clients are, and they will touch nothing now from a firm with a German name.

Your new attitude I cannot discuss. But you must understand me. I did not expect you would take up arms for my people because they are my people, but because you were a man who loved justice.

I commend my rash Griselle to you. The child does not realize what a risk she is taking. I shall not write again.

Goodbye, my friend,

MAX

EISENSTEIN GALLERIES
SAN FRANCISCO, CALIFORNIA, U. S. A.
NOVEMBER 5, 1933

Herrn Martin Schulse
c/o Deutsch-Voelkische Bank
und Handelsgesellschaft
Munich, Germany

MARTIN:

I write again because I must. A black foreboding has taken possession of me. I wrote Griselle as soon as I knew she was in Berlin and she answered briefly. Rehearsals were going brilliantly; the play would open shortly. My second letter was more encouragement than warning, and it has been returned to me, the envelope unopened, marked only addressee unknown, (*Adressat Unbekannt*). What a darkness those words carry! How can she be unknown? It is surely a message that she has come to harm. They know what has happened to her, those stamped letters say, but I am not to know. She has gone into some sort of void and it will be useless to seek her. All this they tell me in two words, *Adressat Unbekannt*.

Martin, need I ask you to find her, to succor her? You have known her graciousness, her beauty and sweetness. You have had her love, which she has given to no other man. Do not attempt to write to me. I know I need not even ask you to aid. It is enough to tell you that something has gone wrong, that she must be in danger.

I leave her in your hands, for I am helpless.

MAX

EISENSTEIN GALLERIES

SAN FRANCISCO, CALIFORNIA, U. S. A.

NOVEMBER 23, 1933

Herrn Martin Schulse
c/o Deutsch-Voelkische Bank
und Handelsgesellschaft
Munich, Germany

MARTIN:

I turn to you in despair. I could not wait for another month to pass so I am sending some information as to your investments. You may wish to make some changes and I can thus enclose my appeal with a bank letter.

It is Griselle. For two months there has been only silence from her, and now the rumors begin to come in to me. From Jewish mouth to Jewish mouth the tales slowly come back from Germany, tales so full of dread I would close my ears if I dared, but I cannot. I must know what has happened to her. I must be sure.

She appeared in the Berlin play for a week. Then she was jeered from the audience as a Jewess. She is so headstrong, so foolhardy, the splendid child! She threw the word back in their teeth. She told them proudly that she was a Jewess.

Some of the audience started after her. She ran backstage. Someone must have helped her for she got away with the whole pack at her heels and took refuge with a Jewish family in a cellar for several days. After that she changed her appearance as much as she could and started south, hoping to walk back to Vienna. She did not dare to try the railroads. She told those she left that she would be safe if she could reach friends in Munich. That is my hope, that she has gone to you, for she has never reached Vienna. Send me word, Martin, and if she has not yet come there make a quiet investigation if you can. My mind cannot rest. I torture myself by day and by night, seeing the brave little thing trudging all those long miles through hostile country, with winter coming on. God grant you can send me a word of relief.

MAX

Deutſch-Völkiſche Bank und Handelsgeſellſchaft,
München

DECEMBER 8, 1933

Mr. Max Eisenstein
Eisenstein Galleries
San Francisco, California, U. S. A.

DEAR MAX:

Heil Hitler! I much regret that I have bad news for you. Your sister is dead. Unfortunately she was, as you have said, very much a fool. Not quite a week ago she came here, with a bunch of storm troopers almost right behind her. The house was very active—Elsa has not been well since little Adolph was born last month—the doctor was here, and two nurses, with all the servants and children scurrying around.

By luck I answered the door. At first I think it is an old woman and then I see the face, and then I see the storm troopers have turned in the park gates. Can I hide her? It is one chance in thousands. A servant will be on us at any minute. Can I endure to have my house ransacked with Elsa ill in bed and to risk being arrested for harboring a Jew and to lose all I have built up here? Of course as a German I have one plain duty. She has displayed her Jewish body on the stage before pure young German men. I should hold her and turn her over to the storm troopers. But this I cannot do.

"You will destroy us all, Griselle," I tell her. "You must run back further in the park." She looks at me and smiles (she was always a brave girl) and makes her own choice.

"I would not bring you harm, Martin," she says, and she runs down the steps and out toward the trees. But she must be tired. She does not run very fast and the storm troopers have caught sight of her. I am helpless, I go in the house and in a few minutes she stops screaming, and in the morning I have the body sent down to the village for burial. She was a fool to come to Germany. Poor little Griselle. I grieve with you, but as you see, I was helpless to aid her.

I must now demand you do not write again. Every word that comes to the house is now censored, and I cannot tell how soon they may start to open the mail to the bank. And I will no longer have any dealings with Jews, except for the receipt of money. It is not so good for me that a Jewess came here for refuge, and no further association can be tolerated.

A new Germany is being shaped here. We will soon show the world great things under our Glorious Leader.

MARTIN

CABLEGRAM

MUNICH, JANUARY 2, 1934.

MARTIN SCHULSE

YOUR TERMS ACCEPTED NOVEMBER TWELVE AUDIT
SHOWS THIRTEEN PERCENT INCREASE FEBRUARY SECOND
FOUR-FOLD ASSURED PAN EXHIBITION MAY FIRST PRE-
PARE LEAVE FOR MOSCOW IF MARKET OPENS UNEXPECT-
EDLY FINANCIAL INSTRUCTIONS MAILED NEW ADDRESS

EISENSTEIN

EISENSTEIN GALLERIES

SAN FRANCISCO, CALIFORNIA, U. S. A.

JANUARY 3, 1934

Herrn Martin Schulse
Schloss Rantzenburg
Munich, Germany

OUR DEAR MARTIN:

Don't forget grandma's birthday. She will be 64 on
the 8th. American contributors will furnish 1000
brushes for your German Young Painters' League.
Mandelberg has joined in supporting the league. You
must send 11 Picasso reproductions, 20 by 90 to branch
galleries on the 25th, no sooner. Reds and blues must
predominate. We can allow you $8,000 on this transac-
tion at present. Start new accounts book 2.

Our prayers follow you daily, dear brother,

EISENSTEIN

EISENSTEIN GALLERIES
SAN FRANCISCO, CALIFORNIA, U. S. A.
JANUARY 17, 1934

Herrn Martin Schulse
Schloss Rantzenburg
Munich, Germany

MARTIN, DEAR BROTHER:

Good news! Our stock reached 116 five days ago. The Fleishmans have advanced another $10,000. This will fill your Young Painters' League quota for a month but let us know if opportunities increase. Swiss miniatures are having a vogue. You must watch the market and plan to be in Zurich after May first if any unexpected opportunities develop. Uncle Solomon will be glad to see you and I know you will rely heavily on his judgment.

The weather is clear and there is little danger of storms during the next two months. You will prepare for your students the following reproductions: Van Gogh 15 by 103, red; Poussin 20 by 90, blue and yellow; Vermeer 11 by 33, red and blue.

Our hopes will follow your new efforts.

EISENSTEIN

EISENSTEIN GALLERIES
SAN FRANCISCO, CALIFORNIA, U. S. A.
JANUARY 29, 1934

DEAR MARTIN:

Your last letter was delivered by mistake at 457 Geary St., Room 4. Aunt Rheba says tell Martin he must write more briefly and clearly so his friends can understand all that he says. I am sure everyone will be in readiness for your family reunion on the 15th. You will be tired after these festivities and may want to take your family with you on your trip to Zurich.

Before leaving however, procure the following reproductions for branches of German Young Painters' League, looking forward to the joint exhibit in May or earlier: Picasso 17 by 81, red; Van Gogh 5 by 42, white; Rubens 15 by 204, blue and yellow.

Our prayers are with you.

EISENSTEIN

SCHLOSS RANTZENBURG
MUNICH, GERMANY
FEBRUARY 12, 1934

Mr. Max Eisenstein
Eisenstein Galleries
San Francisco, California, U. S. A.

MAX, MY OLD FRIEND:

My God, Max, do you know what you do? I shall have to try to smuggle this letter out with an American I have met here. I write in appeal from a despair you cannot imagine. This crazy cable! These letters you have sent. I am called in to account for them. The letters are not delivered, but they bring me in and show me letters from you and demand I give them the code. A code? And how can you, a friend of long years, do this to me?

Do you realize, have you any idea that you destroy me? Already the results of your madness are terrible. I am bluntly told I must resign my office. Heinrich is no longer in the boys' corps. They tell him it will not be good for his health. God in heaven, Max, do you see what that means? And Elsa, to whom I dare not tell anything, comes in bewildered that the officials refuse her invitations and Baron von Freische does not speak to her upon the street.

Yes, yes, I know why you do it—but do you not understand I could do nothing? What could I have done? I did not dare to try. I beg of you, not for myself, but for Elsa and the boys—think what it means to them if I am taken away and they do not know if I live or die. Do you know what it is to be taken to a concentration camp? Would you stand me against a wall and level the gun? I beg of you, stop. Stop now, while everything is not yet destroyed. I am in fear for my life, for my life, Max.

Is it you who does this? It cannot be you. I have loved you like a brother, my old Maxel. My God, have you no mercy? I beg you, Max, no more, no more! Stop while I can be saved. From a heart filled with old affection I ask it.

MARTIN

EISENSTEIN GALLERIES
SAN FRANCISCO, CALIFORNIA, U. S. A.
FEBRUARY 15, 1934

Herrn Martin Schulse
Schloss Rantzenburg
Munich, Germany

OUR DEAR MARTIN:

Seven inches of rainfall here in 18 days. What a season! A shipment of 1500 brushes should reach the Berlin branch for your painters by this week-end. This will allow time for practice before the big exhibition. American patrons will help with all the artists' supplies that can be provided, but you must make the final arrangements. We are too far out of touch with the European market and you are in a position to gauge the extent of support such a showing would arouse in Germany. Prepare these for distribution by March 24th: Rubens 12 by 77, blue; Giotti 1 by 317, green and white; Poussin 20 by 90, red and white.

Young Blum left last Friday with the Picasso specifications. He will leave oils in Hamburg and Leipzig and will then place himself at your disposal.

Success to you!

EISENSTEIN

EISENSTEIN GALLERIES
SAN FRANCISCO, CALIFORNIA, U. S. A.
MARCH 3, 1934

MARTIN OUR BROTHER:

Cousin Julius has two nine-pound boys. The family is happy. We regard the success of your coming artists' exhibition as assured. The last shipment of canvases was delayed due to difficulties of international exchange but will reach your Berlin associates in plenty of time. Consider reproduction collection complete. Your best support should come from Picasso enthusiasts but neglect no other lines.

We leave all final plans to your discretion but urge an early date for wholly successful exhibit.

The God of Moses be at your right hand.

EISENSTEIN

EISENSTEIN GALLERIES
SAN FRANCISCO, CALIFORNIA, U. S. A.

SAN FRANCISCO
5 PM
MAR 3
1934
CALIFORNIA

MÜNCHEN
18.3.34. 4-5
h

Adressat
unbekannt

Mr. Martin Schulse
Schloss Rantzenburg
Munich

GERMANY

American Verse

PAUL REVERE'S RIDE

BY HENRY WADSWORTH LONGFELLOW

Listen, my children, and you shall hear
Of the midnight ride of Paul Revere,
On the eighteenth of April, in Seventy-five;
Hardly a man is now alive
Who remembers that famous day and year.

He said to his friend, "If the British march
By land or sea from the town tonight,
Hang a lantern aloft in the belfry arch
Of the North Church tower as a signal light,—
One, if by land, and two, if by sea;
And I on the opposite shore will be,
Ready to ride and spread the alarm
Through every Middlesex village and farm,
For the country folk to be up and to arm."

Then he said, "Good night!" and with muffled oar
Silently rowed to the Charlestown shore,
Just as the moon rose over the bay,
Where swinging wide at her moorings lay
The *Somerset*, British man-of-war;
A phantom ship, with each mast and spar
Across the moon like a prison bar,
And a huge black hulk that was magnified
By its own reflection in the tide.

Meanwhile, his friend, through alley and street,
Wanders and watches with eager ears,

Till in the silence around him he hears
The muster of men at the barrack door,
The sound of arms, and the tramp of feet,
And the measured tread of the grenadiers,
Marching down to their boats on the shore.

Then he climbed the tower of the Old North Church,
By the wooden stairs, with stealthy tread,
To the belfry chamber overhead,
And startled the pigeons from their perch
On the somber rafters, that round him made
Masses and moving shapes of shade,—
By the trembling ladder, steep and tall,
To the highest window in the wall,
Where he paused to listen and look down
A moment on the roofs of the town,
And the moonlight flowing over all.

Beneath, in the churchyard, lay the dead,
In their night-encampment on the hill,
Wrapped in silence so deep and still
That he could hear, like a sentinel's tread,
The watchful night-wind, as it went
Creeping along from tent to tent,
And seeming to whisper, "All is well!"
A moment only he feels the spell
Of the place and the hour, and the secret dread
Of the lonely belfry and the dead;
For suddenly all his thoughts are bent
On a shadowy something far away,
Where the river widens to meet the bay,—
A line of black that bends and floats
On the rising tide, like a bridge of boats.

Meanwhile, impatient to mount and ride,

Booted and spurred, with a heavy stride
On the opposite shore walked Paul Revere.
Now he patted his horse's side,
Now gazed at the landscape far and near,
Then, impetuous, stamped the earth,
And turned and tightened his saddle-girth;
But mostly he watched with eager search
The belfry-tower of the Old North Church,
As it rose above the graves on the hill,
Lonely and spectral and somber and still.
And lo! as he looks, on the belfry's height
A glimmer, and then a gleam of light!
He springs to the saddle, the bridle he turns,
But lingers and gazes, till full on his sight
A second lamp in the belfry burns!

A hurry of hoofs in a village street,
A shape in the moonlight, a bulk in the dark,
And beneath, from the pebbles, in passing, a spark
Struck out by a steed flying fearless and fleet:
That was all! And yet, through the gloom and
      the light,
The fate of a nation was riding that night;
And the spark struck out by that steed, in his flight,
Kindled the land into flame with its heat.

He has left the village and mounted the steep,
And beneath him, tranquil and broad and deep,
Is the Mystic, meeting the ocean tides;
And under the alders, that skirt its edge,
Now soft on the sand, now loud on the ledge,
Is heard the tramp of his steed as he rides.

It was twelve by the village clock
When he crossed the bridge into Medford town.

He heard the crowing of the cock,
And the barking of the farmer's dog,
And felt the damp of the river fog,
That rises after the sun goes down.

It was one by the village clock
When he galloped into Lexington.
He saw the gilded weathercock
Swim in the moonlight as he passed,
And the meetinghouse window, blank and bare,
Gaze at him with a spectral glare,
As if they already stood aghast
At the bloody work they would look upon.

It was two by the village clock
When he came to the bridge in Concord town.
He heard the bleating of the flock,
And the twitter of birds among the trees,
And felt the breath of the morning breeze
Blowing over the meadows brown.
And one was safe and asleep in his bed
Who at the bridge would be first to fall,
Who that day would be lying dead,
Pierced by a British musket-ball.

You know the rest. In the books you have read,
How the British Regulars fired and fled,—
How the farmers gave them ball for ball,
From behind each fence and farmyard wall,
Chasing the red-coats down the lane,
Then crossing the fields to emerge again
Under the trees at the turn of the road,
And only pausing to fire and load.

So through the night rode Paul Revere;
And so through the night went his cry of alarm

To every Middlesex village and farm,—
A cry of defiance and not of fear,
A voice in the darkness, a knock at the door,
And a word that shall echo forevermore!
For, borne on the night-wind of the Past,
Through all our history, to the last,
In the hour of darkness and peril and need,
The people will waken and listen to hear
The hurrying hoof-beats of that steed,
And the midnight message of Paul Revere.

THE CONCORD HYMN

BY RALPH WALDO EMERSON

By the rude bridge that arched the flood,
Their flag to April's breeze unfurled,
Here once the embattled farmers stood,
And fired the shot heard round the world.

The foe long since in silence slept;
Alike the conqueror silent sleeps;
And Time the ruined bridge has swept
Down the dark stream which seaward creeps.

On this green bank, by this soft stream,
We set today a votive stone;
That memory may their deed redeem,
When, like our sires, our sons are gone.

Spirit, that made those spirits dare
To die, and leave their children free,
Bid Time and Nature gently spare
The shaft we raise to them and thee.

DEATH AND GENERAL PUTNAM

BY ARTHUR GUITERMAN

His iron arm had spent its force,
No longer might he rein a horse;
Lone, beside the dying blaze
Dreaming dreams of younger days
    Sat old Israel Putnam.

Twice he heard, then three times more
A knock upon the oaken door,
A knock he could not fail to know,
That old man in the ember-glow.
    "Come," said General Putnam.

The door swung wide; in cloak and hood
Lean and tall the pilgrim stood
And spoke in tones none else might hear,
"Once more I come to bring you Fear!"
    "Fear?" said General Putnam.

"You know not Fear? And yet this face
Your eyes have seen in many a place
Since first in stony Pomfret, when
You dragged the mad wolf from her den."
    "Yes," said General Putnam.

"Was I not close, when, stripped and bound
With blazing fagots heaped around
You heard the Huron war cry shrill?

Was I not close at Bunker Hill?"
        "Close," said General Putnam.

"Am I not that which strong men dread
On stricken field or fevered bed
On gloomy trail and stormy sea,
And dare you name my name to me?"
        "Death," said General Putnam.

"We have been comrades, you and I,
In chase and war beneath this sky;
And now, whatever Fate may send,
Old comrade, can you call me friend?"
        "Friend!" said General Putnam.

Then up he rose, and forth they went
Away from battleground, fortress, tent,
Mountain, wilderness, field and farm,
Death and the General, arm-in-arm,
        Death and General Putnam.

HOME, SWEET HOME

BY JOHN HOWARD PAYNE

*This not unfamiliar lyric was the song hit of an otherwise for-
gotten show called "Clari; or, The Maid of Milan," the work of
an author who, at the age of fifty, retreated to a snug berth in the
consular service. His appointment by President Tyler to the post
where he lived and died, acquires, just a hundred years later, a certain topical interest for it was in May 1843 that he took office
as the American Consul at Tunis.*

Mid pleasures and palaces though we may roam,
Be it ever so humble, there's no place like home;
A charm from the sky seems to hallow us there,
Which, seek through the world, is ne'er met with else-
    where.
Home, home, sweet, sweet home!
There's no place like home, oh, there's no place like
    home!

An exile from home, splendor dazzles in vain;
Oh, give me my lowly thatched cottage again!
The birds singing gayly, that came at my call—
Give me them—and the peace of mind, dearer than all!
Home, home, sweet, sweet home!
There's no place like home, oh, there's no place like
    home!

I gaze on the moon as I tread the drear wild,
And feel that my mother now thinks of her child,
As she looks on that moon from our own cottage door

Thro' the woodbine, whose fragrance shall cheer me no
    more.
Home, home, sweet, sweet home!
There's no place like home, oh, there's no place like
    home!

How sweet 'tis to sit 'neath a fond father's smile,
And the caress of a mother to soothe and beguile!
Let others delight mid new pleasures to roam,
But give me, oh, give me, the pleasures of home,
Home, home, sweet, sweet home!
There's no place like home, oh, there's no place like
    home!

To thee I'll return, overburdened with care;
The heart's dearest solace will smile on there;
No more from that cottage again will I roam;
Be it ever so humble, there's no place like home.
Home, home, sweet, sweet home!
There's no place like home, oh, there's no place like
    home!

TO HELEN

BY EDGAR ALLAN POE

Helen, thy beauty is to me
　Like those Nicèan barks of yore
That gently, o'er a perfumed sea,
　The weary way-worn wanderer bore
　To his own native shore.

On desperate seas long wont to roam,
　Thy hyacinth hair, thy classic face,
Thy Naiad airs have brought me home
　To the glory that was Greece,
And the grandeur that was Rome.

Lo, in yon brilliant window-niche
　How statue-like I see thee stand,
　The agate lamp within thy hand,
Ah! Psyche, from the regions which
　Are holy land!

ANNABEL LEE

BY EDGAR ALLAN POE

It was many and many a year ago,
  In a kingdom by the sea,
That a maiden there lived, whom you may know
  By the name of Annabel Lee;
And this maiden she lived with no other thought
  Than to love, and be loved by me.

I was a child and she was a child,
  In this kingdom by the sea;
But we loved with a love that was more than love,
  I and my Annabel Lee,—
With a love that the wingèd seraphs of heaven
  Coveted her and me.

And this was the reason that long ago,
  In this kingdom by the sea,
A wind blew out of a cloud, chilling
  My beautiful Annabel Lee;
So that her high-born kinsmen came,
  And bore her away from me,
To shut her up in a sepulcher,
  In this kingdom by the sea.

The angels, not so happy in heaven,
  Went envying her and me.
Yes! that was the reason (as all men know)
  In this kingdom by the sea,
That the wind came out of the cloud by night,
  Chilling and killing my Annabel Lee.

But our love it was stronger by far than the love
  Of those who were older than we—
  Of many far wiser than we—
And neither the angels in Heaven above,
  Nor the demons down under the sea,
Can ever dissever my soul from the soul
  Of the beautiful Annabel Lee:—

For the moon never beams without bringing me
      dreams
  Of the beautiful Annabel Lee;
And the stars never rise but I feel the bright eyes
  Of the beautiful Annabel Lee;
And so, all the night-tide, I lie down by the side
Of my darling,—my darling,—my life and my
      bride,
  In the sepulcher there by the sea—
  In her tomb by the sounding sea.

BATTLE HYMN
OF THE REPUBLIC

BY JULIA WARD HOWE

Mine eyes have seen the glory of the coming of the
    Lord:
He is trampling out the vintage where the grapes of
    wrath are stored;
He hath loosed the fateful lightning of his terrible
    swift sword.
        His truth is marching on.

I have seen him in the watch-fires of a hundred circling
    camps;
They have builded him an altar in the evening dews
    and damps;
I can read his righteous sentence by the dim and flar-
    ing lamps.
        His day is marching on.

I have read a fiery gospel, writ in burnished rows of
    steel:
"As ye deal with my contemners, so with you my
    grace shall deal;
Let the Hero, born of woman, crush the serpent with
    his heel,
        Since God is marching on."

He has sounded forth the trumpet that shall never call
    retreat;

He is sifting out the hearts of men before his judgment-
seat:
O, be swift, my soul, to answer him! be jubilant my feet!
Our God is marching on.

In the beauty of the lilies Christ was born across the sea,
With a glory in his bosom that transfigures you and me;
As he died to make men holy, let us die to make men
free,
While God is marching on.

NANCY HANKS

BY ROSEMARY BENÉT

If Nancy Hanks
Came back as a ghost,
Seeking news
Of what she loved most,
She'd ask first,
"Where's my son?
What's happened to Abe?
What's he done?

"Poor little Abe,
Left all alone
Except for Tom,
Who's a rolling stone;
He was only nine
The year I died.
I remember still
How hard he cried.

"Scraping along
In a little shack
With hardly a shirt
To cover his back,
And a prairie wind
To blow him down,
Or pinching times
If he went to town.

"You wouldn't know
About my son?

Did he grow tall?
Did he have fun?
Did he learn to read?
Did he get to town?
Do you know his name?
Did he get on?"

ETHIOPIA
SALUTING THE COLORS

BY WALT WHITMAN

Who are you dusky woman, so ancient hardly human,
With your woolly-white and turban'd head, and bare
bony feet?
Why rising by the roadside here, do you the colors
greet?

('Tis while our army lines Carolina's sands and pines,
Forth from thy hovel door thou Ethiopia com'st to me,
As under doughty Sherman I march toward the sea.)

*Me master years a hundred since from my parents
sunder'd,*
*A little child, they caught me as the savage beast is
caught,*
Then hither me across the sea the cruel slaver brought.

No further does she say, but lingering all the day,
Her high-borne turban'd head she wags, and rolls her
darkling eye,
And courtesies to the regiments, the guidons moving by.

What is it fateful woman, so blear, hardly human?
Why wag your head with turban bound, yellow, red
and green?
Are the things so strange and marvelous you see or
have seen?

AS TOILSOME I WANDERED VIRGINIA'S WOODS

BY WALT WHITMAN

As toilsome I wander'd Virginia's woods,
To the music of rustling leaves kick'd by my feet, (for
    'twas autumn,)
I mark'd at the foot of a tree the grave of a soldier;
Mortally wounded he and buried on the retreat, (easily
    all could I understand,)
The halt of a mid-day hour, when up! no time to lose—
    yet this sign left,
On a tablet scrawl'd and nail'd on the tree by the grave,
Bold, cautious, true, and my loving comrade.

Long, long I muse, then on my way go wandering,
Many a changeful season to follow, and many a scene
    of life,
Yet at times through changeful season and scene,
    abrupt, alone, or in the crowded street,
Comes before me the unknown soldier's grave, comes
    the inscription rude in Virginia's woods,
Bold, cautious, true, and my loving comrade.

LITTLE BOY BLUE

BY EUGENE FIELD

The little toy dog is covered with dust,
  But sturdy and stanch it stands;
And the little toy soldier is red with rust,
  And his musket molds in his hands.
Time was when the little toy dog was new
  And the soldier was passing fair,
And that was the time when our Little Boy Blue
  Kissed them and put them there.

"Now, don't you go till I come," he said,
  "And don't you make any noise!"
So toddling off to his trundle-bed
  He dreamed of the pretty toys.
And as he was dreaming, an angel song
  Awakened our Little Boy Blue—
Oh, the years are many, the years are long,
  But the little toy friends are true.

Ay, faithful to Little Boy Blue they stand,
  Each in the same old place,
Awaiting the touch of a little hand,
  And the smile of a little face.
And they wonder, as waiting these long years through,
  In the dust of that little chair,
What has become of our Little Boy Blue
  Since he kissed them and put them there.

THE LAST LEAF

BY OLIVER WENDELL HOLMES

I saw him once before,
As he passed by the door,
   And again
The pavement stones resound
As he totters o'er the ground
   With his cane.

They say that in his prime,
Ere the pruning-knife of Time
   Cut him down,
Not a better man was found
By the crier on his round
   Through the town.

But now he walks the streets,
And he looks at all he meets
   Sad and wan,
And he shakes his feeble head,
That it seems as if he said,
   "They are gone."

The mossy marbles rest
On the lips that he has pressed
   In their bloom,
And the names he loved to hear
Have been carved for many a year
   On the tomb.

My grandmamma has said—
Poor old lady, she is dead
    Long ago—
That he had a Roman nose,
And his cheek was like a rose
    In the snow.

But now his nose is thin,
And it rests upon his chin
    Like a staff,
And a crook is in his back,
And a melancholy crack
    In his laugh.

I know it is a sin
For me to sit and grin
    At him here;
But the old three-cornered hat,
And the breeches, and all that,
    Are so queer!

And if I should live to be
The last leaf upon the tree
    In the spring,
Let them smile, as I do now,
At the old forsaken bough
    Where I cling.

A VISIT
FROM ST. NICHOLAS

BY CLEMENT C. MOORE

'Twas the night before Christmas, when all through
    the house
Not a creature was stirring, not even a mouse;
The stockings were hung by the chimney with care,
In hopes that St. Nicholas soon would be there;
The children were nestled all snug in their beds,
While visions of sugar-plums danced in their heads;
And mamma in her kerchief, and I in my cap,
Had just settled our brains for a long winter's nap,—
When out on the lawn there arose such a clatter,
I sprang from my bed to see what was the matter.
Away to the window I flew like a flash,
Tore open the shutters and threw up the sash.
The moon on the breast of the new-fallen snow
Gave a lustre of midday to objects below;
When, what to my wondering eyes should appear,
But a miniature sleigh and eight tiny reindeer,
With a little old driver, so lively and quick
I knew in a moment it must be St. Nick.
More rapid than eagles his coursers they came,
And he whistled and shouted, and called them by name:
"Now, Dasher! now, Dancer! now, Prancer and Vixen!
On, Comet! on, Cupid! on, Donder and Blitzen!
To the top of the porch, to the top of the wall!
Now dash away, dash away, dash away all!"
As dry leaves that before the wild hurricane fly,
When they meet with an obstacle, mount to the sky,

So, up to the house-top the coursers they flew,
With a sleigh full of toys,—and St. Nicholas too.
And then in a twinkling I heard on the roof
The prancing and pawing of each little hoof,
As I drew in my head and was turning around,
Down the chimney St. Nicholas came with a bound.
He was dressed all in fur from his head to his foot,
And his clothes were all tarnished with ashes and soot;
A bundle of toys he had flung on his back,
And he looked like a pedler just opening his pack.
His eyes how they twinkled! his dimples how merry!
His cheeks were like roses, his nose like a cherry;
His droll little mouth was drawn up like a bow,
And the beard on his chin was as white as the snow.
The stump of a pipe he held tight in his teeth,
And the smoke it encircled his head like a wreath.
He had a broad face, and a little round belly
That shook, when he laughed, like a bowl full of jelly.
He was chubby and plump,—a right jolly old elf—
And I laughed when I saw him, in spite of myself.
A wink of his eye and a twist of his head
Soon gave me to know I had nothing to dread.
He spoke not a word, but went straight to his work,
And filled all the stockings; then turned with a jerk,
And laying his finger aside of his nose,
And giving a nod, up the chimney he rose.
He sprang to his sleigh, to his team gave a whistle,
And away they all flew like the down of a thistle;
But I heard him exclaim, ere he drove out of sight:
"Happy Christmas to all, and to all a goodnight!"

AMERICAN LAUGHTER

BY KENNETH ALLAN ROBINSON

Oh, the men who laughed the American laughter
Whittled their jokes from the tough bull-pines;
They were tall mén, sharpened before and after;
They studied the sky for the weather-signs;
They tilted their hats and they smoked long-nines!

Their laughter was ladled in Western flagons
And poured down throats that were parched for more;
This was the laughter of democrat wagons
And homely men at the crossroads store
—It tickled the shawl that a lawyer wore!

It hurt the ears of the dainty and pretty
But they laughed the louder and laughed their fill,
A laughter made for Virginia City,
Springfield, and Natchez-under-the-Hill,
And the river that flows past Hannibal still!

American laughter was lucky laughter,
A coonskin tune by a homespun bard;
It tasted of hams from the smokehouse rafter
And locust trees in the courthouse yard,
And Petroleum Nasby and Artemus Ward!

They laughed at the Mormons and Mike Fink's daugh-
ter,
And the corncob tale of Sut Lovingood's dog,
Till the ague fled from the fever-water

And the damps deserted the tree-stump bog,
—They laughed at the tale of the jumping frog!

They laughed at the British, they laughed at Shakers,
At Horace Greeley, and stovepipe hats;
They split their fences and ploughed their acres,
And treed their troubles like mountain-cats;
—They laughed calamity out of the flats!

Now the Boston man, according to rumor,
Said, as he turned in his high-backed bed,
"This doesn't conform to my rules for humor,"
And he settled his nightcap over his head,
—But it shook the earth like the buffalo-tread!

And the corn grew tall and the fields grew wider,
And the land grew sleek with the mirth they sowed;
They laughed the fat meat into the spider,
They laughed the blues from the Wilderness Road,
—They crossed hard times to the Comstock Lode!

PLAIN LANGUAGE
FROM TRUTHFUL JAMES

BY BRET HARTE

Which I wish to remark,
And my language is plain,
That for ways that are dark
And for tricks that are vain,
The heathen Chinee is peculiar,
Which the same I would rise to explain.

Ah Sin was his name;
And I shall not deny,
In regard to the same,
What that name might imply;
But his smile it was pensive and childlike,
As I frequent remarked to Bill Nye.

It was August the third,
And quite soft was the skies;
Which it might be inferred
That Ah Sin was likewise;
Yet he played it that day upon William
And me in a way I despise.

Which we had a small game,
And Ah Sin took a hand:
It was Euchre. The same
He did not understand;
But he smiled as he sat by the table,
With the smile that was childlike and bland.

Yet the cards they were stocked
In a way that I grieve,
And my feelings were shocked
At the state of Nye's sleeve,
Which was stuffed full of aces and bowers,
And the same with intent to deceive.

But the hands that were played
By that heathen Chinee,
And the points that he made,
Were quite frightful to see—
Till at last he put down a right bower
Which the same Nye had dealt unto me. .

Then I looked up at Nye,
And he gazed upon me;
And he rose with a sigh,
And said, "Can this be?
We are ruined by Chinese cheap labor"—
And he went for that heathen Chinee.

In the scene that ensued
I did not take a hand,
But the floor it was strewed
Like the leaves on the strand
With the cards that Ah Sin had been hiding,
In the game "he did not understand."

In his sleeves, which were long,
He had twenty-four packs—
Which was coming it strong,
Yet I state but the facts;
And we found on his nails, which were taper,
What is frequent in tapers—that's wax.

Which is why I remark,
And my language is plain,
That for ways that are dark,
And for tricks that are vain,
The heathen Chinee is peculiar—
Which the same I am free to maintain.

LITTLE WILLIE

BY EUGENE FIELD

When Willie was a little boy,
Not more than five or six,
Right constantly did he annoy
His mother with his tricks,
Not yet a picayune cared I
For what he did or said,
Unless, as happened frequently,
The rascal wet the bed.

Closely he cuddled up to me,
And put his hands in mine,
'Til all at once I seemed to be
Afloat in seas of brine.
Sabean odors clogged the air,
And filled my soul with dread,
Yet I could only grin and bear
When Willie wet the bed.

'Tis many times that rascal has
Soaked all the bedclothes through,
Whereat I'd feebly light the gas
And wonder what to do.
Yet there he'd lie, so peaceful like;
God bless his curly head;
I quite forgave the little tyke
For wetting of the bed.

Ah me, those happy days have flown;
My boy's a father too,

And little Willies of his own
Do what he used to do.
And I! Ah, all that's left of me
Is dreams of pleasure fled;
Our boys ain't what they used to be
When Willie wet the bed.

Had I my choice, no shapely dame
Should share my couch with me,
No amorous jade of tarnished fame,
No wench of high degree;
But I should choose and choose again
The little curly head
Who cuddled close beside me when
He used to wet the bed.

THE MYSTERY OF GILGAL

BY JOHN HAY

The darkest, strangest mystery
I ever read, or heern, or see,
Is 'long of a drink at Taggart's Hall,—
   Tom Taggart's of Gilgal.

I've heern the tale a thousand ways,
But never could git through the maze
That hangs around that queer day's doin's;
   But I'll tell the yarn to youans.

Tom Taggart stood behind his bar,
The time was fall, the skies was far,
The neighbors round the counter drawed,
   And ca'mly drinked and jawed.

At last come Colonel Blood of Pike,
And old Jedge Phinn, permiscus-like,
And each, as he meandered in,
   Remarked, "A whisky-skin."

Tom mixed the beverage full and far,
And slammed it, smoking, on the bar.
Some says three fingers, some says two,—
   I'll leave the choice to you.

Phinn to the drink put forth his hand;
Blood drawed his knife, with accent bland,
"I ax yer parding, Mister Phinn—
   Jest drap that whisky-skin."

No man high-toneder could be found
Than old Jedge Phinn the country round.
Says he, "Young man, the tribe of Phinns
    Knows their own whisky-skins!"

He went for his 'leven-inch bowie-knife:—
"I tries to foller a Christian life;
But I'll drap a slice of liver or two,
    My bloomin' shrub, with you."

They carved in a way that all admired,
Tell Blood drawed iron at last, and fired.
It took Seth Bludso 'twixt the eyes,
    Which caused him great surprise.

Then coats went off, and all went in;
Shots and bad language swelled the din;
The short, sharp bark of Derringers,
    Like bull-pups, cheered the furse.

They piled the stiffs outside the door;
They made, I reckon, a cord or more.
Girls went that winter, as a rule,
    Alone to spellin'-school.

I've sarched in vain, from Dan to Beer-
Sheba, to make this mystery clear;
But I end with *hit* as I did begin,—
    "WHO GOT THE WHISKY-SKIN?"

I HEAR AMERICA SINGING

BY WALT WHITMAN

I hear America singing, the varied carols I hear,
Those of mechanics, each one singing his as it should
    be blithe and strong,
The carpenter singing his as he measures his plank
    or beam,
The mason singing his as he makes ready for work,
    or leaves off work,
The boatman singing what belongs to him in his boat,
    the deckhand singing on the steamboat deck,
The shoemaker singing as he sits on his bench, the
    hatter singing as he stands,
The wood-cutter's song, the ploughboy's on his way in
    the morning, or at noon intermission or at sundown,
The delicious singing of the mother, or of the young
    wife at work, or of the girl sewing or washing,
Each singing what belongs to him or her and to none
    else,
The day what belongs to the day—at night the party
    of young fellows, robust, friendly,
Singing with open mouths their strong melodious songs.

THE OLD MAN AND JIM

BY JAMES WHITCOMB RILEY

Old man never had much to say—
  'Ceptin' to Jim,—
And Jim was the wildest boy he had—
  And the old man jes' wrapped up in him!
Never heerd him speak but once
Er twice in my life,—and first time was
When the army broke out, and Jim he went,
The old man backin' him, fer three months:
And all 'at I heerd the old man say
Was, jes' as we turned to start away,—
    "Well, good-by, Jim:
        Take keer of yourse'f!"

'Peared-like, he was more satisfied
  Jes' *lookin'* at Jim
And likin' him all to hisse'f-like, see?—
  'Cause he was jes' wrapped up in him!
And over and over I mind the day
The old man come and stood round in the way
While we was drillin', a-watchin' Jim—
And down at the deepot a-heerin' him say,
    "Well, good-by, Jim:
        Take keer of yourse'f!"

Never was nothin' about the *farm*
  Disting'ished Jim;
Neighbors all ust to wonder why
  The old man 'peared wrapped up in him:

421

But when Cap. Biggler he writ back
'At Jim was the bravest boy we had
In the whole dern rigiment, white er black,
And his fightin' good as his farmin' bad—
'At he had led, with a bullet clean
Bored through his thigh, and carried the flag
Through the bloodiest battle you ever seen.—
The old man wound up a letter to him
'At Cap. read to us, 'at said: "Tell Jim Good-by,
    And take keer of hisse'f!"

Jim come home jes' long enough
    To take the whim
'At he'd like to go back in the calvery—
    And the old man jes' wrapped up in him!
Jim 'lowed 'at he'd had sich luck afore,
Guessed he'd tackle her three years more.
And the old man give him a colt he'd raised,
And follered him over to Camp Ben Wade,
And laid around fer a week er so,
Watchin' Jim on dress-parade—
Tel finally he rid away,
And last he heerd was the old man say,—
    "Well, good-by, Jim:
        Take keer of yourse'f!"

Tuk the papers, the old man did,
    A-watchin' fer Jim—
Fully believin' he'd make his mark
    Some way—jes' wrapped up in him!—
And many a time the word 'u'd come
'At stirred him up like the tap of a drum—
At Petersburg, fer instance, where
Jim rid right into their cannons there,
And tuk 'em, and p'inted 'em t'other way,

And socked it home to the boys in gray,
As they scooted fer timber, and on and on—
Jim a lieutenant and one arm gone,
And the old man's words in his mind all day,—
  "Well, good-by, Jim:
     Take keer of yourse'f!"

Think of a private, now, perhaps,
  We'll say like Jim,
'At's clumb clean up to the shoulder-straps—
  And the old man jes' wrapped up in him!
Think of him—with the war plum' through,
And the glorious old Red-White-and-Blue
A-laughin' the news down over Jim,
And the old man, bendin' over him—
The surgeon turnin' away with tears
'At hadn't leaked fer years and years,
As the hand of the dyin' boy clung to
His father's, the old voice in his ears,—
  "Well, good-by, Jim:
     Take keer of yourse'f!"

JOHN L. SULLIVAN,
THE STRONG BOY OF BOSTON

BY VACHEL LINDSAY

When I was nine years old, in 1889
I sent my love a lacy Valentine.
Suffering boys were dressed like Fauntleroys,
While Judge and Puck in giant humor vied.
The Gibson Girl came shining like a bride
To spoil the cult of Tennyson's Elaine.
Louisa Alcott was my gentle guide. . . .
Then . . .
I heard a battle trumpet sound.
Nigh New Orleans
Upon an emerald plain
John L. Sullivan
The strong boy
Of Boston
Fought seventy-five red rounds with Jake Kilrain.

In simple sheltered 1889
Nick Carter I would piously deride.
Over the Elsie Books I moped and sighed.
St. Nicholas Magazine was all my pride,
While coarser boys on cellar doors would slide.
The grown ups bought refinement by the pound.
Rogers groups had not been told to hide.
E. P. Roe had just begun to wane.
Howells was rising, surely to attain!
The nation for a jamboree was gowned:—
Her hundredth year of roaring freedom crowned.

The British Lion ran and hid from Blaine.
The razzle-dazzle hip-hurrah from Maine.
The mocking bird was singing in the lane. . . .
Yet . . .
"East side, west side, all around the town
The tots sang: 'Ring a rosie—'
'London Bridge a falling down.' "
And . . .
John L. Sullivan
The strong boy
Of Boston
Broke every single rib of Jake Kilrain.

In dear provincial 1889,
Barnum's bears and tigers could astound.
Ingersoll was called a most vile hound,
And named with Satan, Judas, Thomas Paine!
Robert Elsmere riled the pious brain.
Phillips Brooks for heresy was fried.
Boston Brahmins patronized Mark Twain.
The base ball rules were changed. That was a gain.
Pop Anson was our darling, pet and pride.
Native sons in Irish votes were drowned.
Tammany once more escaped its chain.
Once more each raw saloon was raising Cain.
The mocking bird was singing in the lane. . . .
Yet . . .
"East side, west side, all around the town
The tots sang: 'Ring a rosie'
'London Bridge is falling down.' "
And . . .
John L. Sullivan
The strong boy
Of Boston
Finished the ring career of Jake Kilrain.

In mystic, ancient 1889,
Wilson with pure learning was allied.
Roosevelt gave forth a chirping sound.
Stanley found old Emin and his train.
Stout explorers sought the pole in vain.
To dream of flying proved a man insane.
The newly rich were bathing in champagne.
Van Bibber Davis, at a single bound
Displayed himself, and simpering glory found.
John J. Ingalls, like a lonely crane
Swore and swore, and stalked the Kansas plain.
The Cronin murder was the ages' stain.
Johnstown was flooded, and the whole world cried.
We heard not of Louvain nor of Lorraine,
Or a million heroes for their freedom slain.
Of Armageddon and the world's birth-pain—
The League of Nations, and the world one posy.
We *thought* the world would loaf and sprawl and mosey.
The gods of Yap and Swat were sweetly dozy.
We *thought* the far off gods of Chow had died.
The mocking bird was singing in the lane. . . .
Yet . . .
"East side, west side, all around the town
The tots sang: 'Ring a rosie'
'London Bridge is falling down.'"
And . . .
John L. Sullivan knocked out Jake Kilrain.

AFTERNOON ON A HILL

BY EDNA ST. VINCENT MILLAY

In the spring of 1918, this poem was published in The Stars and Stripes *over the signature of a Private 1 Cl. then attached, though not deeply, to a medical unit at Vincennes on the outskirts of Paris. He had successfully submitted it as his own work to an editorial council which was made up of semi-illiterate enlisted men who, even so, ought to have known better.*

I will be the gladdest thing
   Under the sun!
I will touch a hundred flowers
   And not pick one.

I will look at cliffs and clouds
   With quiet eyes,
Watch the wind bow down the grass,
   And the grass rise.

And when lights begin to show
   Up from the town,
I will mark which must be mine,
   And then start down!

MINIVER CHEEVY

BY EDWIN ARLINGTON
ROBINSON

Miniver Cheevy, child of scorn,
  Grew lean while he assailed the seasons;
He wept that he was ever born,
  And he had reasons.

Miniver loved the days of old
  When swords were bright and steeds were prancing;
The vision of a warrior bold
  Would set him dancing.

Miniver sighed for what was not,
  And dreamed, and rested from his labors;
He dreamed of Thebes and Camelot,
  And Priam's neighbors.

Miniver mourned the ripe renown
  That made so many a name so fragrant;
He mourned Romance, now on the town,
  And Art, a vagrant.

Miniver loved the Medici,
  Albeit he had never seen one;
He would have sinned incessantly
  Could he have been one.

Miniver cursed the commonplace
  And eyed a khaki suit with loathing;

He missed the mediaeval grace
  Of iron clothing.

Miniver scorned the gold he sought,
  But sore annoyed was he without it;
Miniver thought, and thought, and thought,
  And thought about it.

Miniver Cheevy, born too late,
  Scratched his head and kept on thinking;
Miniver coughed, and called it fate,
  And kept on drinking.

I HAVE A RENDEZVOUS
WITH DEATH

BY ALAN SEEGER

I have a rendezvous with Death
At some disputed barricade,
When Spring comes back with rustling shade
And apple-blossoms fill the air—
I have a rendezvous with Death
When Spring brings back blue days and fair.

It may be he shall take my hand
And lead me into his dark land
And close my eyes and quench my breath—
It may be I shall pass him still.
I have a rendezvous with Death
On some scarred slope of battered hill,
When Spring comes round again this year
And the first meadow-flowers appear.

God knows 'twere better to be deep
Pillowed in silk and scented down,
Where love throbs out in blissful sleep,
Pulse nigh to pulse, and breath to breath,
Where hushed awakenings are dear . . .
But I've a rendezvous with Death
At midnight in some flaming town,
When Spring trips north again this year,
And I to my pledged word am true,
I shall not fail that rendezvous.

my sweet old etcetera

by e. e. cummings

my sweet old etcetera
aunt lucy during the recent

war could and what
is more did tell you just
what everybody was fighting

for,
my sister

isabel created hundreds
(and
hundreds) of socks not to
mention shirts fleaproof earwarmers

etcetera wristers etcetera, my
mother hoped that

i would die etcetera
bravely of course my father used
to become hoarse talking about how it was
a privilege and if only he
could meanwhile my

self etcetera lay quietly
in the deep mud et
cetera

(dreaming
et cetera, of
your smile
eyes knees and of your etcetera)

TWO-VOLUME NOVEL

BY DOROTHY PARKER

The sun's gone dim, and
   The moon's turned black;
For I loved him, and
   He didn't love back.

ABRAHAM LINCOLN WALKS AT MIDNIGHT

BY VACHEL LINDSAY

It is portentous, and a thing of state
  That here at midnight, in our little town
A mourning figure walks, and will not rest
  Near the old court-house pacing up and down.

Or by his homestead, or the shadowed yards
  He lingers where his children used to play,
Or through the market, on the well-worn stones
  He stalks until the dawn-stars burn away.

A bronzed, lank man! His suit of ancient black,
  A famous high-top-hat and plain worn shawl
Make him the quaint great figure that men love,
  The prairie-lawyer, master of us all.

He cannot sleep upon his hillside now.
  He is among us, as in times before!
And we who toss and lie awake for long
  Breathe deep, and start, to see him pass the door.

His head is bowed. He thinks on men and kings.
  Yea, when the sick world cries, how can he sleep?
Too many peasants fight, they know not why,
  Too many homesteads in black terror weep.

The sins of all the war-lords burn his heart.
  He sees the dreadnaughts scouring every main.

He carries on his shawl-wrapt shoulders now
  The bitterness, the folly and the pain.

He cannot rest until a spirit-dawn
  Shall come;—the shining hope of Europe free;
The league of sober folk, the Workers' Earth
  Bringing long peace to Cornland, Alp and Sea.

It breaks his heart that kings must murder still,
  That all his hours of travail here for men
Seem yet in vain. And who will bring white peace
  That he may sleep upon his hill again?

THE MAID-SERVANT
AT THE INN

BY DOROTHY PARKER

"It's queer," she said; "I see the light
  As plain as I beheld it then,
All silver-like and calm and bright—
  We've not had stars like that again!

"And she was such a gentle thing
  To birth a baby in the cold.
The barn was dark and frightening—
  This new one's better than the old.

"I mind my eyes were full of tears,
  For I was young, and quick distressed,
But she was less than me in years
  That held a son against her breast.

"I never saw a sweeter child—
  The little one, the darling one!—
I mind I told her, when she smiled
  You'd know he was his mother's son.

"It's queer that I should see them so—
  The time they came to Bethlehem
Was more than thirty years ago;
  I've prayed that all is well with them."

THE DEATH
OF THE HIRED MAN

BY ROBERT FROST

Mary sat musing on the lamp-flame at the table
Waiting for Warren. When she heard his step,
She ran on tip-toe down the darkened passage
To meet him in the doorway with the news
And put him on his guard. "Silas is back."
She pushed him outward with her through the door
And shut it after her. "Be kind," she said.
She took the market things from Warren's arms
And set them on the porch, then drew him down
To sit beside her on the wooden steps.

"When was I ever anything but kind to him?
But I'll not have the fellow back," he said.
"I told him so last haying, didn't I?
'If he left then,' I said, 'that ended it.'
What good is he? Who else will harbor him
At his age for the little he can do?
What help he is there's no depending on.
Off he goes always when I need him most.
'He thinks he ought to earn a little pay,
Enough at least to buy tobacco with,
So he won't have to beg and be beholden.'
'All right,' I say, 'I can't afford to pay
Any fixed wages, though I wish I could.'
'Someone else can.' 'Then someone else will have to.'
I shouldn't mind his bettering himself
If that was what it was. You can be certain,

When he begins like that, there's someone at him
Trying to coax him off with pocket-money,—
In haying time, when any help is scarce.
In winter he comes back to us. I'm done."

"Sh! not so loud: he'll hear you," Mary said.

"I want him to: he'll have to soon or late."

"He's worn out. He's asleep beside the stove.
When I came up from Rowe's I found him here,
Huddled against the barn-door fast asleep,
A miserable sight, and frightening, too—
You needn't smile—I didn't recognize him—
I wasn't looking for him—and he's changed.
Wait till you see."

                    "Where did you say he'd been?"

"He didn't say. I dragged him to the house,
And gave him tea and tried to make him smoke.
I tried to make him talk about his travels,
Nothing would do: he just kept nodding off."

"What did he say? Did he say anything?"

"But little."

                    "Anything? Mary, confess
He said he'd come to ditch the meadow for me."

"Warren!"

                    "But did he? I just want to know."

"Of course he did. What would you have him say?
Surely you wouldn't grudge the poor old man
Some humble way to save his self-respect.
He added, if you really care to know,
He meant to clear the upper pasture, too.
That sounds like something you have heard before?
Warren, I wish you could have heard the way
He jumbled everything. I stopped to look
Two or three times—he made me feel so queer—
To see if he was talking in his sleep.
He ran on Harold Wilson—you remember—
The boy you had in haying four years since.
He's finished school, and teaching in his college.
Silas declares you'll have to get him back.
He says they two will make a team for work:
Between them they will lay this farm as smooth!
The way he mixed that in with other things.
He thinks young Wilson a likely lad, though daft
On education—you know how they fought
All through July under the blazing sun,
Silas up on the cart to build the load,
Harold along beside to pitch it on."

"Yes, I took care to keep well out of earshot."

"Well, those days trouble Silas like a dream.
You wouldn't think they would. How some things linger!
Harold's young college boy's assurance piqued him.
After so many years he still keeps finding
Good arguments he sees he might have used.
I sympathize. I know just how it feels
To think of the right thing to say too late.
Harold's associated in his mind with Latin.
He asked me what I thought of Harold's saying
He studied Latin like the violin

Because he liked it——that an argument!
He said he couldn't make the boy believe
He could find water with a hazel prong——
Which showed how much good school had ever done
     him.
He wanted to go over that. But most of all
He thinks if he could have another chance
To teach him how to build a load of hay——"

"I know, that's Silas' one accomplishment.
He bundles every forkful in its place,
And tags and numbers it for future reference,
So he can find and easily dislodge it
In the unloading. Silas does that well.
He takes it out in bunches like birds' nests.
You never see him standing on the hay
He's trying to lift, straining to lift himself."

"He thinks if he could teach him that, he'd be
Some good perhaps to someone in the world.
He hates to see a boy the fool of books.
Poor Silas, so concerned for other folk,
And nothing to look backward to with pride,
And nothing to look forward to with hope,
So now and never any different."

Part of a moon was falling down the west,
Dragging the whole sky with it to the hills.
Its light poured softly in her lap. She saw
And spread her apron to it. She put out her hand
Among the harp-like morning-glory strings,
Taut with the dew from garden bed to eaves,
As if she played unheard the tenderness
That wrought on him beside her in the night.

"Warren," she said, "he has come home to die:
You needn't be afraid he'll leave you this time."

"Home," he mocked gently.

                              "Yes, what else but home?
It all depends on what you mean by home.
Of course he's nothing to us, any more
Than was the hound that came a stranger to us
Out of the woods, worn out upon the trail."

"Home is the place where, when you have to go there,
They have to take you in."

                              "I should have called it
Something you somehow haven't to deserve."

Warren leaned out and took a step or two,
Picked up a little stick, and brought it back
And broke it in his hand and tossed it by.
"Silas has better claim on us, you think,
Than on his brother? Thirteen little miles
As the road winds would bring him to his door.
Silas has walked that far no doubt today.
Why didn't he go there? His brother's rich,
A somebody—director in the bank."

"He never told us that."

                              "We know it though."

"I think his brother ought to help, of course.
I'll see to that if there is need. He ought of right
To take him in, and might be willing to—
He may be better than appearances.

But have some pity on Silas. Do you think
If he'd had any pride in claiming kin
Or anything he looked for from his brother,
He'd keep so still about him all this time?"

"I wonder what's between them."

                                    "I can tell you.
Silas is what he is—we wouldn't mind him—
But just the kind that kinsfolk can't abide.
He never did a thing so very bad.
He don't know why he isn't quite as good
As anyone. He won't be made ashamed
To please his brother, worthless though he is."

"I can't think Si ever hurt anyone."

"No, but he hurt my heart the way he lay
And rolled his old head on that sharp-edged chair-back.
He wouldn't let me put him on the lounge.
You must go in and see what you can do.
I made the bed up for him there tonight.
You'll be surprised at him—how much he's broken.
His working days are done; I'm sure of it."

"I'd not be in a hurry to say that."

"I haven't been. Go, look, see for yourself.
But, Warren, please remember how it is:
He's come to help you ditch the meadow.
He has a plan. You mustn't laugh at him.
He may not speak of it, and then he may.
I'll sit and see if that small sailing cloud
Will hit or miss the moon."

It hit the moon.
Then there were three there, making a dim row,
The moon, the little silver cloud, and she.

Warren returned—too soon, it seemed to her,
Slipped to her side, caught up her hand and waited.

"Warren?" she questioned.

"Dead," was all he answered.

LAMENT

BY EDNA ST. VINCENT MILLAY

Listen, children:
Your father is dead.
From his old coats
I'll make you little jackets;
I'll make you little trousers
From his old pants.
There'll be in his pockets
Things he used to put there,
Keys and pennies
Covered with tobacco;
Dan shall have the pennies
To save in his bank;
Anne shall have the keys
To make a pretty noise with.
Life must go on,
And the dead be forgotten;
Life must go on,
Though good men die;
Anne, eat your breakfast;
Dan, take your medicine;
Life must go on;
I forget just why.

MENDING WALL

BY ROBERT FROST

Something there is that doesn't love a wall,
That sends the frozen ground swell under it,
And spills the upper boulders in the sun;
And makes gaps even two can pass abreast.
The work of hunters is another thing:
I have come after them and made repair
Where they have left not one stone on stone,
But they would have the rabbit out of hiding,
To please the yelping dogs. The gaps I mean,
No one has seen them made or heard them made,
But at spring mendingtime we find them there.
I let my neighbor know beyond the hill;
And on a day we meet to walk the line
And set the wall between us once again.
We keep the wall between us as we go.
To each the boulders that have fallen to each.
And some are loaves and some so nearly balls
We have to use a spell to make them balance:
"Stay where you are until our backs are turned!"
We wear our fingers rough with handling them.
Oh, just another kind of outdoor game,
One on a side. It comes to little more:
There where it is we do not need the wall:
He is all pine and I am apple orchard.
My apple trees will never get across
And eat the cones under his pines, I tell him.
He only says, "Good fences make good neighbors."
Spring is the mischief in me, and I wonder

If I could put a notion in his head:
"*Why* do they make good neighbors? Isn't it
Where there are cows? But here there are no cows.
Before I built a wall I'd ask to know
What I was walling in or walling out,
And to whom I was like to give offense.
Something there is that doesn't love a wall,
That wants it down." I could say "Elves" to him,
But it's not elves exactly, and I'd rather
He said it for himself. I see him there
Bringing a stone grasped firmly by the top
In each hand, like an old stone savage armed.
He moves in darkness as it seems to me,
Not of woods only and the shade of trees.
He will not go behind his father's saying,
And he likes having thought of it so well
He says again, "Good fences make good neighbors."

EARLY MOON

BY CARL SANDBURG

The baby moon, a canoe, a silver papoose canoe, sails
and sails in the Indian west.

A ring of silver foxes, a mist of silver foxes, sit and sit
around the Indian moon.

One yellow star for a runner, and rows of blue stars for
more runners, keep a line of watchers.

O foxes, baby moon, runners, you are the panel of
memory, fire-white writing tonight of the Red Man's
dreams.

Who squats, legs crossed and arms folded, matching its
look against the moon-face, the star-faces, of the
West?

Who are the Mississippi Valley Ghosts, of copper foreheads, riding wiry ponies in the night?—no bridles,
love-arms on the pony necks, riding in the night a
long old trail?

Why do they always come back when the silver foxes sit
around the early moon, a silver papoose, in the Indian west?

STOPPING BY WOODS
ON A SNOWY EVENING

BY ROBERT FROST

Whose woods these are I think I know.
His house is in the village though;
He will not see me stopping here
To watch his woods fill up with snow.

My little horse must think it queer
To stop without a farmhouse near
Between the woods and frozen lake
The darkest evening of the year.

He gives his harness bells a shake
To ask if there is some mistake.
The only other sound's the sweep
Of easy wind and downy flake.

The woods are lovely, dark and deep,
But I have promises to keep,
And miles to go before I sleep,
And miles to go before I sleep.

GRASS

BY CARL SANDBURG

Pile the bodies high at Austerlitz and Waterloo.
Shovel them under and let me work—
      I am the grass; I cover all.

And pile them high at Gettysburg
And pile them high at Ypres and Verdun.
Shovel them under and let me work.
Two years, ten years, and the passengers ask the
    conductor:
      What place is this?
      Where are we now?

      I am the grass.
      Let me work.

SHENANDOAH ROAD

BY E. B. WHITE

"Yassir, yonder's the highway."
Sing it, nigger boy, sing it to me—
Song of a big road going along,
A slow-time Southland song:
New corn in a red clay field,
Red as blood where the highway cuts it,
Song of a road in the sun of morning,
A dogwood blossom, river-bending road,
Winding the hill, looking for the town,
Down, down,
A drug store, a main street, a Carolina town—
Sing that song to me!

In the soft days—
Salesmen, traveling folks,
Let them ride the cushions in the soft white-lilac days,
But let me go the valley pike
That's crazy with red-bud running wild.
There was an old tune I remember
From the jazz baby of the four-a-day:
"In the Blue Ridge Mountains of Virginia" . . .
Pucker up now,
Whistle it to new fat lambs,
Whistle it loud to new wobbly foals,
Yes, sir, let the mountains hear—
Let me whistle that tune!

An apple tree in baby pink
Throwing a shadow across a whitewashed fence to a
    green lawn;
A locomotive engineer, tooting a long sigh,
Waving from the cab as the tracks swing down across
    the road;
A black boy, riding mule-back into town—
Long ears for the mule,
Long, dangly feet for the boy—
Riding mule-back, gazing at the New York license plates
Of a tourist up from Florida,
Dreaming of the big town he's never been to.
Sit your mule, black boy,
Dreams are taller than cities;
Water your mule in the Shenandoah
In the springtime;
Sing your slow songs, never mind the city;
A grey cabin, chinked with red mud,
At the end of a row of boxwoods:
Dark hole for a door,
Dark hole for a window,
Little dark faces at a sunshine doorstep . . .
"It's pretty weather," says the man at the filling station.

Ever seen the long shadows go along green willows by
    a stream?
Ever seen a cow stand stock still, in the long shadows?
Ever seen a hen in a sheep pasture
Stand stock still in May,
Waiting for something to happen?

The sun leaves the bottom lands
Long before it leaves the ridge—
And the cows are patient in the cool light

Down beneath the willow trees
Where the stream runs slow.
The old, old woman of Maggotty Creek,
She says there's still arbutus to pick
If you know where to go.

Wish on a white horse—
Make a crazy, never-come-true wish:
That the fragrance of blossoms shall last forever,
That boy-and-girl love shall last forever,
Oh, wish on a white horse
Going down the valley!

Red, yellow, and green,
The spangled lady bareback rider
Laughs from the circus billboard—
And the town girl
Walking to the circus with the cadet from the military
    school,
Hand in hand, free and easy,
Laughs.
The road will be lit by flares
When the drivers march the camels home to bed
Under the moon;
But the by-roads lead away from the light,
And the bent grass is warm and smooth
Where the tents have been,
Under the moon.

                        *   *   *

"Yassir, yonder's the highway."
Sing it, nigger boy, sing it to me—
Song of a big road going along,
Winding the hill, looking for the town,
A drug store, a main street, a Carolina town—
Sing that song to me!

AGED FOUR

BY MILDRED FOCHT

Christmas is a cruel day
For Mothers who are poor;
The wistful eyes of children
Are daggers to endure.

Though shops are crammed with playthings,
Enough for every one,
If a mother's purse is empty
There might as well be none.

My purse is full of money,
But I cannot buy a toy;
Only a wreath of holly
For the grave of my little boy.

MR. FLOOD'S PARTY

BY EDWIN ARLINGTON ROBINSON

Old Eben Flood, climbing alone one night
Over the hill between the town below
And the forsaken upland hermitage
That held as much as he should ever know
On earth again of home, paused warily.
The road was his with not a native near;
And Eben, having leisure, said aloud,
For no man else in Tilbury Town to hear:

"Well, Mr. Flood, we have the harvest moon
Again, and we may not have many more;
The bird is on the wing, the poet says,
And you and I have said it here before.
Drink to the bird." He raised up to the light
The jug that he had gone so far to fill,
And answered huskily: "Well, Mr. Flood,
Since you propose it, I believe I will."

Alone, as if enduring to the end
A valiant armor of scarred hopes outworn,
He stood there in the middle of the road
Like Roland's ghost winding a silent horn.
Below him, in the town among the trees,
Where friends of other days had honored him,
A phantom salutation of the dead
Rang thinly till old Eben's eyes were dim.

Then, as a mother lays her sleeping child
Down tenderly, fearing it may awake,
He set the jug down slowly at his feet
With trembling care, knowing that most things break;
And only when assured that on firm earth
It stood, as the uncertain lives of men
Assuredly did not, he paced away,
And with his hand extended paused again:

"Well, Mr. Flood, we have not met like this
In a long time; and many a change has come
To both of us, I fear, since last it was
We had a drop together. Welcome home!"
Convivially returning with himself,
Again he raised the jug up to the light;
And with an acquiescent quaver said:
"Well, Mr. Flood, if you insist, I might.

"Only a very little, Mr. Flood——
For auld lang syne. No more, sir; that will do."
So, for the time, apparently it did,
And Eben evidently thought so too;
For soon amid the silver loneliness
Of night he lifted up his voice and sang,
Secure, with only two moons listening,
Until the whole harmonious landscape rang—

"For auld lang syne." The weary throat gave out,
The last word wavered; and the song being done,
He raised again the jug regretfully
And shook his head, and was again alone.
There was not much that was ahead of him,
And there was nothing in the town below—
Where strangers would have shut the many doors
That many friends had opened long ago.

TO FIGHT ALOUD
IS VERY BRAVE

BY EMILY DICKINSON

To fight aloud is very brave,
But gallanter, I know,
Who charge within the bosom,
The cavalry of woe.

Who win, and nations do not see,
Who fall, and none observe,
Whose dying eyes no country
Regards with patriot love.

We trust, in plumed procession,
For such the angels go,
Rank after rank, with even feet
And uniforms of snow.

SONG IN EXILE

BY ALICE DUER MILLER

The rustling palms bend readily
   Between the sun and me;
The trades blow warm and steadily
   Across the turquoise sea;
But I'd rather feel the March wind bite
   In the country of the free.

Hibiscus and camellias
   Bloom here abundantly,
And roses and gardenias—
   The sweetest flowers there be—
But I'd rather see through the bare north woods
   One bridal dogwood tree.

The tropic light is mellow
   As a lamp in a lighted room;
The sun shines high and yellow
   In the quivering cloudless dome;
But, oh, for the snow and the cruel cold
   And the rigors of my home!

"SCUM O' THE EARTH"

BY ROBERT HAVEN SCHAUFFLER

I

At the gate of the West I stand,
On the island where nations throng.
We call them "scum o' the earth";

Stay, are we doing you wrong,
Young fellow from Socrates' land?—
You, like a Hermes so lithe and strong
Fresh from the master Praxiteles' hand?
So you're of Spartan birth?
Descended, perhaps, from one of the band—
Deathless in story and song—
Who combed their long hair at Thermopylæ's pass? . . .
Ah, I forget what straits (alas!),
More tragic than theirs, more compassion-worth,
Have doomed you to march in our "immigrant class"
Where you're nothing but "scum o' the earth."

II

You Pole with the child on your knee,
What dower have you for the land of the free?
Hark! does she croon
The sad little tune
Chopin once mined from the Polish air
And mounted in gold for us to wear?
Now a ragged young fiddler answers
In wild Czech melody

That Dvořák took whole from the dancers.
And the heavy faces bloom
In the wonderful Slavic way;
The dull little eyes, the foreheads' gloom,
Are suddenly fair and gay.
While, watching these folk and their mystery,
I forget that we,
In our scornful mirth,
Brand them as "polacks"—and "scum o' the earth."

III

Genoese boy of the level brow,
Lad of the lustrous, dreamy eyes
Agaze at Manhattan's pinnacles now
In the first, glad shock of a hushed surprise;
Within your far-rapt seer's eyes
I catch the glow of the wild surmise
That played on the Santa Maria's prow
In that still gray dawn,—
Four centuries gone,
When a world from the wave began to rise.
Oh, who shall foretell what high emprise
Is the goal that gleams
When Italy's dreams
Spread wing and sweep into the skies?
Cæsar dreamed him a world ruled well;
Dante dreamed heaven out of hell;
Angelo brought us there to dwell;
And you, are you of a different birth?—
You're only a "dago,"—and "scum o' the earth"!

IV

Stay, are we doing you wrong
Calling you "scum o' the earth,"
Man of the sorrow-bowed head,

Of the features tender yet strong,—
Man of the eyes full of wisdom and mystery
Mingled with patience and dread?
Have not I known you in history,
Sorrow-bowed head?
Were you the poet-king, worth
Treasures of Ophir unpriced?
Or were you the prophet, whose art
Foretold how the rabble would mock
That shepherd of spirits, ere long,
Who should gather the lambs to his heart
And tenderly feed his flock?
Man—lift that sorrow-bowed head. . . .
Behold, the face of the Christ!

The vision dies at its birth.
You're merely a butt for our mirth.
You're a "sheeny"—and therefore despised
And rejected as "scum o' the earth."

v

Countrymen, bend and invoke
Mercy for us blasphemers,
For that we spat on these marvellous folk,
Nations of darers and dreamers,
Scions of singers and seers,
Our peers, and more than our peers.
"Rabble and refuse," we name them
And "scum o' the earth," to shame them.
Mercy for us of the few, young years,
Of the culture so callow and crude,
Of the hands so grasping and rude,
The lips so ready for sneers
At the sons of our ancient more-than-peers.
Mercy for us who dare despise

Men in whose loins our Homer lies;
Mothers of men who shall bring to us
The glory of Titian, the grandeur of Huss;
Children in whose frail arms may rest
Prophets and singers and saints of the West.

Newcomers all from the eastern seas,
Help us incarnate dreams like these.
Forgive and forget that we did you wrong.
Help us to father a nation strong
In the comradeship of an equal birth,
In the wealth of the richest bloods of earth.

MY CITY

BY JAMES WELDON JOHNSON

When I come down to sleep death's endless night,
The threshold of the unknown dark to cross,
What to me then will be the keenest loss,
When this bright world blurs on my fading sight?
Will it be that no more I shall see the trees
Or smell the flowers or hear the singing birds
Or watch the flashing streams or patient herds?
No. I am sure it will be none of these.

But, ah! Manhattan's sights and sounds, her smells,
Her crowds, her throbbing force, the thrill that comes
From being of her a part, her subtle spells,
Her shining towers, her avenues, her slums—
O God! the stark, unutterable pity,
To be dead, and never again behold my city.

FAREWELL, MY FRIENDS

BY CLARENCE DAY

Farewell, my friends—farewell and hail!
I'm off to seek the Holy Grail.
   I cannot tell you why.
Remember, please, when I am gone,
'Twas Aspiration led me on.
Tiddlely-widdlely tootle-oo,
All I want is to stay with you,
   But here I go. Good-bye.

American Fact

THE DECLARATION
OF INDEPENDENCE

WHEN in the Course of human Events, it becomes necessary for one People to dissolve the Political Bands which have connected them with another, and to assume among the Powers of the Earth, the separate and equal Station to which the Laws of Nature and of Nature's God entitle them, a decent Respect to the Opinions of Mankind requires that they should declare the causes which impel them to the Separation.

WE hold these Truths to be self-evident, that all Men are created equal, that they are endowed by their Creator with certain unalienable Rights, that among these are Life, Liberty, and the Pursuit of Happiness—That to secure these Rights, Governments are instituted among Men, deriving their just Powers from the Consent of the Governed, that whenever any Form of Government becomes destructive of these Ends, it is the Right of the People to alter or to abolish it, and to institute new Government, laying its Foundation on such Principles, and organizing its Powers in such Form, as to them shall seem most likely to effect their Safety and Happiness. Prudence, indeed, will dictate that Governments long established should not be changed for light and transient Causes; and accordingly all Experience hath shewn, that Mankind are more disposed to suffer, while Evils are sufferable, than to right themselves by abolishing the Forms to which they are accustomed. But when a long Train of Abuses and Usurpations, pursuing invariably the same Object, evinces a Design to reduce them under absolute Despotism, it is their Right, it is their Duty, to throw off such Government, and to provide new Guards for their future Security. Such has been the patient Sufferance of these Colonies; and such is now the Necessity which constrains them to alter their former Systems of Government. The History of the present King of Great-Britain is a History of repeated Injuries and Usurpations, all having in direct Object the Establishment of an absolute Tyranny over these States. To prove this, let Facts be submitted to a candid World.

HE has refused his Assent to Laws, the most wholesome and necessary for the public Good.

HE has forbidden his Governors to pass Laws of immediate and pressing Importance, unless suspended in their Operation till his Assent should be obtained; and when so suspended, he has utterly neglected to attend to them.

HE has refused to pass other Laws for the Accommodation of large Districts of People, unless those People would relinquish the Right of Representation in the Legislature, a Right inestimable to them, and formidable to Tyrants only.

HE has called together Legislative Bodies at Places unusual, uncomfortable, and distant from the Depository of their public Records, for the sole Purpose of fatiguing them into Compliance with his Measures.

HE has dissolved Representative Houses repeatedly, for opposing with manly Firmness his Invasions on the Rights of the People.

HE has refused for a long Time, after such Dissolutions, to cause others to be elected; whereby the Legislative Powers, incapable of Annihilation, have returned to the People at large for their exercise; the State remaining in the mean time exposed to all the Dangers of Invasion from without, and Convulsions within.

HE has endeavoured to prevent the Population of these States; for that Purpose obstructing the Laws for Naturalization of Foreigners; refusing to pass others to encourage their Migrations hither, and raising the Conditions of new Appropriations of Lands.

HE has obstructed the Administration of Justice, by refusing his Assent to Laws for establishing Judiciary Powers.

HE has made Judges dependent on his Will alone, for the Tenure of their Offices, and the Amount and Payment of their Salaries.

HE has erected a Multitude of new Offices, and sent hither Swarms of Officers to harass our People, and eat out their Substance.

HE has kept among us, in Times of Peace, Standing Armies, without the consent of our Legislatures.

HE has affected to render the Military independent of and superior to the Civil Power.

HE has combined with others to subject us to a Jurisdiction foreign to our Constitution, and unacknowledged by our Laws; giving his Assent to their Acts of pretended Legislation:

FOR quartering large Bodies of Armed Troops among us:

FOR protecting them, by a mock Trial, from Punishment for any Murders which they should commit on the Inhabitants of these States:

FOR cutting off our Trade with all Parts of the World:

FOR imposing Taxes on us without our Consent:

FOR depriving us, in many Cases, of the Benefits of Trial by Jury:

FOR transporting us beyond Seas to be tried for pretended Offences:

FOR abolishing the free System of English Laws in a neighbouring Province, establishing therein an arbitrary

Government, and enlarging its Boundaries, so as to render it at once an Example and fit Instrument for introducing the same absolute Rule into these Colonies:

FOR taking away our Charters, abolishing our most valuable Laws, and altering fundamentally the Forms of our Governments:

FOR suspending our own Legislatures, and declaring themselves invested with Power to legislate for us in all Cases whatsoever.

HE has abdicated Government here, by declaring us out of his Protection and waging War against us.

HE has plundered our Seas, ravaged our Coasts, burnt our Towns, and destroyed the Lives of our People.

HE is, at this Time, transporting large Armies of foreign Mercenaries to compleat the Works of Death, Desolation, and Tyranny, already begun with circumstances of Cruelty and Perfidy, scarcely paralleled in the most barbarous Ages, and totally unworthy the Head of a civilized Nation.

HE has constrained our fellow Citizens taken Captive on the high Seas to bear Arms against their Country, to become the Executioners of their Friends and Brethren, or to fall themselves by their Hands.

HE has excited domestic Insurrections amongst us, and has endeavoured to bring on the Inhabitants of our Frontiers, the merciless Indian Savages, whose known Rule of Warfare, is an undistinguished Destruction, of all Ages, Sexes and Conditions.

IN every stage of these Oppressions we have Petitioned for Redress in the most humble Terms: Our repeated Petitions have been answered only by repeated Injury. A Prince, whose Character is thus marked by every act which may define a Tyrant, is unfit to be the Ruler of a free People.

NOR have we been wanting in Attentions to our British Brethren. We have warned them from Time to Time of Attempts by their Legislature to extend an unwarrantable Jurisdiction over us. We have reminded them of the Circumstances of our Emigration and Settlement here. We have appealed to their native Justice and Magnanimity, and we have conjured them by the Ties of our common Kindred to disavow these Usurpations, which, would inevitably interrupt our Connections and Correspondence. They too have been deaf to the Voice of Justice and of Consanguinity. We must, therefore, acquiesce in the Necessity, which denounces our Separation, and hold them, as we hold the rest of Mankind, Enemies in War, in Peace, Friends.

WE, therefore, the Representatives of the UNITED STATES OF AMERICA, in GENERAL CONGRESS, Assembled, appealing to the Supreme Judge of the World for the Rectitude of our Intentions, do, in the Name, and by Authority of the good People of these Colonies, solemnly Publish and Declare, That these United Colonies are, and of Right ought to be, FREE AND INDEPENDENT STATES; that they are absolved from all Allegiance to the British Crown, and that all political Connection between them and the State of Great-Britain, is and ought to be totally dissolved; and that as FREE AND INDEPENDENT STATES, they have full Power to levy War, conclude Peace, contract Alliances, establish Commerce, and to do all other Acts and Things which INDEPENDENT STATES may of right do. And for the support of this Declaration, with a firm Reliance on the Protection of divine Providence, we mutually pledge to each other our Lives, our Fortunes, and our sacred Honor.

Signed by ORDER *and in* BEHALF *of the* CONGRESS,

JOHN HANCOCK, PRESIDENT.

ATTEST.

CHARLES THOMSON, SECRETARY.

A LETTER
FROM BENJAMIN FRANKLIN
TO GEORGE WASHINGTON

Passy, March 5, 1780.

SIR,

I have received but lately the letter your Excellency did me the honor of writing to me in recommendation of the Marquis de la Fayette. His modesty detained it long in his own hands. We became acquainted however from the time of his arrival at Paris; and his zeal for the honor of our country, his activity in our affairs here, and his firm attachment to our cause, and to you, impressed me with the same regard and esteem for him that your Excellency's letter would have done, had it been immediately delivered to me.

Should peace arrive after another campaign or two, and afford us a little leisure, I should be happy to see your Excellency in Europe, and to accompany you, if my age and strength would permit, in visiting some of its ancient and most famous kingdoms. You would on this side the sea, enjoy the great reputation you have acquired, pure and free from those little shades that the jealousy and envy of a man's countrymen and cotemporaries are ever endeavouring to cast over living merit. Here you would know, and enjoy, what posterity will say of Washington. For a thousand leagues have nearly the same effect with a thousand years. The feeble voice of those grovelling passions cannot extend so far either in time or distance. At present I enjoy that pleasure for you: as I frequently hear the old Generals of this martial country (who study the maps of America, and mark upon them all your operations) speak with sincere approbation and great applause of your conduct; and join in giving you the character of one of the greatest captains of the age.

I must soon quit the scene, but you may live to see our country flourish; as it will amazingly and rapidly after the war is over; like a field of young Indian corn, which long fair weather and sunshine had enfeebled and discolored, and which in that weak state, by a thunder gust of violent wind, hail, and rain, seemed to be threatened with absolute destruction; yet the storm being past, it recovers fresh verdure, shoots up with double vigor, and delights the eye not of its owner only, but of every observing traveller.

The best wishes that can be formed for your health, honor, and happiness, ever attend you, from your Excellency's most obedient and most humble servant,

B. FRANKLIN.

UNDER A CLOUD OF SAIL

FROM *Two Years Before the Mast*

BY RICHARD HENRY DANA

FRIDAY, *July 22d* [1835]. This day we had a steady gale from the southward, and stood on under close sail, with the yards eased a little by the weather braces, the clouds lifting a little, and showing signs of breaking away.

In the afternoon, I was below with Mr. H——, the third mate, and two others, filling the bread locker in the steerage from the casks, when a bright gleam of sunshine broke out and shone down the companionway and through the skylight, lighting up everything below, sending a warm glow through the hearts of everyone. It was a sight we had not seen for weeks—an omen, a godsend. Even the roughest and hardest face acknowledged its influence.

Just at that moment we heard a loud shout from all parts of the deck, and the mate called out down the companionway to the captain, who was sitting in the cabin. What he said, we could not distinguish, but the captain kicked over his chair, and was on deck at one jump. We could not tell what it was; and, anxious as we were to know, the discipline of the ship would not allow of our leaving our places. Yet, as we were not called, we knew there was no danger.

We hurried to get through with our job, when, seeing the steward's black face peering out of the

472

pantry, Mr. H—— hailed him, to know what was the matter. "Lan' O, to be sure, sir! No you hear 'em sing out, 'Lan' O'? De cap'em say 'im Cape Horn!"

This gave us a new start, and we were soon through our work, and on deck; and there lay the land, fair upon the larboard beam, and slowly edging away upon the quarter. All hands were busy looking at it—the captain and mates from the quarter-deck, the cook from his galley, and the sailors from the forecastle; and even Mr. N——, the passenger, who had kept in his shell for nearly a month, and hardly been seen by anybody, and who we had almost forgotten was on board, came out like a butterfly, and was hopping round as bright as a bird.

The land was the island of Staten Land, just to the eastward of Cape Horn; and a more desolate looking spot I never wish to set eyes upon—bare, broken, and girt with rocks and ice, with here and there, between the rocks and broken hillocks, a little stunted vegetation of shrubs. It was a place well suited to stand at the juncture of the two oceans, beyond the reach of human cultivation, and encounter the blasts and snows of a perpetual winter.

Yet, dismal as it was, it was a pleasant sight to us; not only as being the first land we had seen, but because it told us that we had passed the Cape—were in the Atlantic—and that, with twenty-four hours of this breeze, might bid defiance to the Southern ocean. It told us, too, our latitude and longitude better than any observation; and the captain now knew where we were, as well as if we were off the end of Long Wharf.

In the general joy, Mr. N—— said he should like to go ashore upon the island and examine a spot which probably no human being had ever set foot upon; but

the captain intimated that he would see the island—
specimens and all—in another place, before he would
get out a boat or delay the ship one moment for him.

We left the land gradually astern; and at sundown
had the Atlantic Ocean clear before us.

It is usual, in voyages round the Cape from the
Pacific, to keep to the eastward of the Falkland Islands;
but as it had now set in a strong, steady, and clear south-
wester, with every prospect of its lasting, and we had
had enough of high latitudes, the captain determined to
stand immediately to the northward, running inside the
Falkland Islands. Accordingly, when the wheel was
relieved at eight o'clock, the order was given to keep her
due north, and all hands were turned up to square away
the yard and make sail.

In a moment, the news ran through the ship that the
captain was keeping her off, with her nose straight for
Boston, and Cape Horn over her taffrail. It was a moment of enthusiasm. Everyone was on the alert, and even
the two sick men turned out to lend a hand at the halyards. The wind was now due southwest, and blowing a
gale to which a vessel close-hauled could have shown
no more than a single close-reefed sail; but as we were
going before it, we could carry on. Accordingly, hands
were sent aloft, and a reef shaken out of the topsails,
and the reefed foresail set. When we came to masthead
the topsail yards, with all hands at the halyards, we
struck up "Cheerily, men," with a chorus which might
have been heard half way to Staten Land.

Under her increased sail, the ship drove on through
the water. Yet she could bear it well; and the captain
sung out from the quarter-deck—"Another reef out of
that fore-topsail, and give it to her!" Two hands sprung
aloft; the frozen reef points and earings were cast

adrift, the halyards manned, and the sail gave out her increased canvas to the gale. All hands were kept on deck to watch the effect of the change. It was as much as she could well carry, and with a heavy sea astern, it took two men at the wheel to steer her. She flung the foam from her bows; the spray breaking aft as far as the gangway. She was going at a prodigious rate. Still, everything held. Preventer braces were reeved and hauled taut; tackles got upon the backstays; and each thing done to keep all snug and strong.

The captain walked the deck at a rapid stride, looked aloft at the sails, and then to windward; the mate stood in the gangway, rubbing his hands, and talking aloud to the ship—"Hurrah, old bucket! the Boston girls have got hold of the towrope!" and the like; and we were on the forecastle, looking to see how the spars stood it, and guessing the rate at which she was going—when the captain called out——

"Mr. Brown, get up the topmast studding sail! What she can't carry she may drag!"

The mate looked a moment: but he would let no man be before him in daring. He sprung forward——

"Hurrah, men! rig out the topmast studding-sail boom! Lay aloft, and I'll send the rigging up to you!"

We sprung aloft into the top; lowered a girtline down, by which he hauled up the rigging; rove the tacks and halyards; ran out the boom and lashed it fast, and sent down the lower halyards, as a preventer.

It was a clear starlight night, cold and blowing; but everybody worked with a will. Some, indeed, looked as though they thought the "old man" was mad, but no one said a word. We had had a new topmast studding sail made with a reef in it—a thing hardly ever heard of, and which the sailors had ridiculed a good deal, saying that when it was time to reef a studding sail, it was time to take it in. But we found a use for it now; for, there being a reef in the topsail, the studding sail could not be set without one in it also. To be sure, a studding sail with reefed topsails was rather a new thing; yet there was some reason in it, for if we carried that away, we should lose only a sail and a boom; but a whole topsail might have carried away the mast and all.

While we were aloft, the sail had been got out, bent to the yard, reefed, and ready for hoisting. Waiting for a good opportunity, the halyards were manned and the yard hoisted fairly up to the block; but when the mate came to shake the catspaw out of the downhaul, and we began to boom-end the sail, it shook the ship to her center. The boom buckled up and bent like a whipstick, and we looked every moment to see something go; but, being of the short, tough, upland spruce, it bent like whalebone, and nothing could break it. The carpenter said it was the best stick he had ever seen.

The strength of all hands soon brought the tack to the boom end, and the sheet was trimmed down, and the preventer and the weather brace hauled taut to take off the strain. Every rope yarn seemed stretched to the utmost, and every thread of canvas; and with this sail added to her, the ship sprung through the water like a thing possessed. The sail being nearly all forward, it lifted her out of the water, and she seemed actually to jump from sea to sea. From the time her keel was laid, she had never been so driven; and had it been life or death with every one of us, she should not have borne another stitch of canvas.

Finding that she would bear the sail, the hands were sent below, and our watch remained on deck. Two men at the wheel had as much as they could do to keep her within three points of her course, for she steered as wild as a young colt.

The mate walked the deck, looking at the sails, and then over the side to see the foam fly by her—slapping his hands upon his thighs and talking to the ship—"Hurrah, you jade, you've got the scent!—you know where you're going!" And when she leaped over the seas, and almost out of the water, and trembled to her very keel, the spars and masts snapping and creaking, "There she goes! There she goes—handsomely! As long as she cracks she holds!"—while we stood with the rigging laid down fair for letting go, and ready to take in sail and clear away, if anything went.

At four bells we hove the log, and she was going eleven knots fairly; and had it not been for the sea from aft which sent the ship home, and threw her continually off her course, the log would have shown her to have been going much faster. I went to the wheel with a young fellow from the Kennebec, who was a good helmsman; and for two hours we had our hands full.

A few minutes showed us that our monkey jackets must come off; and cold as it was, we stood in our shirt sleeves in a perspiration; and were glad enough to have it eight bells, and the wheel relieved. We turned in and slept as well as we could, though the sea made a constant roar under her bows, and washed over the forecastle like a small cataract.

At four o'clock, we were called again. The same sail was still on the vessel, and the gale, if there was any change, had increased a little. No attempt was made to take the studding sail in; and, indeed, it was too late now. If we had started anything toward taking it in, either tack or halyards, it would have blown to pieces, and carried something away with it. The only way now was to let everything stand, and if the gale went down, well and good; if not, something must go—the weakest stick or rope first—and then we could get it in.

For more than an hour she was driven on at such a rate that she seemed actually to crowd the sea into a heap before her; and the water poured over the sprit-sail yard as it would over a dam. Toward daybreak the gale abated a little, and she was just beginning to go more easily along, relieved of the pressure, when Mr. Brown, determined to give her no respite, and depending upon the wind's subsiding as the sun rose, told us to get along the lower studding sail.

This was an immense sail, and held wind enough to last a Dutchman a week—hove to. It was soon ready, the boom topped up, preventer guys rove, and the idlers called up to man the halyards; yet such was still the force of the gale, that we were nearly an hour setting the sail; carried away the overhaul in doing it, and came very near snapping off the swinging boom.

No sooner was it set than the ship tore on again like one that was mad, and began to steer as wild as a hawk. The men at the wheel were puffing and blowing at their work, and the helm was going hard up and hard down, constantly. Add to this, the gale did not lessen as the day came on, but the sun rose in clouds. A sudden lurch threw the man from the weather wheel across the deck and against the side. The mate sprung to the wheel, and the man, regaining his feet, seized the spokes and they hove the wheel up just in time to save her from bracing to; though nearly half the studding sail went under water; and as she came to, the boom stood up at an angle of forty-five degrees.

She had evidently more on her than she could bear; yet it was in vain to try to take it in—the clew line was not strong enough; and they were thinking of cutting away, when another wide yaw and a come to snapped the guys, and the swinging boom came in, with a crash, against the lower rigging. The outhaul block gave way, and the topmast studding-sail boom bent in a manner which I never before supposed a stick could bend.

I had my eye on it when the guys parted, and it made one spring and buckled up so as to form nearly a half circle, and sprung out again to its shape. The clew line gave way at the first pull; the cleat to which the halyards were belayed was wrenched off, and the sail blew round the spritsail yard and head guys, which gave us a bad job to get it in. A half hour served to clear all away, and she was suffered to drive on with her topmast studding sail set, it being as much as she could stagger under.

During all this day and the next night, we went on under the same sail, the gale blowing with undiminished force; two men at the wheel all the time; watch and watch, and nothing to do but to steer and look out for the ship, and be blown along;—until the noon of the next day——

Sunday, *July 24th,* when we were in latitude 50° 27' S., longitude 62° 13' W., having made four degrees of latitude in the last twenty-four hours. Being now to the northward of the Falkland Islands, the ship was kept off, northeast, for the equator; and with her head for the equator, and Cape Horn over her taffrail, she went gloriously on; every heave of the sea leaving the Cape astern and every hour bringing us nearer to home, and to warm weather.

Many a time, when blocked up in the ice, with everything dismal and discouraging about us, had we said—if we were only fairly round, and standing north on the other side, we should ask for no more:—and now we had it all with a clear sea, and as much wind as a sailor could pray for.

If the best part of a voyage is the last part, surely we had all now that we could wish. Everyone was in the

highest spirits, and the ship seemed as glad as any of
us at getting out of her confinement. At each change of
the watch, those coming on deck asked those going
below—"How does she go along?" and got for answer,
the rate, and the customary addition—"Ay! and the
Boston girls have had hold of the towrope all the watch,
and can't haul half the slack in!"

Each day the sun rose higher in the horizon, and the
nights grew shorter; and at coming on deck each morning, there was a sensible change in the temperature. The
ice, too, began to melt from off the rigging and spars,
and, except a little which remained in the tops and
round the hounds of the lower masts, was soon gone.

As we left the gale behind us, the reefs were shaken
out of the topsails, and sail made as fast as she could
bear it; and every time all hands were sent to the halyards, a song was called for, and we hoisted away with
a will.

Sail after sail was added, as we drew into fine
weather; and in one week after leaving Cape Horn, the
long topgallant masts were got up, topgallant and royal
yards crossed, and the ship restored to her fair proportions.

The Southern Cross we saw no more after the first
night; the Magellan Clouds settled lower and lower in
the horizon; and so great was our change of latitude
each succeeding night, that we sunk some constellation
in the south, and raised another in the northern horizon.

Sunday, *July 31st.* At noon we were in lat. 36° 41′ S.,
long. 38° 08′ W.; having traversed the distance of two
thousand miles, allowing for changes of course, in nine
days. A thousand miles in four days and a half! This is
equal to steam.

Soon after eight o'clock, the appearance of the ship
gave evidence that this was the first Sunday we had yet

had in fine weather. As the sun came up clear, with the promise of a fair, warm day, and as usual on Sunday, there was no work going on, all hands turned to upon clearing out the forecastle.

The wet and soiled clothes which had accumulated there during the past month, were brought up on deck; the chests moved; brooms, buckets of water, swabs, scrubbing brushes, and scrapers carried down, and applied, until the forecastle floor was as white as chalk, and everything neat and in order. The bedding from the berths was then spread on deck, and dried, and aired; the deck tub filled with water; and a grand washing began of all the clothes which were brought up.

Shirts, frocks, drawers, trousers, jackets, stockings, of every shape and color, wet and dirty—many of them moldy from having been lying a long time wet in a foul corner—these were all washed and scrubbed out, and finally towed overboard for half an hour; and then made fast to the rigging to dry. Wet boots and shoes were spread out to dry in sunny places on deck; and the whole ship looked like a back yard on a washing day.

After we had done with our clothes, we began upon our own persons. A little fresh water, which we had saved from our allowance, was put in buckets, and with soap and towels, we had what sailors call a fresh-water wash. The same bucket, to be sure, had to go through several hands, and was spoken for by one after another, but as we rinsed off in salt water, pure from the ocean, and the fresh was used only to start the accumulated grime and blackness of five weeks, it was held of little consequence.

We soaped down and scrubbed one another with towels and pieces of canvas, stripping to it; and then, getting into the head, threw buckets of water upon each other. After this, came shaving, and combing, and brushing; and when, having spent the first part of the day in this way, we sat down on the forecastle, in the afternoon with clean duck trousers, and shirts on, washed, shaved, and combed, and looking a dozen shades lighter for it, reading, sewing, and talking at our ease, with a clear sky and warm sun over our heads, a steady breeze over the larboard quarter, studding sails out alow and aloft, and all the flying kites abroad;— we felt that we had got back into the pleasantest part of a sailor's life.

At sundown the clothes were all taken down from the rigging clean and dry—and stowed neatly away in our chests; and our southwesters, thick boots, guernsey frocks, and other accompaniments of bad weather, put out of the way, we hoped, for the rest of the voyage, as we expected to come upon the coast early in the autumn.

Notwithstanding all that has been said about the beauty of a ship under full sail, there are very few who have ever seen a ship literally, under all her sail. A ship coming in or going out of port, with her ordinary sails, and perhaps two or three studding sails, is commonly said to be under full sail; but a ship never has all her sail upon her, except when she has a light, steady breeze, very nearly, but not quite, dead aft, and so regular that it can be trusted, and is likely to last for some time. Then, with all her sails, light and heavy, and studding sails, on each side alow and aloft, she is the most glorious moving object in the world. Such a sight, very few, even some who have been at sea a good deal have ever beheld; for from the deck of your own vessel you cannot see her, as you would a separate object.

One night, while we were in these tropics, I went out to the end of the flying jib boom, upon some duty, and, having finished it, turned round, and lay over the boom for a long time, admiring the beauty of the sight before me. Being so far out from the deck, I could look at the ship, as at a separate vessel;—and there rose up from the water, supported only by the small black hull a pyramid of canvas, spreading out far beyond the hull, and towering up almost, as it seemed in the indistinct night air, to the clouds.

The sea was as still as an inland lake; the light trade wind was gently and steadily breathing from astern; the dark blue sky was studded with the tropical stars; there was no sound but the rippling of the water under the stem; and the sails were spread out, wide and high; the two lower studding sails stretching, on each side, far beyond the deck; the topmast studding sails, like wings to the topsails; the topgallant studding sails spreading fearlessly out above them; still higher, the two royal studding sails, looking like two kites flying from the same string; and highest of all, the little skysail, the apex of the pyramid, seeming actually to touch the stars, and to be out of reach of human hands. So quiet, too, was the sea, and so steady the breeze, that if these sails had been sculptured marble, they could not have been more motionless. Not a ripple upon the surface of the canvas; not even a quivering of the extreme edges of the sail—so perfectly were they distended by the breeze.

I was so lost in the sight, that I forgot the presence of the man who came out with me, until he said (for he too, rough old man-of-war's man as he was, had been gazing at the show), half to himself, still looking at the marble sails,—"How quietly they do their work!"

WHERE I LIVED,
AND WHAT I LIVED FOR

FROM *Walden*

BY HENRY DAVID THOREAU

AT a certain season of our life we are accustomed to consider every spot as the possible site of a house. I have thus surveyed the country on every side within a dozen miles of where I live. In imagination I have bought all the farms in succession, for all were to be bought, and I knew their price. I walked over each farmer's premises, tasted his wild apples, discoursed on husbandry with him, took his farm at his price, at any price, mortgaging it to him in my mind; even put a higher price on it,—took everything but a deed of it,—took his word for his deed, for I dearly love to talk,—cultivated it, and him too to some extent, I trust, and withdrew when I had enjoyed it long enough, leaving him to carry it on. This experience entitled me to be regarded as a sort of real-estate broker by my friends. Wherever I sat, there I might live, and the landscape radiated from me accordingly. What is a house but a *sedes*, a seat?— better if a country seat. I discovered many a site for a house not likely to be soon improved, which some might have thought too far from the village, but to my eyes the village was too far from it. Well, there I might live, I said; and there I did live, for an hour, a summer and a winter life; saw how I could let the years run off, buffet the winter through, and see the spring come in. The future inhabitants of this region, wherever they may place their houses, may be sure that they have been anticipated. An afternoon sufficed to lay out the land into orchard, wood-lot, and pasture, and to decide what fine oaks or pines should be left to stand before the door, and whence each blasted tree could be seen to the best advantage; and then I let it lie, fallow perchance, for a man is rich in proportion to the number of things which he can afford to let alone.

My imagination carried me so far that I even had the refusal of several farms,—the refusal was all I wanted,—but I never got my fingers burned by actual possession. The nearest that I came to actual possession was when I bought the Hollowell place, and had begun to sort my seeds, and collected materials with which to make a wheelbarrow to carry it on or off with; but before the owner gave me a deed of it, his wife—every man has such a wife—changed her mind and wished to keep it, and he offered me ten dollars to release him. Now, to speak the truth, I had but ten cents in the world, and it surpassed my arithmetic to tell, if I was that man who had ten cents, or who had a farm, or ten dollars, or all together. However, I let him keep the ten dollars and the farm too, for I had carried it far enough; or rather, to be generous, I sold him the farm for just what I gave for it, and, as he was not a rich man, made him a present of ten dollars, and still had my ten cents, and seeds, and materials for a wheelbarrow left. I found thus that I had been a rich man without any damage to my poverty. But I retained the landscape, and I have since annually carried off what it yielded without a wheelbarrow. With respect to landscapes,—

> "I am monarch of all I *survey*,
>   My right there is none to dispute."

I have frequently seen a poet withdraw, having en-

joyed the most valuable part of a farm, while the crusty
farmer supposed that he had got a few wild apples only.
Why, the owner does not know it for many years when
a poet has put his farm in rime, the most admirable kind
of invisible fence, has fairly impounded it, milked it,
skimmed it, and got all the cream, and left the farmer
only the skimmed milk.

The real attractions of the Hollowell farm, to me,
were: its complete retirement, being about two miles
from the village, half a mile from the nearest neighbor,
and separated from the highway by a broad field; its
bounding on the river, which the owner said protected
it by its fogs from frosts in the spring, though that was
nothing to me; the gray color and ruinous state of the
house and barn, and the dilapidated fences, which put
such an interval between me and the last occupant; the
hollow and lichen-covered apple trees, gnawed by rabbits, showing what kind of neighbors I should have; but
above all, the recollection I had of it from my earliest
voyages up the river, when the house was concealed behind a dense grove of red maples, through which I heard
the house-dog bark. I was in haste to buy it, before the
proprietor finished getting out some rocks, cutting down
the hollow apple trees, and grubbing up some young
birches which had sprung up in the pasture, or, in short,
had made any more of his improvements. To enjoy these
advantages I was ready to carry it on; like Atlas, to take
the world on my shoulders,—I never heard what com-
pensation he received for that,—and do all those things
which had no other motive or excuse but that I might
pay for it and be unmolested in my possession of it; for
I knew all the while that it would yield the most abundant crop of the kind I wanted, if I could only afford
to let it alone. But it turned out as I have said.

All that I could say, then, with respect to farming on

a large scale—I have always cultivated a garden—was, that I had had my seeds ready. Many think that seeds improve with age. I have no doubt that time discriminates between the good and the bad; and when at last I shall plant, I shall be less likely to be disappointed. But I would say to my fellows, once for all, As long as possible live free and uncommitted. It makes but little difference whether you are committed to a farm or the county jail.

Old Cato, whose "De Re Rustica" is my "Cultivator," says,—and the only translation I have seen makes sheer nonsense of the passage,—"When you think of getting a farm turn it thus in your mind, not to buy greedily; nor spare your pains to look at it, and do not think it enough to go round it once. The oftener you go there the more it will please you, if it is good." I think I shall not buy greedily, but go round and round it as long as I live, and be buried in it first, that it may please me the more at last.

The present was my next experiment of this kind, which I purpose to describe more at length, for convenience putting the experience of two years into one. As I have said, I do not propose to write an ode to dejection, but to brag as lustily as chanticleer in the morning, standing on his roost, if only to wake my neighbors up.

When first I took up my abode in the woods, that is, began to spend my nights as well as days there, which, by accident, was on Independence Day, or the Fourth of July, 1845, my house was not finished for winter, but was merely a defence against the rain, without plastering or chimney, the walls being of rough, weather-stained boards, with wide chinks, which made it cool at night. The upright white hewn studs and freshly planed door and window casings gave it a clean and airy look, especially in the morning, when its timbers were saturated with dew, so that I fancied that by noon some sweet gum would exude from them. To my imagination it retained throughout the day more or less of this auroral character, reminding me of a certain house on a mountain which I had visited a year before. This was an airy and unplastered cabin, fit to entertain a travelling god, and where a goddess might trail her garments. The winds which passed over my dwelling were such as sweep over the ridges of mountains, bearing the broken strains, or celestial parts only, of terrestrial music. The morning wind forever blows, the poem of creation is uninterrupted; but few are the ears that hear it. Olympus is but the outside of the earth everywhere.

The only house I had been the owner of before, if I except a boat, was a tent, which I used occasionally when making excursions in the summer, and this is still rolled up in my garret; but the boat, after passing from hand to hand, has gone down the stream of time. With this more substantial shelter about me, I had made some progress toward settling in the world. This frame, so slightly clad, was a sort of crystallization around me, and reacted on the builder. It was suggestive somewhat as a picture in outlines. I did not need to go outdoors to take the air, for the atmosphere within had lost none of its freshness. It was not so much within-doors as behind a door where I sat, even in the rainiest weather. The Harivansa says, "An abode without birds is like a meat without seasoning." Such was not my abode, for I found myself suddenly neighbor to the birds; not by having imprisoned one, but having caged myself near them. I was not only nearer to some of those which commonly frequent the garden and the orchard, but to those wilder and more thrilling songsters of the forest which never, or rarely, serenade a villager,—the wood thrush, the veery, the scarlet tanager, the field sparrow, the whip-poor-will, and many others.

I was seated by the shore of a small pond, about a mile and a half south of the village of Concord and somewhat higher than it, in the midst of an extensive wood between that town and Lincoln, and about two miles south of that our only field known to fame, Concord Battle Ground; but I was so low in the woods that the opposite shore, half a mile off, like the rest, covered with wood, was my most distant horizon. For the first week, whenever I looked out on the pond it impressed me like a tarn high up on the side of a mountain, its bottom far above the surface of other lakes, and, as the sun arose, I saw it throwing off its nightly clothing of mist, and here and there, by degrees, its soft ripples or its smooth reflecting surface was revealed, while the mists, like ghosts, were stealthily withdrawing in every direction into the woods, as at the breaking up of some nocturnal conventicle. The very dew seemed to hang upon the trees later into the day than usual, as on the sides of mountains.

This small lake was of most value as a neighbor in the intervals of a gentle rain-storm in August, when, both air and water being perfectly still, but the sky overcast, mid-afternoon had all the serenity of evening, and the wood thrush sang around, and was heard from shore to shore. A lake like this is never smoother than at such a time; and the clear portion of the air above it being shallow and darkened by clouds, the water, full of light and re-flections, becomes a lower heaven itself so much the more important. From a hilltop near by, where the wood had been recently cut off, there was a pleasing vista southward across the pond, through a wide indentation in the hills which form the shore there, where their opposite sides sloping toward each other suggested a stream flowing out in that direction through a wooded valley, but stream there was none. That way I looked between and over the near green hills to some distant and higher ones in the horizon, tinged with blue. Indeed, by standing on tiptoe I could catch a glimpse of some of the peaks of the still bluer and more distant mountain ranges in the northwest, those true-blue coins from heaven's own mint, and also of some portion of the village. But in other directions, even from this point, I could not see over or beyond the woods which surrounded me. It is well to have some water in your neighborhood, to give buoyancy to and float the earth. One value even of the smallest well is, that when you look into it you see that earth is not continent but insular. This is as important as that it keeps butter cool. When I looked across the pond from this peak toward the Sudbury meadows, which in time of flood I distinguished elevated perhaps by a mirage in their seething valley, like a coin in a basin, all the earth beyond the pond appeared like a thin crust insulated and floated even by this small sheet of intervening water, and I was reminded that this on which I dwelt was but *dry land*.

Though the view from my door was still more contracted, I did not feel crowded or confined in the least. There was pasture enough for my imagination. The low shrub oak plateau to which the opposite shore arose stretched away toward the prairies of the West and the steppes of Tartary, affording ample room for all the roving families of men. "There are none happy in the world but beings who enjoy freely a vast horizon,"—said Damodara, when his herds required new and larger pastures.

Both place and time were changed, and I dwelt nearer to those parts of the universe and to those eras in history which had most attracted me. Where I lived was as far off as many a region viewed nightly by astronomers. We are wont to imagine rare and delectable places in some remote and more celestial corner of the system, behind the constellation of Cassiopeia's Chair, far from noise and disturbance. I discovered that my house actually had its site in such a withdrawn, but forever new and unprofaned, part of the universe. If it were worth the while to settle in those parts near to the Pleiades or the Hyades, to Aldebaran or Altair, then I was really there, or at an equal remoteness from the life which I had left behind, dwindled and twinkling with as fine a ray to my nearest neighbor. and to be seen only in moonless nights by him. Such was that part of creation where I had squatted;—

> "There was a shepherd that did live,
>   And held his thoughts as high
> As were the mounts whereon his flocks
>   Did hourly feed him by."

What should we think of the shepherd's life if his flocks always wandered to higher pastures than his thoughts?

Every morning was a cheerful invitation to make my life of equal simplicity, and I may say innocence, with Nature herself. I have been as sincere a worshipper of Aurora as the Greeks. I got up early and bathed in the pond; that was a religious exercise, and one of the best things which I did. They say that characters were engraven on the bathing tub of King Tching-thang to this effect: "Renew thyself completely each day; do it again, and again, and forever again." I can understand that. Morning brings back the heroic ages. I was as much affected by the faint hum of a mosquito making its invisible and unimaginable tour through my apartment at earliest dawn, when I was sitting with door and windows open, as I could be by any trumpet that ever sang of fame. It was Homer's requiem; itself an Iliad and Odyssey in the air, singing its own wrath and wanderings. There was something cosmical about it; a standing advertisement, till forbidden, of the everlasting vigor and fertility of the world. The morning, which is the most memorable season of the day, is the awakening hour. Then there is least somnolence in us; and for an hour, at least, some part of us awakes which slumbers all the rest of the day and night. Little is to be expected of that day, if it can be called a day, to which we are not awakened by our Genius, but by the mechanical nudgings of of some servitor, are not awakened by our own newly acquired force and aspirations from within, accompanied by the undulations of celestial music, instead of factory bells, and a fragrance filling the air—to a higher life than we fell asleep from; and thus the darkness bear its fruit, and prove itself to be good, no less than the light. That man who does not believe that each day contains an earlier, more sacred, and auroral hour than he has yet profaned, has despaired of life, and is pursuing a descending and darkening way. After a partial cessation of his sensuous life, the soul of man, or its organs rather, are reinvigorated each day, and his Genius tries again what noble life it can make. All memorable events, I should say, transpire in morning time and in a morning atmosphere. The Vedas say, "All intelligences awake with the morning." Poetry and art, and the fairest and most memorable of the actions of men, date from such an hour. All poets and heroes, like Memnon, are the children of Aurora, and emit their music at sunrise. To him whose elastic and vigorous thought keeps pace with the sun, the day is a perpetual morning. It matters not what the clocks say or the attitudes and labors of men. Morning is when I am awake and there is a dawn in me. Moral reform is the effort to throw off sleep. Why is it that men give so poor an account of their day if they have not been slumbering? They are not such poor calculators. If they had not been overcome with drowsiness, they would have performed something. The millions are awake enough for physical labor; but only one in a million is awake enough for effective intellectual exertion, only one in a hundred millions to a poetic or divine life. To be awake is to be alive. I have never yet met a man who was quite awake. How could I have looked him in the face?

We must learn to reawaken and keep ourselves awake, not by mechanical aids, but by an infinite expectation of the dawn, which does not forsake us in our soundest sleep. I know of no more encouraging fact than the un-questionable ability of man to elevate his life by a con-scious endeavor. It is something to be able to paint a particular picture, or to carve a statue, and so to make a few objects beautiful; but it is far more glorious to carve and paint the very atmosphere and medium through which we look, which morally we can do. To affect the quality of the day, that is the highest of arts. Every man is tasked to make his life, even in its details, worthy of the contemplation of his most elevated and critical hour. If we refused, or rather used up, such paltry information as we get, the oracles would dis-tinctly inform us how this might be done.

I went to the woods because I wished to live delib-erately, to front only the essential facts of life, and see if I could not learn what it had to teach, and not, when I came to die, discover that I had not lived. I did not wish to live what was not life, living is so dear; nor did I wish to practise resignation, unless it was quite necessary. I wanted to live deep and suck out all the marrow of life, to live so sturdily and Spartan-like as to put to rout all that was not life, to cut a broad swath and shave close, to drive life into a corner, and reduce it to its lowest terms, and, if it proved to be mean, why then to get the whole and genuine meanness of it, and publish its meanness to the world; or if it were sublime, to know it by experience, and be able to give a true account of it in my next excursion. For most men, it appears to me, are in a strange uncertainty about it, whether it is of the devil or of God, and have *somewhat hastily* concluded that it is the chief end of man here to "glorify God and enjoy him forever."

Still we live meanly, like ants; though the fable tells us that we were long ago changed into men; like pygmies we fight with cranes; it is error upon error, and clout upon clout, and our best virtue has for its occasion a superfluous and evitable wretchedness. Our life is frittered away by detail. An honest man has hardly need to count more than his ten fingers, or in extreme cases he may add his ten toes, and lump the rest. Simplicity, simplicity, simplicity! I say, let your affairs be as two or three, and not a hundred or a thousand; instead of a million count half a dozen, and keep your accounts on your thumb-nail. In the midst of this chopping sea of civilized life, such are the clouds and storms and quicksands and thousand-and-one items to be allowed for, that a man has to live, if he would not founder and go to the bottom and not make his port at all, by dead reckoning, and he must be a great calculator indeed who succeeds. Simplify, simplify. Instead of three meals a day, if it be necessary eat but one; instead of a hundred dishes, five; and reduce other things in proportion. Our life is like a German Confederacy, made up of petty states, with its boundary forever fluctuating, so that even a German cannot tell you how it is bounded at any moment. The nation itself, with all its so-called internal improvements, which, by the way, are

all external and superficial, is just such an unwieldy and
overgrown establishment, cluttered with furniture and
tripped up by its own traps, ruined by luxury and heed-
less expense, by want of calculation and a worthy aim,
as the million households in the land; and the only cure
for it, as for them, is in a rigid economy, a stern and
more than Spartan simplicity of life and elevation of
purpose. It lives too fast. Men think that it is essential
that the *Nation* have commerce, and export ice, and talk
through a telegraph, and ride thirty miles an hour,
without a doubt, whether *they* do or not; but whether we
should live like baboons or like men, is a little uncertain.
If we do not get out sleepers, and forge rails, and devote
days and nights to the work, but go to tinkering upon
our *lives* to improve *them,* who will build railroads? And
if railroads are not built, how shall we get to Heaven in
season? But if we stay at home and mind our business,
who will want railroads? We do not ride on the railroad;
it rides upon us. Did you ever think what those sleepers
are that underlie the railroad? Each one is a man, an
Irishman, or a Yankee man. The rails are laid on them,
and they are covered with sand, and the cars run
smoothly over them. They are sound sleepers, I assure
you. And every few years a new lot is laid down and
run over; so that, if some have the pleasure of riding on
a rail, others have the misfortune to be ridden upon.
And when they run over a man that is walking in his
sleep, a supernumerary sleeper in the wrong position,
and wake him up, they suddenly stop the cars, and make
a hue and cry about it, as if this were an exception. I
am glad to know that it takes a gang of men for every
five miles to keep the sleepers down and level in their
beds as it is, for this is a sign that they may sometime
get up again.

Why should we live with such hurry and waste of

life? We are determined to be starved before we are hungry. Men say that a stitch in time saves nine, and so they take a thousand stitches to-day and save nine to-morrow. As for *work*, we haven't any of any consequence. We have the Saint Vitus' dance, and cannot possibly keep our heads still. If I should only give a few pulls at the parish bell-rope, as for a fire, that is, without setting the bell, there is hardly a man on his farm in the outskirts of Concord, notwithstanding that press of engagements which was his excuse so many times this morning, nor a boy, nor a woman, I might almost say, but would forsake all and follow that sound, not mainly to save property from the flames, but, if we will confess the truth, much more to see it burn, since burn it must, and we, be it known, did not set it on fire,—or to see it put out, and have a hand in it, if that is done as handsomely; yes, even if it were the parish church itself. Hardly a man takes a half-hour's nap after dinner, but when he wakes he holds up his head and asks, "What's the news?" as if the rest of mankind had stood his sentinels. Some give directions to be waked every half-hour, doubtless for no other purpose; and then, to pay for it, they tell what they have dreamed. After a night's sleep the news is as indispensable as the breakfast. "Pray tell me anything new that has happened to a man anywhere on this globe,"—and he reads it over his coffee and rolls, that a man has had his eyes gouged out this morning on the Wachito River; never dreaming the while that he lives in the dark unfathomed mammoth cave of this world, and has but the rudiment of an eye himself.

For my part, I could easily do without the post-office. I think that there are very few important communications made through it. To speak critically, I never received more than one or two letters in my life—I wrote this some years ago—that were worth the postage. The penny-post is, commonly, an institution through which you seriously offer a man that penny for his thoughts which is so often safely offered in jest. And I am sure that I never read any memorable news in a newspaper. If we read of one man robbed, or murdered, or killed by accident, or one house burned, or one vessel wrecked, or one steamboat blown up, or one cow run over on the Western Railroad, or one mad dog killed, or one lot of grasshoppers in the winter,—we never need read of another. One is enough. If you are acquainted with the principle, what do you care for a myriad instances and applications? To a philosopher all *news*, as it is called, is gossip, and they who edit and read it are old women over their tea. Yet not a few are greedy after this gossip. There was such a rush, as I hear, the other day at one of the offices to learn the foreign news by the last arrival, that several large squares of plate glass belonging to the establishment were broken by the pressure,—news which I seriously think a ready wit might write a twelvemonth, or twelve years, beforehand with sufficient accuracy. As for Spain, for instance, if you know how to throw in Don Carlos and the Infanta, and Don Pedro and Seville and Granada, from time to time in the right proportions,—they may have changed the names a little since I saw the papers,—and serve up a bull-fight when other entertainments fail, it will be true to the letter, and give us as good an idea of the exact state or ruin of things in Spain as the most succinct and lucid reports under this head in the newspapers: and as for England, almost the last significant scrap of news from that quarter was the revolution of 1649; and if you have learned the history of her crops for an average year, you never need attend to that thing again, unless your speculations are of a merely pecuniary character. If one may judge who rarely looks into the newspapers, nothing new does ever happen in foreign parts, a French revolution not excepted.

What news! how much more important to know what that is which was never old! "Kieou-he-yu (great dignitary of the state of Wei) sent a man to Khoung-tseu to know his news. Khoung-tseu caused the messenger to be seated near him, and questioned him in these terms: What is your master doing? The messenger answered with respect: My master desires to diminish the number of his faults, but he cannot come to the end of them. The messenger being gone, the philosopher remarked: What a worthy messenger! What a worthy messenger!" The preacher, instead of vexing the ears of drowsy farmers on their day of rest at the end of the week,—for Sunday is the fit conclusion of an ill-spent week, and not the fresh and brave beginning of a new one,—with this one other draggle-tail of a sermon, should shout with thundering voice, "Pause! Avast! Why so seeming fast, but deadly slow?"

Shams and delusions are esteemed for soundest truths, while reality is fabulous. If men would steadily observe realities only, and not allow themselves to be deluded, life, to compare it with such things as we know, would be like a fairy tale and the Arabian Nights' Entertainments. If we respected only what is inevitable and has a right to be, music and poetry would resound along the streets. When we are unhurried and wise, we perceive that only great and worthy things have any permanent and absolute existence, that petty fears and petty pleasures are but the shadow of the reality. This is always exhilarating and sublime. By closing the eyes and slumbering, and consenting to be deceived by shows, men establish and confirm their daily life of routine and habit everywhere, which still is built on purely illusory foundations. Children, who play life, discern its true law and relations more clearly than men, who fail to live it worthily, but who think that they are wiser by experience, that is, by failure. I have read in a Hindoo book, that "there was a king's son, who, being expelled in infancy from his native city, was brought up by a forester, and, growing up to maturity in that state, imagined himself to belong to the barbarous race with which he lived. One of his father's ministers having discovered him, revealed to him what he was, and the misconception of his character was removed, and he knew himself to be a prince. So soul," continues the Hindoo philosopher, "from the circumstances in which it is placed, mistakes its own character, until the truth is revealed to it by some holy teacher, and then it knows itself to be *Brahme*." I perceive that we inhabitants of New England live this mean life that we do because our vision does not penetrate the surface of things. We think that that *is* which *appears* to be. If a man should walk through this town and see only the reality, where, think you, would the "Mill-dam" go to? If he should give us an account of the realities he beheld there, we should not recognize the place in his description. Look at a meeting-house, or a court-house, or a jail, or a shop, or a dwelling-house, and say what that thing really is before a true gaze, and they would all go to pieces in your account of them. Men esteem truth remote, in the outskirts of the system, behind the farthest star, before Adam and after the last man. In eternity there is indeed something true and sublime. But all these times and places and occasions are now and here. God himself culminates in the present moment, and will never be more divine in the lapse of all the ages. And we are enabled to apprehend at all what is sublime and noble only by the perpetual instilling and drenching of the reality that surrounds us. The universe constantly and obediently answers to our conceptions; whether we travel fast or slow, the track is laid for us. Let us spend our lives in conceiving then. The poet or the artist never yet had so fair and noble a design but some of his posterity at least could accomplish it.

Let us spend one day as deliberately as Nature, and not be thrown off the track by every nutshell and mosquito's wing that falls on the rails. Let us rise early and fast, or break fast, gently and without perturbation; let company come and let company go, let the bells ring and the children cry,—determined to make a day of it. Why should we knock under and go with the stream? Let us not be upset and overwhelmed in that terrible rapid and whirlpool called a dinner, situated in the meridian shallows. Weather this danger and you are safe, for the rest of the way is down hill. With unrelaxed nerves, with morning vigor, sail by it, looking another way, tied to the mast like Ulysses. If the engine whistles, let it whistle till it is hoarse for its pains. If the bell rings, why should we run? We will consider what kind of music they are like. Let us settle ourselves, and work and wedge our feet downward through the mud and slush of opinion, and prejudice, and tradition, and delusion, and appearance, that alluvion which covers the globe, through Paris and London, through New York and Boston and Concord, through Church and State, through poetry and philosophy and religion, till we come to a hard bottom and rocks in place, which we can call *reality*, and say, This is, and no mistake; and then begin, having a *point d'appui*, below freshet and frost and fire, a place where you might found a wall or a state, or set a lamp-post safely, or perhaps a gauge, not a Nilometer, but a Realometer, that future ages might know how deep a freshet of shams and appearances had gathered from time to time. If you stand right fronting and face to face to a fact, you will see the sun glimmer on both its surfaces, as if it were a cimeter, and feel its sweet edge dividing you through the heart and marrow, and so you will happily conclude your mortal career. Be it life or death, we crave only reality. If we are really dying, let us hear the rattle in our throats and feel cold in the extremities; if we are alive, let us go about our business.

Time is but the stream I go a-fishing in. I drink at it; but while I drink I see the sandy bottom and detect how shallow it is. Its thin current slides away, but eternity remains. I would drink deeper; fish in the sky, whose bottom is pebbly with stars. I cannot count one. I know not the first letter of the alphabet. I have always been regretting that I was not as wise as the day I was born. The intellect is a cleaver; it discerns and rifts its way into the secret of things. I do not wish to be any more busy with my hands than is necessary. My head is hands and feet. I feel all my best faculties concentrated in it. My instinct tells me that my head is an organ for burrowing, as some creatures use their snout and fore paws, and with it I would mine and burrow my way through these hills. I think that the richest vein is somewhere hereabouts; so by the divining-rod and thin rising vapors I judge; and here I will begin to mine.

THE HUNTING CAMP

FROM *The Oregon Trail*

BY FRANCIS PARKMAN

LONG before daybreak the Indians broke up their camp. The women of Mene-Seela's lodge were as usual among the first that were ready for departure, and I found the old man himself sitting by the embers of the decayed fire, over which he was warming his withered fingers, as the morning was very chill and damp. The preparations for moving were even more confused and disorderly than usual. While some families were leaving the ground the lodges of others were still standing untouched. At this old Mene-Seela grew impatient, and walking out to the middle of the village, he stood with his robe wrapped close around him, and harangued the people in a loud, sharp voice. Now, he said, when they were on an enemy's hunting-grounds, was not the time to behave like children; they ought to be more active and united than ever. His speech had some effect. The delinquents took down their lodges and loaded their pack-horses; and when the sun rose, the last of the men, women, and children had left the deserted camp.

This movement was made merely for the purpose of finding a better and safer position. So we advanced only three or four miles up the little stream, when each family assumed its relative place in the great ring of the village, and the squaws set actively at work in preparing the camp. But not a single warrior dismounted from his horse. All the men that morning were mounted on inferior animals, leading their best horses by a cord, or confiding them to the care of boys. In small parties they began to leave the ground and ride rapidly away over the plains to the westward. I had taken no food, and not being at all ambitious of farther abstinence, I went into my host's lodge, which his squaws had set up with wonderful despatch, and sat down in the centre, as a gentle hint that I was hungry. A wooden bowl was soon set before me, filled with the nutritious preparation of dried meat, called *pemmican* by the northern voyagers, and *wasna* by the Dahcotah. Taking a handful to break my fast upon, I left the lodge just in time to see the last band of hunters disappear over the ridge of the neighboring hill. I mounted Pauline and galloped in pursuit, riding rather by the balance than by any muscular strength that remained to me. From the top of the hill I could overlook a wide extent of desolate prairie, over which, far and near, little parties of naked horsemen were rapidly passing. I soon came up to the nearest, and we had not ridden a mile before all were united into one large and compact body. All was haste and eagerness. Each hunter whipped on his horse, as if anxious to be the first to reach the game. In such movements among the Indians this is always more or less the case; but it was especially so in the present instance, because the head chief of the village was absent, and there were but few "soldiers," a sort of Indian police, who among their other functions usually assume the direction of a buffalo hunt. No man turned to the right hand or to the left. We rode at a swift canter straight forward, up hill and down hill, and through the stiff, obstinate growth of the endless wild-sage bushes. For an hour and a half the same red shoulders, the same long black hair rose and fell with the motion of the horses before me. Very little was said, though once I observed an old man severely reproving Raymond for having left his rifle behind him, when there was some probability of encountering an enemy before the day was over. As we galloped across a plain thickly set with sage bushes, the foremost riders vanished suddenly from sight, as if diving into the earth. The arid soil was cracked into a deep ravine. Down we all went in succession and galloped in a line along the bottom, until we found a point where, one by one, the horses could scramble out. Soon after, we came upon a wide shallow stream, and as we rode swiftly over the hard sand-beds and through the thin sheets of rippling water, many of the savage horsemen threw themselves to the ground, knelt on the sand, snatched a hasty draught, and leaping back again to their seats, galloped on as before.

Meanwhile scouts kept in advance of the party; and now we began to see them on the ridges of the hills, waving their robes in token that buffalo were visible. These however proved to be nothing more than old straggling bulls, feeding upon the neighboring plains, who would stare for a moment at the hostile array and then gallop clumsily off. At length we could discern several of these scouts making their signals to us at once; no longer waving their robes boldly from the top of the hill, but standing lower down, so that they could not be seen from the plains beyond. Game worth pursuing had evidently been discovered. The excited Indians now urged forward their tired horses even more rapidly than before. Pauline, who was still sick and jaded, began to groan heavily; and her yellow sides were darkened with sweat. As we were crowding together over a lower intervening hill, I heard Reynal and Raymond shouting to me from the left; and, looking in that direction, I saw them riding away behind a party of about twenty mean-looking Indians. These were the relatives of Reynal's squaw, Margot, who, not wishing to take part in the general hunt, were riding towards a distant hollow, where they saw a small band of buffalo which they meant to appropriate to themselves. I answered to the call by ordering Raymond to turn back and follow me. He reluctantly obeyed, though Reynal, who had relied on his assistance in skinning, cutting up, and carrying to camp the buffalo that he and his party should kill, loudly protested, and declared that we should see no sport if we went with the rest of the Indians. Followed by Raymond, I pursued the main body of hunters, while Reynal, in a great rage, whipped his horse over the hill after his ragamuffin relatives. The Indians, still about a hundred in number, galloped in a dense body at some distance in advance, a cloud of dust flying in the wind behind them. I could not overtake them until they had stopped on the side of the hill where the scouts were standing. Here each hunter sprang in haste from the tired animal he had ridden, and leaped upon the fresh horse he had brought with him. There was not a saddle or a bridle in the whole party. A piece of buffalo-robe, girthed over the horse's back, served in the place of the one, and a cord of twisted hair, lashed round his lower jaw, answered for the other. Eagle feathers dangled from every mane and tail, as marks of courage and speed. As for the rider, he wore no other clothing than a light cincture at his waist, and a pair of moccasins. He had a heavy whip, with a handle of solid elk-horn, and a lash of

knotted bull-hide, fastened to his wrist by a band. His
bow was in his hand, and his quiver of otter or panther
skin hung at his shoulder. Thus equipped, some thirty
of the hunters galloped away towards the left, in order
to make a circuit under cover of the hills, that the
buffalo might be assailed on both sides at once. The
rest impatiently waited until time enough had elapsed
for their companions to reach the required position.
Then riding upward in a body, we gained the ridge
of the hill, and for the first time came in sight of the
buffalo on the plain beyond.

They were a band of cows, four or five hundred in
number, crowded together near the bank of a wide
stream that was soaking across the sand-beds of the
valley. This valley was a large circular basin, sun-
scorched and broken, scantily covered with herbage,
and surrounded with high barren hills, from an opening in which we could see our allies galloping out upon
the plain. The wind blew from that direction. The
buffalo, aware of their approach, had begun to move,
though very slowly and in a compact mass. I have no
farther recollection of seeing the game until we were
in the midst of them, for as we rode down the hill
other objects engrossed my attention. Numerous old
bulls were scattered over the plain, and ungallantly
deserting their charge at our approach began to wade
and plunge through the quicksands of the stream,
and gallop away towards the hills. One old veteran
was straggling behind the rest, with one of his fore-
legs, which had been broken by some accident, dan-
gling about uselessly. His appearance as he went sham-
bling along on three legs, was so ludicrous that I could
not help pausing for a moment to look at him. As I
came near, he would try to rush upon me, nearly
throwing himself down at every awkward attempt.

Looking up, I saw the whole body of Indians full an hundred yards in advance. I lashed Pauline in pursuit and reached them just in time; for, at that moment, each hunter, as if by a common impulse, violently struck his horse, each horse sprang forward, and, scattering in the charge in order to assail the entire herd at once, we all rushed headlong upon the buffalo. We were among them in an instant. Amid the trampling and the yells I could see their dark figures running hither and thither through clouds of dust, and the horsemen darting in pursuit. While we were charging on one side, our companions attacked the bewildered and panic-stricken herd on the other. The uproar and confusion lasted but a moment. The dust cleared away, and the buffalo could be seen scattering as from a common centre, flying over the plain singly, or in long files and small compact bodies, while behind them followed the Indians, riding at furious speed, and yelling as they launched arrow after arrow into their sides. The carcasses were strewn thickly over the ground. Here and there stood wounded buffalo, their bleeding sides feathered with arrows; and as I rode by them their eyes would glare, they would bristle like gigantic cats, and feebly attempt to rush up and gore my horse.

I left camp that morning with a philosophic resolution. Neither I nor my horse were at that time fit for such sport, and I had determined to remain a quiet spectator; but amid the rush of horses and buffalo, the uproar and the dust, I found it impossible to sit still; and as four or five buffalo ran past me in a line, I lashed Pauline in pursuit. We went plunging through the water and the quicksands, and clambering the bank, chased them through the wild-sage bushes that covered the rising ground beyond. But neither her native spirit nor the blows of the knotted bull-hide could supply the place of poor Pauline's exhausted strength. We could not gain an inch upon the fugitives. At last, however, they came full upon a ravine too wide to leap over; and as this compelled them to turn abruptly to the left, I contrived to get within ten or twelve yards of the hindmost. At this she faced about, bristled angrily, and made a show of charging. I shot at her, and hit her somewhere in the neck. Down she tumbled into the ravine, whither her companions had descended before her. I saw their dark backs appearing and disappearing as they galloped along the bottom; then, one by one, they scrambled out on the other side, and ran off as before, the wounded animal following with the rest.

Turning back, I saw Raymond coming on his black mule to meet me; and as we rode over the field together, we counted scores of carcasses lying on the plain, in the ravines, and on the sandy bed of the stream. Far away in the distance, horsemen and buffalo were still scouring along, with clouds of dust rising behind them; and over the sides of the hills long files of the frightened animals were rapidly ascending. The hunters began to return. The boys, who had held the horses behind the hill, made their appearance, and the work of flaying and cutting up began in earnest all over the field. I noticed my host Kongra-Tonga beyond the stream, just alighting by the side of a cow which he had killed. Riding up to him, I found him in the act of drawing out an arrow, which, with the exception of the notch at the end, had entirely disappeared in the animal. I asked him to give it to me, and I still retain it as a proof, though by no means the most striking one that could be offered, of the force and dexterity with which the Indians discharge their arrows.

The hides and meat were piled upon the horses, and the hunters began to leave the ground. Raymond and I, too, getting tired of the scene, set out for the village, riding straight across the intervening desert. There was no path, and as far as I could see, no landmarks sufficient to guide us; but Raymond seemed to have an instinctive perception of the point on the horizon towards which we ought to direct our course. Antelope were bounding on all sides, and as is always the case in the presence of buffalo, they seemed to have lost their natural shyness. Bands of them would run lightly up the rocky declivities, and stand gazing down upon us from the summit. At length we could distinguish the tall white rocks and the old pine-trees that, as we well remembered, were just above the site of the encampment. Still we could see nothing of the camp itself, until, mounting a grassy hill, we saw the circle of lodges, dingy with storms and smoke, standing on the plain at our feet.

I entered the lodge of my host. His squaw instantly brought me food and water, and spread a buffalo-robe for me to lie upon; and being much fatigued I lay down and fell asleep. In about an hour, the entrance of Kongra-Tonga, with his arms smeared with blood to the elbows, awoke me; he sat down in his usual seat, on the left side of the lodge. His squaw gave him a vessel of water for washing, set before him a bowl of boiled meat, and, as he was eating, pulled off his bloody moccasins and placed fresh ones on his feet; then outstretching his limbs, my host composed himself to sleep.

And now the hunters, two or three at a time, came

rapidly in, and each consigning his horses to the squaws, entered his lodge with the air of a man whose day's work was done. The squaws flung down the load from the burdened horses, and vast piles of meat and hides were soon gathered before every lodge. By this time it was darkening fast, and the whole village was illumined by the glare of fires. All the squaws and children were gathered about the piles of meat, exploring them in search of the daintiest portions. Some of these they roasted on sticks before the fires, but often they dispensed with this superfluous operation. Late into the night the fires were still glowing upon the groups of feasters engaged in this savage banquet around them.

Several hunters sat down by the fire in Kongra-Tonga's lodge to talk over the day's exploits. Among the rest, Mene-Seela came in. Though he must have seen full eighty winters, he had taken an active share in the day's sport. He boasted that he had killed two cows that morning, and would have killed a third if the dust had not blinded him so that he had to drop his bow and arrows and press both hands against his eyes to stop the pain. The fire-light fell upon his wrinkled face and shrivelled figure as he sat telling his story with such inimitable gesticulation that every man in the lodge broke into a laugh.

Old Mene-Seela was one of the few Indians in the village with whom I would have trusted myself alone without suspicion, and the only one from whom I should have received a gift or a service without the certainty that it proceeded from an interested motive. He was a great friend to the whites. He liked to be in their society, and was very vain of the favors he had received from them. He told me one afternoon, as we were sitting together in his son's lodge, that he considered the beaver and the whites the wisest people on earth; indeed, he was convinced they were the same; and an incident which had happened to him long before had assured him of this. So he began the following story, and as the pipe passed in turn to him, Reynal availed himself of these interruptions to translate what had preceded. But the old man accompanied his words with such admirable pantomime that translation was hardly necessary.

He said that when he was very young, and had never yet seen a white man, he and three or four of his companions were out on a beaver hunt, and he crawled into a large beaver-lodge, to see what was there. Sometimes he crept on his hands and knees, sometimes he was obliged to swim, and sometimes to lie flat on his face and drag himself along. In this way he crawled a great distance under ground. It was very dark, cold, and close, so that at last he was almost suffocated, and fell into a swoon. When he began to recover, he could just distinguish the voices of his companions outside, who had given him up for lost, and were singing his death-song. At first he could see nothing, but soon discerned something white before him, and at length plainly distinguished three people, entirely white, one man and two women, sitting at the edge of a black pool of water. He became alarmed, and thought it high time to retreat. Having succeeded, after great trouble, in reaching daylight again, he went to the spot directly above the pool of water where he had seen the three mysterious beings. Here he beat a hole with his war-club in the ground, and sat down to watch. In a moment the nose of an old male beaver appeared at the opening. Mene-Seela instantly seized him and dragged him up, when two other beavers, both females, thrust out their heads, and these he served in the same way. "These," said the old man, concluding his story, for which he was probably indebted to a dream, "must have been the three white people whom I saw sitting at the edge of the water."

Mene-Seela was the grand depositary of the legends and traditions of the village. I succeeded, however, in getting from him only a few fragments. Like all Indians, he was excessively superstitious, and continually saw some reason for withholding his stories. "It is a bad thing," he would say, "to tell the tales in summer. Stay with us till next winter, and I will tell you every thing I know; but now our war-parties are going out, and our young men will be killed if I sit down to tell stories before the frost begins."

But to leave this digression. We remained encamped on this spot five days, during three of which the hunters were at work incessantly, and immense quantities of meat and hides were brought in. Great alarm, however, prevailed in the village. All were on the alert. The young men ranged the country as scouts, and the old men paid careful attention to omens and prodigies, and especially to their dreams. In order to convey to the enemy (who, if they were in the neighborhood, must inevitably have known of our presence) the impression that we were constantly on the watch, piles of sticks and stones were erected on all the surrounding hills, in such a manner as to appear at a distance like sentinels. Often, even to this hour, that scene will rise before my mind like a visible reality; the tall white rocks; the old pine-trees on their summits; the sandy stream that ran along their bases and half encircled the village; and the wild-sage bushes, with their dull green hue and their medicinal odor, that covered all the neighboring declivities. Hour after hour the squaws would pass and repass with their vessels of water between the stream and the lodges. For the most part, no one was to be seen in the camp but women and children, two or three superannuated old men, and a few lazy and worthless young ones. These, together with the dogs, now grown fat and good-natured with the abundance in the camp, were its only tenants. Still it presented a busy and bustling scene. In all quarters the meat, hung on cords of hide, was drying in the sun, and around the lodges, the squaws, young and old, were laboring on the fresh hides stretched upon the ground, scraping the hair from one side and the still adhering flesh from the other, and rubbing into them the brains of the buffalo, in order to render them soft and pliant.

In mercy to myself and my horse, I did not go out with the hunters after the first day. Of late, however, I had been gaining strength rapidly, as was always the case upon every respite of my disorder. I was soon able to walk with ease. Raymond and I would go out upon the neighboring prairies to shoot antelope, or sometimes to assail straggling buffalo, on foot; an attempt in which we met with rather indifferent success. As I came out of Kongra-Tonga's lodge one morning, Reynal called to me from the opposite side of the village, and asked me over to breakfast. The breakfast was a substantial one. It consisted of the rich, juicy hump-ribs of a fat cow; a repast absolutely unrivalled in its way. It was roasting before the fire, impaled upon a stout stick, which Reynal took up and planted in the ground before his lodge; when he, with Raymond and myself, taking our seats around it, unsheathed our knives and assailed it with good will. In spite of all medical experience, this solid fare, without bread or salt, seemed to agree with me admirably.

"We shall have strangers here before night," said Reynal.

"How do you know that?" I asked.

"I dreamed so. I am as good at dreaming as an Indian. There's the Hail-Storm; he dreamed the same thing, and he and his crony, The Rabbit, have gone out on discovery."

I laughed at Reynal for his credulity, went over to my host's lodge, took down my rifle, walked out a mile or two on the prairie, saw an old bull standing alone, crawled up a ravine, shot him, and saw him escape. Then, exhausted and rather ill-humored, I walked back to the village. By a strange coincidence, Reynal's prediction had been verified; for the first persons whom I saw were the two trappers, Rouleau and Saraphin, coming to meet me. These men, as the reader may possibly recollect, had left our party about a fortnight before. They had been trapping among the Black Hills, and were now on their way to the Rocky Mountains, intending in a day or two to set out for the neighboring Medicine Bow. They were not the most elegant or refined of companions, yet they made a very welcome addition to the limited society of the village. For the rest of that day we lay smoking and talking in Reynal's lodge. This indeed was no better than a hut, made of hides stretched on poles, and entirely open in front. It was well carpeted with soft buffalo-robes, and here we remained, sheltered from the sun, surrounded by the domestic utensils of Madame Margot's household. All was quiet in the village. Though the hunters had not gone out that day, they lay sleeping in their lodges, and most of the women were silently engaged in their heavy tasks. A few young men were playing at a lazy game of ball in the area of the village; and when they became tired, some girls supplied their place with a more boisterous sport. At a little distance, among the lodges, some children and half-grown squaws were playfully tossing one of their number in a buffalo-robe, an exact counterpart of the ancient pastime from which Sancho Panza suffered so much. Farther out on the prairie, a host of little naked boys were roaming about, engaged in various rough games, or pursuing birds and ground-squirrels with their bows and arrows; and woe to the unhappy little animals that fell into their merciless, torture-loving hands. A squaw from the next lodge, a notable housewife, named Weah Washtay, or the Good Woman, brought us a large bowl of *wasna*, and went into an ecstasy of delight when I presented her with a green glass ring, such as I usually wore with a view to similar occasions.

The sun went down, and half the sky was glowing fiery red, reflected on the little stream as it wound away among the sage-bushes. Some young men left the village, and soon returned, driving in before them all the horses, hundreds in number, and of every size, age, and color. The hunters came out, and each securing those that belonged to him, examined their condition, and tied them fast by long cords to stakes driven in front of his lodge. It was half an hour before the bustle subsided and tranquillity was restored again. By this time it was nearly dark. Kettles were hung over the fires, around which the squaws were gathered with their children, laughing and talking merrily. A circle of a different kind was formed in the centre of the village. This was composed of the old men and warriors of repute, who sat together with their white buffalo-robes drawn close around their shoulders; and as the pipe passed from hand to hand, their conversation had not a particle of the gravity and reserve usually ascribed to Indians. I sat down with them as usual. I had in my hand half a dozen squibs and serpents, which I had made one day when encamped upon Laramie Creek, with gunpowder and charcoal, and the leaves of "Frémont's Expedition," rolled round a stout lead-pencil. I waited till I could get hold of the large piece of burning *bois-de-vache* which the Indians kept by them on the ground for lighting their pipes. With this I lighted all the fireworks at once, and tossed them whizzing and sputtering into the air, over the heads of the company. They all jumped up and ran off with yelps of astonishment and consternation. After a moment or two, they ventured to come back one by one, and some of the boldest, picking up the cases of burnt paper, examined them with eager curiosity to discover their mysterious secret. From that time forward I enjoyed great repute as a "fire-medicine."

The camp was filled with the low hum of cheerful voices. There were other sounds, however, of a different kind; for from a large lodge, lighted up like a gigantic lantern by the blazing fire within, came a chorus of dismal cries and wailings, long drawn out, like the howling of wolves, and a woman, almost naked, was crouching close outside, crying violently, and gashing her legs with a knife till they were covered with blood. Just a year before, a young man belonging to this family had been slain by the enemy, and his relatives were thus lamenting his loss. Still other sounds might be heard; loud earnest cries often repeated from amid the gloom, at a distance beyond the village. They proceeded from some young men who, being about to set out in a few days on a war-party, were standing at the top of a hill, calling on the Great Spirit to aid them in their enterprise. While I was listening, Rouleau, with a laugh on his careless face, called to me and directed my attention to another quarter. In front of the lodge where Weah Washtay lived, another squaw was standing, angrily scolding an old yellow dog, who lay on the ground with his nose resting between his paws, and his eyes turned sleepily up to her face, as if pretending to give respectful attention, but resolved to fall asleep as soon as it was all over.

"You ought to be ashamed of yourself!" said the old woman. "I have fed you well, and taken care of you ever since you were small and blind, and could only crawl about and squeal a little, instead of howling as you do now. When you grew old, I said you were a good dog. You were strong and gentle when the load was put on your back, and you never ran among the feet of the horses when we were all travelling together over the prairie. But you had a bad heart! Whenever a rabbit jumped out of the bushes, you were always the first to run after him and lead away all the other dogs behind you. You ought to have known that it was very dangerous to act so. When you had got far out on the prairie, and no one was near to help you, perhaps a wolf would jump out of the ravine; and then what could you do? You would certainly have been killed, for no dog can fight well with a load on his back. Only three days ago you ran off in that way, and turned over the bag of wooden pins with which I used to fasten up the front of the lodge. Look up there, and you will see that it is all flapping open. And now to-night you have stolen a great piece of fat meat which was roasting before the fire for my children. I tell you, you have a bad heart, and you must die!"

So saying, the squaw went into the lodge, and coming out with a large stone mallet, killed the unfortunate dog at one blow. This speech is worthy of notice, as illustrating a curious characteristic of the Indians, who ascribe intelligence and a power of understanding speech to the inferior animals; to whom, indeed, according to many of their traditions, they are linked in close affinity; and they even claim the honor of a lineal descent from bears, wolves, deer, or tortoises.

As it grew late, I walked across the village to the lodge of my host, Kongra-Tonga. As I entered I saw him, by the blaze of the fire in the middle, reclining half asleep in his usual place. His couch was by no means an uncomfortable one. It consisted of buffalo-robes, laid together on the ground, and a pillow made of whitened deer-skin, stuffed with feathers and ornamented with beads. At his back was a light frame-work of poles and slender reeds, against which he could lean with ease when in a sitting posture; and at the top of it, just above his head, hung his bow and quiver. His squaw, a laughing, broad-faced woman, apparently had not yet completed her domestic arrangements, for she was bustling about the lodge, pulling over the utensils and the bales of dried meat that were ranged carefully around it. Unhappily, she and her partner were not the only tenants of the dwelling; for half a dozen children were scattered about, sleeping in every imaginable posture. My saddle was in its place at the head of the lodge, and a buffalo-robe was spread on the ground before it. Wrapping myself in my blanket, I lay down; but had I not been extremely fatigued, the noise in the next lodge would have prevented my sleeping. There was the monotonous thumping of the Indian drum, mixed with occasional sharp yells, and a chorus chanted by twenty voices. A grand scene of gambling was going forward with all the appropriate formalities. The players were staking on the chances of the game their ornaments, their horses, and as the excitement rose, their garments, and even their weapons; for desperate gambling is not confined to the hells of Paris. The men of the plains and forests no less resort to it as a relief to the tedious monotony of their lives, which alternate between fierce excitement and listless inaction. I fell asleep with the dull notes of the drum still sounding on my ear; but these orgies lasted without intermission till daylight. I was soon awakened by one of the children crawling over me, while another larger one was tugging at my blanket and nestling himself in a very disagreeable proximity. I immediately repelled these advances by punching the heads of these miniature savages with a short stick which I always kept by me for the purpose; and as sleeping half the day and eating much more than is good for them makes them extremely restless, this operation usually had to be repeated four or five times in the course of the night. My host himself was the author of another formidable annoyance. All these Indians, and he among the rest, think themselves bound to the constant performance of certain acts as the condition on which their success in life depends, whether in war, love, hunting, or any other employment. These "medicines," as they are called, which are usually communicated in dreams, are often absurd enough. Some Indians will strike the butt of the pipe against the ground every time they smoke; others will insist that every thing they say shall be interpreted by contraries; and Shaw once met an old man who conceived that all would be lost unless he compelled every white man he met to drink a bowl of cold water. My host ·was particularly unfortunate in his allotment. The spirits had told him in a dream that he must sing a certain song in the middle of every night; and regularly at about twelve o'clock his dismal

monotonous chanting would awaken me, and I would
see him seated bolt upright on his couch, going through
his dolorous performance with a most business-like air.
There were other voices of the night, still more in-
harmonious. Twice or thrice, between sunset and
dawn, all the dogs in the village, and there were
hundreds of them, would bay and yelp in chorus; a
horrible clamor, resembling no sound that I have ever
heard, except perhaps the frightful howling of wolves
that we used sometimes to hear, long afterward, when
descending the Arkansas on the trail of General Kear-
ney's army. This canine uproar is, if possible, more
discordant than that of the wolves. Heard at a distance
slowly rising on the night, it has a strange unearthly
effect, and would fearfully haunt the dreams of a
nervous man; but when you are sleeping in the midst
of it, the din is outrageous. One long, loud howl
begins it, and voice after voice takes up the sound,
till it passes around the whole circumference of the
village, and the air is filled with confused and discordant cries, at once fierce and mournful. It lasts a
few moments, and then dies away into silence.

Morning came, and Kongra-Tonga, mounting his
horse, rode out with the hunters. It may not be amiss
to glance at him for an instant in his character of
husband and father. Both he and his squaw, like most
other Indians, were very fond of their children, whom
they indulge to excess, and never punished, except in
extreme cases, when they would throw a bowl of
cold water over them. Their offspring became sufficiently undutiful and disobedient under this system of
education, which tends not a little to foster that wild
idea of liberty and utter intolerance of restraint which
lie at the foundation of the Indian character. It would
be hard to find a fonder father than Kongra-Tonga.

There was one urchin in particular, rather less than two meet high, to whom he was exceedingly attached; and sometimes spreading a buffalo-robe in the lodge, he would seat himself upon it, place his small favorite upright before him, and chant in a low tone some of the words used as an accompaniment to the war-dance. The little fellow, who could just manage to balance himself by stretching out both arms, would lift his feet and turn slowly round and round in time to his father's music, while my host would laugh with delight, and look smiling up into my face to see if I were admiring this precocious performance of his offspring. In his capacity of husband he was less tender. The squaw who lived in the lodge with him had been his partner for many years. She took good care of his children and his household concerns. He liked her well enough, and as far as I could see, they never quarrelled; but his warmer affections were reserved for younger and more recent favorites. Of these he had at present only one, who lived in a lodge apart from his own. One day while in this camp, he became displeased with her, pushed her out, threw after her her ornaments, dresses, and every thing she had, and told her to go home to her father. Having consummated this summary divorce, for which he could show good reasons, he came back, seated himself in his usual place, and began to smoke with an air of the utmost tranquillity and self-satisfaction.

I was sitting in the lodge with him on that very afternoon, when I felt some curiosity to learn the history of the numerous scars that appeared on his naked body. Of some of them, however, I did not venture to inquire, for I already understood their origin. Each of his arms was marked as if deeply gashed with a knife at regular intervals, and there were other scars also, of a different character, on his back and on either breast. They were the traces of the tortures which these Indians, in common with a few other tribes, inflict upon themselves at certain seasons; in part, it may be, to gain the glory of courage and endurance, but chiefly as an act of self-sacrifice to secure the favor of the spirits. The scars upon the breast and back were produced by running through the flesh strong splints of wood, to which heavy buffalo-skulls are fastened by cords of hide, and the wretch runs forward with all his strength, assisted by two companions, who take hold of each arm, until the flesh tears apart and the skulls are left behind. Others of Kongra-Tonga's scars were the result of accidents; but he had many received in war. He was one of the most noted warriors in the village. In the course of his life he had slain, as he boasted to me, fourteen men; and though, like other Indians, he was a braggart and liar, yet in this statement common report bore him out. Being flattered by my inquiries, he told me tale after tale, true or false, of his warlike exploits; and there was one among the rest illustrating the worst features of Indian character too well for me to omit it. Pointing out of the opening of the lodge towards the Medicine Bow Mountain, not many miles distant, he said that he was there a few summers ago with a war-party of his young men. Here they found two Snake Indians, hunting. They shot one of them with arrows, and chased the other up the side of the mountain till they surrounded him, and Kongra-Tonga himself, jumping forward among the trees, seized him by the arm. Two of his young men then ran up and held him fast while he scalped him alive. They then built a great fire, and cutting the tendons of their captive's wrists and feet, threw him in, and held him down with long poles until he was burnt to death. He garnished his story with descriptive particulars much too revolting to mention. His features were remarkably mild and open, without the fierceness of expression common among these Indians; and as he detailed these devilish cruelties, he looked up into my face with the air of earnest simplicity which a little child would wear in relating to its mother some anecdote of its youthful experience.

Old Mene-Seela's lodge could offer another illustration of the ferocity of Indian warfare. A bright-eyed active little boy was living there who had belonged to a village of the Gros-Ventre Blackfeet, a small but bloody and treacherous band, in close alliance with the Arapahoes. About a year before, Kongra-Tonga and a party of warriors had found about twenty lodges of these Indians upon the plains a little to the eastward of our present camp; and surrounding them in the night, they butchered men, women, and children, preserving only this little boy alive. He was adopted into the old man's family, and was now fast becoming identified with the Ogillallah children, among whom he mingled on equal terms. There was also a Crow warrior in the village, a man of gigantic stature and most symmetrical proportions. Having been taken prisoner many years before and adopted by a squaw in place of a son whom she had lost, he had forgotten his old nationality, and was now both in act and inclination an Ogillallah.

It will be remembered that the scheme of the grand war-party against the Snake and Crow Indians originated in this village; and though this plan had fallen to the ground, the embers of martial ardor continued to glow. Eleven young men had prepared to go out against the enemy, and the fourth day of our stay in this camp was fixed upon for their departure. At the head of this party was a well-built, active little Indian, called the White Shield, whom I had always noticed for the neat-ness of his dress and appearance. His lodge too, though not a large one, was the best in the village, his squaw was one of the prettiest, and altogether his dwelling was the model of an Ogillallah domestic establishment. I was often a visitor there, for the White Shield being rather partial to white men used to invite me to continual feasts at all hours of the day. Once, when the substantial part of the entertainment was over, and he and I were seated cross-legged on a buffalo-robe smoking together very amicably, he took down his warlike equipments, which were hanging around the lodge, and displayed them with great pride and self-importance. Among the rest was a superb head-dress of feathers. Taking this from its case, he put it on and stood before me, perfectly conscious of the gallant air which it gave to his dark face and his vigorous graceful figure. He told me that upon it were the feathers of three war-eagles, equal in value to the same number of good horses. He took up also a shield gayly painted and hung with feathers. The effect of these barbaric ornaments was admirable. His quiver was made of the spotted skin of a small panther, common among the Black Hills, from which the tail and distended claws were still allowed to hang. The White Shield concluded his entertainment in a manner characteristic of an Indian. He begged of me a little powder and ball, for he had a gun as well as a bow and arrows; but this I was obliged to refuse, because I had scarcely enough for my own use. Making him, however, a parting present of a paper of vermilion, I left him quite contented.

On the next morning the White Shield took cold, and was attacked with an inflammation of the throat. Immediately he seemed to lose all spirit, and though before no warrior in the village had borne himself more proudly, he now moped about from lodge to lodge with a forlorn and dejected air. At length he sat down, close wrapped in his robe, before the lodge of Reynal, but when he found that neither he nor I knew how to relieve him, he arose and stalked over to one of the medicine-men of the village. This old impostor thumped him for some time with both fists, howled and yelped over him, and beat a drum close to his ear to expel the evil spirit. This treatment failing of the desired effect, the White Shield withdrew to his own lodge, where he lay disconsolate for some hours. Making his appearance once more in the afternoon, he again took his seat on the ground before Reynal's lodge, holding his throat with his hand. For some time he sat silent with his eyes fixed mournfully on the ground. At last he began to speak in a low tone.

"I am a brave man," he said; "all the young men think me a great warrior, and ten of them are ready to go with me to the war. I will go and show them the enemy. Last summer the Snakes killed my brother. I cannot live unless I revenge his death. To-morrow we will set out and I will take their scalps."

The White Shield, as he expressed this resolution, seemed to have lost all the accustomed fire and spirit of his look, and hung his head as if in a fit of despondency.

As I was sitting that evening at one of the fires, I saw him arrayed in his splendid war-dress, his cheeks painted with vermilion, leading his favorite war-horse to the front of his lodge. He mounted and rode round the village, singing his war-song in a loud hoarse voice amid the shrill acclamations of the women. Then dismounting, he remained for some minutes prostrate upon the ground, as if in an act of supplication. On the following morning I looked in vain for the departure of the warriors. All was quiet in the village until late in the forenoon, when the White Shield came and seated himself in his old place before us. Reynal asked him why he had not gone out to find the enemy?

"I cannot go," he answered in a dejected voice. "I have given my war-arrows to the Meneaska."

"You have only given him two of your arrows," said Reynal. "If you ask him, he will give them back again."

For some time the White Shield said nothing. At last he spoke in a gloomy tone,—

"One of my young men has had bad dreams. The spirits of the dead came and threw stones at him in his sleep."

If such a dream had actually taken place it might have broken up this or any other war-party, but both Reynal and I were convinced at the time that it was a mere fabrication to excuse his remaining at home.

The White Shield was a warrior of noted prowess. Very probably, he would have received a mortal wound without the show of pain, and endured without flinching the worst tortures that an enemy could inflict upon him. The whole power of an Indian's nature would be summoned to encounter such a trial; every influence of his education from childhood would have prepared him for it; the cause of his suffering would have been visibly and palpably before him, and his spirit would rise to set his enemy at defiance, and gain the highest glory of a warrior by meeting death with fortitude. But when he feels himself attacked by a mysterious evil, before whose assaults his manhood is wasted, and his strength drained away, when he can see no enemy to resist and defy, the boldest warrior falls prostrate at once. He believes that a bad spirit has taken possession of him, or that he is the victim of some charm. When suffering from a protracted disorder, an Indian will often abandon himself to his supposed destiny, pine away and die, the victim of his own imagination. The same effect will often follow a series of calamities, or a long run of ill-luck, and Indians have been known to ride into the midst of an enemy's camp, or attack a grizzly bear single-handed, to get rid of a life supposed to lie under the doom of fate.

Thus after all his fasting, dreaming, and calling upon the Great Spirit, the White Shield's war-party came to nought.

THE ONLY ONE
BY MAUDE BARNES MILLER

One friend I have who lets me live,
And never tries to make me over.
Completely unreformative—
His name is Rover.

THE DEATH
OF JOHN QUINCY ADAMS

BY CARL SANDBURG

ONE morning in February of 1848 a man sat at his desk in the House of Representatives writing a piece of poetry. He was an old man; he had been born in 1767, or seven years before the Revolutionary War commenced with the firing of shots at Lexington; and he was a very practical man, even though on this morning, as the House was called to order for business, he was writing a piece of poetry.

A resolution was introduced expressing thanks to the generals of the Mexican War for their brave conduct and skilled strategy; the clerk had read, "Resolved by the House, That"—when there was a cry and a stir and the members of the House looked toward the old man; he had stood up as if he might speak once more from the floor where he had spoken hundreds of times; he clutched his desk with groping, convulsive fingers, then he sank back into his chair with a slump; a friend and two doctors carried him to a sofa and he was taken first into the rotunda and then into the Speaker's room. Mustard poultices were placed on his chest and back; he was rubbed and given a friction treatment.

About an hour afterward he spoke a few words. "This is the last of earth, but I am content." His wife, relatives, and friends stood by his side; one was Henry Clay of Kentucky, who held the old man's hand and looked into the old man's face, while tears came into his eyes. At the funeral services in Washington one Repre-

528

sentative from each state was in attendance; they escorted the body to Faneuil Hall in Boston; the body was laid in a grave in Quincy, Massachusetts.

This was the end of John Quincy Adams, his life, career, and works. For seventeen years he had been a member of Congress; during eight of those years he had fought against the "gag rule" by which Congress voted against any petitions relating to slavery being received; each year the majority against him was less until the gag rule was beaten; he had been President of the United States from 1825 to 1829, and before that was Secretary of State under President Monroe and had more of a hand in writing the Monroe Doctrine than did Monroe; earlier yet he had been in London and Paris at work with Henry Clay and Albert Gallatin on the treaty that ended the War of 1812.

This same John Quincy Adams saw Napoleon come back to Paris from Elba; he was in Russia representing President Madison at the time the armies of Napoleon were burned out of Moscow and sent reeling and harried back toward France; before that he had been a professor of rhetoric and oratory at Harvard University; he had come to Harvard after serving as United States Senator from Massachusetts and helping President Jefferson make the Louisiana Purchase; Washington had appointed him Minister to Portugal, after which his father, President John Adams, sent him to Berlin; before his graduation from Harvard he had served as a secretary to the American commissioners who negotiated the treaty of peace that ended the Revolutionary War in 1782; the year before that he was with the American envoy to Russia, following university studies at Paris and Leipzig.

A sweet, lovable man who had led a clean life full of hard work, steady habits, many dangers, furious enemies,

such was John Quincy Adams. Most of the days of his
life he got out of bed and put on his clothes before half-
past four in the morning, and then read one or two chap-
ters in the Bible. When in Washington he took a swim
every morning, summer and winter, in the Potomac
River. He was a little undersized, wore delicate side-
burns, had a mouth with the peace of God on it, and
spoke often as though his body was a rented house and
John Quincy Adams would step out of the tenement and
live on. His last words there in February of 1848 fitted
him. "This is the last of earth, but I am content."

One day four years before he died, John Quincy
Adams of Massachusetts wrote four little verses to another congressman, Alexander Stephens of Georgia, the
wizened, wry, dry member, weighing less than a hundred pounds, known to Jefferson Davis as "the little pale
star from Georgia." The verses were titled "To Alexander H. Stephens, Esq., of Georgia," and two of them
read:

> We meet as strangers in this hall,
> But when our task of duty's done,
> We blend the common good of all
> And melt the multitude in one.
>
> As strangers in this hall we met;
> But now with one united heart,
> Whate'er of life awaits us yet,
> In cordial friendship let us part.

He drew men to him, this Alexander Stephens; in his
black eyes, set deep in a large-boned, homely head, there
was a smolder by which men knew he would play
politics only so far, after which a personal sincerity must
be considered. He stood up one day to speak on the
Mexican War and declared: "All wars, to be just, must
have some distinct and legitimate objects to be accom-

plished. . . . One of the strangest . . . circumstances attending this war is, that though it has lasted upwards of eight months, at a cost of many millions of dollars, and the sacrifice of many valuable lives, both in battle and by the diseases of the camp, no man can tell for what object it is prosecuted. And it is to be doubted whether any man, save the President and his Cabinet, knows the real and secret designs that provoked its existence. To suppress inquiry, and silence all opposition to conduct so monstrous, an executive ukase has been sent forth, strongly intimating, if not clearly threatening, the charge of treason, against all who may dare to call in question the wisdom or propriety of his measures.

"It is to be seen," said Stephens, "whether the free people of this country have so soon forgotten the principles of their ancestors as to be so easily awed by the arrogance of power. For a very little further interference with the freedom of discussion, Charles X, of France, lost his throne; and for a very little greater stretch of royal prerogative, Charles I, of England, lost his head. There are some things more to be dreaded than the loss of a throne, or even the loss of a head—amongst which may be named the anathema of a nation's curse, and the infamy that usually follows it."

And it happened that on February 2, 1848, while sitting at his desk in the House of Representatives, Abraham Lincoln wrote a note to his law partner, Herndon, saying: "I just take up my pen to say that Mr. Stephens, of Georgia, a little slim, pale-faced, consumptive man, with a voice like Logan's, has just concluded the best speech, of an hour's length, I ever heard. My old, withered, dry eyes are full of tears yet. If he writes it out anything like he delivered it, our people shall see a good many copies of it."

FOR US, THE LIVING

BY ALEXANDER WOOLLCOTT

IF you could go back through the years—if, by virtue of some such gift as was the wonder and redemption of an old skin-flint named Scrooge, you could go back through the long file of American years and play eavesdropper on one fateful moment in our history, which one would you choose? Would you choose that moment in which the first starved and despairing settlers in Virginia saw, at long last, the Governor's relief boat coming slowly 'round the bend in the muddy James? Or that moment in which, under the dripping trees at Saratoga, Gentleman Johnny Burgoyne surrendered his sword after the battle which had turned the tide of our own now sanctified revolution? Or would you slip unnoticed into the multitude which stood in the November sunshine on Cemetery Hill at Gettysburg so that you might hear from his own lips that address by Abraham Lincoln which surely will live at least as long as this country does? Always in my own fond recourse to this pastime, that was my choice. But it may not have been a good one. For had I been at Gettysburg when Lincoln spoke, the chances are overwhelming that I would not have heard what he said.

In our own day, it has been an ironic commonplace that that speech which in the long history of liberty and patriotism—as mountain-top signals to mountain-top—calls back across the centuries to the funeral oration of Pericles, made no impression at all on most of the reporters who filed it with the harried telegraph operators at Gettysburg nor on most of the editors who, in composing their papers next day, merely gave their readers the impression that Mr. Lincoln "also spoke." To be sure, "The New York Times" observed the occasion by printing an editorial headed "Two Great Speeches," but if you are persistent enough to read it, you will notice that "The Times" was referring to the stupefying two-hour oration with which Edward Everett had preceded Mr. Lincoln's address and to the stirring speech which Henry Ward Beecher, fresh from his ordeal in England, had just made at the Academy of Music in Brooklyn.

It might be enjoyable and not unprofitable to glance here in passing at the more preposterous comments made by those already hostile to the speaker. In the nearby town of Harrisburg "The Patriot and Union" said, "We pass over the silly remarks of the President; for the credit of the nation we are willing that the veil of oblivion shall be dropped over them and that they shall no more be repeated or thought of." And "The Chicago Times" had this to say: "The cheek of every American must tingle with shame as he reads the silly, flat and dish-watery utterances of the man who has to be pointed out to intelligent foreigners as the President of the United States." One of those whose job it was to enlighten such foreigners, intelligent or otherwise— the American correspondent of "The London Times"— duly kept them posted as follows: "The ceremony was rendered ludicrous by some of the sallies of that poor President Lincoln. Anything more dull and commonplace it wouldn't be easy to produce." These, however, were but spiteful expressions of the same kind of angry partisanship which marked so much of the sniping at Lincoln while he lived and with which even the latest of his successors is by no means unfamiliar.

But here I am concerned only with the immediate

effect upon the fifteen thousand who were actually present at Gettysburg. From the unconscious or reluctant
testimony of many witnesses, one thing is clear. Few of
them suspected for a moment that the world *would* long
remember what was said there. Indeed, that is the
basis of a celebrated and exceedingly sentimental short
story called *The Perfect Tribute* in which Lincoln is
presented as having left Gettysburg, melancholy in the
conviction that he had "failed." The story could have
been written only by someone who knew little about
Lincoln and less about public speaking. But it *is* true
that the first audience, however much *ex post facto*
perceptiveness its members may later have laid claim
to, were at the time quite unimpressed. Historians, with
that wisdom-after-the-event which lends to posterity its
smug air of superiority, have been amused to wonder
why. I know why. I think it can be proved beyond all
doubt that of the fifteen thousand only an inconsiderable few heard what Lincoln said.

It is easy to see why this must have been so. Even
the most inexperienced playwright is careful to postpone past the first ten minutes any crucial line of his
dialogue, not only because stragglers will still be rattling
down the aisles but because there is such a thing as an
arc of attention and, in the relation between the voices
on the stage and the ears beyond the footlights, it takes
a bit of time to establish that arc's trajectory. Listen to
any speaker at a dinner and note how inevitably he de-
votes his first two or three minutes to saying nothing at
all, while his audience, with its varying rate of adjust-
ment, is tuning in. The need for such purely vocal pre-
liminaries is trebled when the gathering is held under
the sky. Mr. Lincoln spoke not only in the open air but
to a multitude of which many, having just escaped from
the trap of a two-hour discourse, were, for reasons you

are free to surmise, moving anxiously toward the exits. Some of these, as it dawned on them that the President had risen, turned in their tracks and started shoving their way back toward the rostrum. So it was not only to a huge crowd in the open air that he spoke, but to one that was not even stationary. He would have had to talk for at least five minutes before even those within reach of his voice could have really begun to listen. But the address is made up of ten sentences. It has only two hundred and seventy-two words. After he had been speaking for two minutes and thirty-five seconds, Mr. Lincoln sat down. Most of those present could not have taken in a word he said.

Now all this I know from my own platform experience. Of course, it was an old story to him who had held the difficult Cooper Union audience in thrall, who had gone down with Douglas into the dust of the arena, and who had spoken by torchlight to many a milling crossroads crowd. No one this country ever produced— not Patrick Henry, nor Henry Ward Beecher, nor Woodrow Wilson—knew better than Lincoln how to *make* an audience listen. If he did not make the one at Gettysburg listen, it must have been for a reason you will find suggested by an anecdote out of Edna Ferber's adventures with the *goyim*. Once, as a guest of the William Lyon Phelpses in New Haven, she heard her host invoke the blessing of God on the excellent menu by muttering confidentially into his soup plate. After the "Amen," Mrs. Phelps complained that she had not heard a word. "My dear," he replied, "I wasn't speaking to you." Is it not clear that, if Mr. Lincoln did not trouble to make the crowd at Gettysburg hear him, it is because he was not speaking to them?

To whom, then? The other day I put that question to John Thomason of the Marines. Smiling as if he knew

the answer, he told me about a letter he had found in a
trunk in a Texas attic. It was written in 1863 by a
young Confederate captain, who had been wounded at
Gettysburg and was still there on crutches when,
months later, the battlefield was dedicated. He must
have been one of the scattered few—there are such
exceptions in every audience—who did hear what Lincoln said. To the folks back home he wrote, "We've got
to stop fighting that man." Wherefore Major Thomason
thinks that if Lincoln was indifferent to those present
at Gettysburg it was because, over their heads, he was
talking to the South.

I think he may have been, but my own inescapable
notion is that, over the heads of the South, he was also
talking to Americans as yet unborn and unbegot.

> . . . whether that nation, or any nation so conceived
> and so dedicated, can long endure. . . .

Have these words, for example, at any time since they
were first spoken, ever had such painful immediacy as
they have seemed to have in our own anxious era? Yes,
he was talking to you and to me. Of this there is no real
question in my mind. The only question—in an age
when beggars on horseback the world around are chal-
lenging all that Lincoln had and was—the only question
is whether we will listen.

> . . . . It is for us, the living, rather, to be dedicated
> here. . . .

For whom was the speech meant? Why, the answer is
in his own words. For us. "For us, the living." For us to
resolve and see to it—and see to it—"that government
of the people, *by* the people, for the people, SHALL
NOT perish from the earth."

THE SECOND INAUGURAL
ADDRESS
BY ABRAHAM LINCOLN

FELLOW-COUNTRYMEN: At this second appearing to take the oath of the presidential office, there is less occasion for an extended address than there was at the first. Then a statement, somewhat in detail, of a course to be pursued, seemed fitting and proper. Now, at the expiration of four years, during which public declarations have been constantly called forth on every point and phase of the great contest which still absorbs the attention and engrosses the energies of the nation, little that is new could be presented. The progress of our arms, upon which all else chiefly depends, is as well known to the public as to myself; and it is, I trust, reasonably satisfactory and encouraging to all. With high hope for the future, no prediction in regard to it is ventured.

On the occasion corresponding to this four years ago, all thoughts were anxiously directed to an impending civil war. All dreaded it—all sought to avert it. While the inaugural address was being delivered from this place, devoted altogether to saving the Union without war, insurgent agents were in the city seeking to destroy it without war—seeking to dissolve the Union, and divide effects, by negotiation. Both parties deprecated war; but one of them would make war rather than let the nation survive; and the other would accept war rather than let it perish. And the war came.

One-eighth of the whole population were colored

slaves, not distributed generally over the Union, but localized in the southern part of it. These slaves constituted a peculiar and powerful interest. All knew that this interest was, somehow, the cause of the war. To strengthen, perpetuate, and extend this interest was the object for which the insurgents would rend the Union, even by war; while the government claimed no right to do more than to restrict the territorial enlargement of it.

Neither party expected for the war the magnitude or the duration which it has already attained. Neither anticipated that the cause of the conflict might cease with, or even before, the conflict itself should cease. Each looked for an easier triumph and a result less fundamental and astounding. Both read the same Bible, and pray to the same God; and each invokes his aid against the other. It may seem strange that any men should dare to ask a just God's assistance in wringing their bread from the sweat of other men's faces; but let us judge not, that we be not judged. The prayers of both could not be answered—that of neither has been answered fully.

The Almighty has his own purposes. "Woe unto the world because of offenses! for it must needs be that offenses comes; but woe to that man by whom the offense cometh." If we shall suppose that American slavery is one of those offenses which in the providence of God, must needs come, but which, having continued through his appointed time, He now wills to remove, and that He gives to both North and South this terrible war, as the woe due to those by whom the offense came, shall we discern therein any departure from those divine attributes which the believers in a living God always ascribe to Him? Fondly do we hope—fervently do we pray—that this mighty scourge of war may speedily pass away. Yet, if God wills that it continue until all the wealth piled by the bondman's two hundred and fifty years of unrequited toil shall be sunk, and until every drop of blood drawn with the lash shall be paid by another drawn with the sword, as was said three thousand years ago, so still it must be said, "The judgments of the Lord are true and righteous altogether."

With malice toward none; with charity for all; with firmness in the right, as God gives us to see the right, let us strive on to finish the work we are in; to bind up the nation's wounds; to care for him who shall have borne the battle, and for his widow and his orphan—to do all which may achieve and cherish a just and lasting peace among ourselves, and with all nations.

THE CONFEDERATE ARMY

BY JOHN W. THOMASON, JR.

This elegy was written a year before Pearl Harbor by an incurable Texan who was a fighting Lieutenant of Marines at Belleau Wood and Soissons in 1918. By the end of 1940, he had dwindled to a mere Lieutenant-Colonel in the Naval Intelligence. The following passage is from a foreword to a collection of his stories called A Lone Star Preacher. The second story in that collection, "A Preacher Goes to War," will be found elsewhere in this volume.

THE Provisional Army of the Confederate States was —as all wartime armies are—a cross-section of the society from which it came. It had its knightly-hearted zealots, consecrated to a Cause, their chins lifted above human fraility. It had its romantics, white plumes of chivalry nodding in their eyes. It had its great grandees, who went out with their body servants and fine linen, as to a tournament; and who, when it was discovered that battlefields were unsalubrious places, fled to safe jobs near the seat of government; or stayed and fought it out in homespun pants and hide brogans, according to the essence of them. It had its solid middle-of-the-road men, who took the sunshine and the sleet with equal minds; and these are the backbone of armies. It had its rascals, corpse-robbers, coffee-coolers, malingerers, deserters—it had a great many deserters. American armies, perhaps because of the unexpected mushiness which streaks American discipline, record appalling highs in the matter of desertion. It had its braggarts, its Falstaffs and its Ancient Pistols, and it had men-at-arms as meek and valiant as Chaucer's very gentle perfect knight.

It was never a really homogeneous army. The Tidewater regiments of Virginia, with their broad vowels, and their cavalier dash, were not quite the same as the sturdy blue-light soldiers from the Valley, whom Stonewall Jackson led down to First Manassas. They were plain and simple men from the hill-farms of North Carolina and Tennessee, in the formations of D. H. Hill, who hardened under fire as steel in a furnace. South Carolina sent high-nosed heroes, critical of family in their officers, but hard-dying men in any company. In the hearts of Alabama and Georgia there smouldered always an angry hell, burning brightest in battle. From Texas and Mississippi and Arkansas came the tall hunters who broke the cane and bridled the western waters; bear killers, Indian fighters, reported as savage and dreadful by civilized patriots called to arms out of rock-fenced New England pastures. And Louisiana sent, under Harry Hayes, those famous cosmopolitan Zouaves called the Louisiana Tigers, who campaigned with the ferocity of Free Companions in the Hundred Years' War. And there were the Florida troops who, undismayed in fire, stampeded the night after Fredericksburg, when the Aurora Borealis snapped and crackled over that field of frozen dead. And the Kentuckians, and the Marylanders served doggedly from divided families.

One thing they had in common—a belief in Southern rights. That one of those rights involved the dark institution of chattel slavery is not pertinent, because few of them owned slaves, or hoped to own them. That tariff and free trade entered into it is not pertinent either—they were pastorals, and their economics were bounded by their fields and woodlots. "What are you

fighting for?" says an officer of Meade's staff to a
hairy Mississippian, captured in Pennsylvania in 1863.
"Fightin' for ouah rights," the Mississippian told him.
"But friend, what earthly right of yours have I ever interfered with?" the major asked him. "I don' know," the
soldier answered honestly, after some thought. "None
that I know of, seh. But maybe I've got rights I haven't
heard tell about, an' if so, I'm fightin' for them, too."

The point is, they all believed in something.

No amount of critical fact-finding detracts from that.
Their effectiveness in war is attested in official records
by their enemies. The heritage they left, of valor and
devotion, is treasured by a united country. The grand-
son of one of Chamberlain's Maine soldiers has been my
adjutant the last two years, and we are proud, both of
us, of the fight our people made on Little Round Top,
the second day at Gettysburg. And perhaps better
marines for it.

As for that enemy, he has his own minnesingers and
saga-men. Let them celebrate him. Under the great
battle names of the Army of Northern Virginia is written a word—Appomattox.

In normal times—that is, when the nations move in
their regular orbits as responsible planets march, and
the children of men sit tranquil in those stations to
which it pleased God to call them—times such as a
whole generation alive today has never seen, and the
rest of us will never see again in our lives—soldiers are
of little account, and soldiering lowly regarded. But
when war breaks on the world, you look around for
men who understand the violent business of war—and
you are genuinely concerned not to find them.

It would be a very comforting thing if we could, in
this urgent year of 1940, call up from the ground those
long-boned, hairy fellows whose armies traversed this

country a lifetime ago. It would be a hopeful thing if they might be mustered again, in their simplicity, their earnestness, and their antique courage. It would be an easy detail to instruct men of their proved and savage aptitude for war in the tactics and techniques introduced by the modern practitioners of that most ancient art. And our enemies would presently be confounded by us in all their knavish tricks.

For those men believed in something. They counted life a light thing to lay down in the faith they bore. They were terrible in battle. They were generous in victory. They rose up from defeat to fight again, and while they lived they were formidable. There were not enough of them; that is all.

THE FIRST G. A. R. PARADE

BY LLOYD LEWIS

IT was May 23, 1865. Sherman sat in a wooden stand
before the White House. Close by sat President Johnson and his Cabinet, and around them governors, senators, notables, and ladies. Crowds jammed Pennsylvania
Avenue, roofs, windows. From a distance came the
blare of bands, shouts. The Army of the Potomac was
being reviewed. The East was having its day. Tomorrow
would come Sherman's day and the West's. Into view
swung General Meade. The crowd shrieked, "Gettysburg!" Here came George Armstrong Custer—a brigadier general at twenty-six—the Eastern army's most
romantic figure. Female voices squealed. The *New York
World* reporter jotted down his description:

> fair and ruddy complexion—a sunrise of golden
> hair which ripples upon his blue shoulders—on
> his left arm hangs a wreath of evergreens—scarlet
> kerchief—white gauntlets.

An overwrought woman threw a wreath. Custer
snatched at it. His horse bolted. The crowd shrieked,
"A runaway!" The *World* man saw Custer's hat blow
off; "in the sunshine his locks, unskeined, stream a foot
behind him . . . it is like the charge of a Sioux chief-
tain." (Prophetic simile; in eleven years Custer would
be dead under a charge of Sioux warriors.) Sherman
watched Custer disappear—"he was not reviewed at
all." (Prophetic dramatization of the end of cavalry as a
major arm of war.)

544

Sherman was critical of Eastern troops, noting that many "turned their eyes around like country gawks to look at the big people on the stand." They did not march well, because of the faulty music from two civilian orchestras—"pampered and well-fed bands that are taught to play the very latest operas." He resolved to eliminate that music tomorrow, and have his own men march to their own regimental bands. Come what might, his army *must* outmarch the Easterners.

Meade walked up onto the stand. Sherman said to him, "I'm afraid my poor tatterdemalion corps will make a poor appearance tomorrow when contrasted with yours." Meade said the people would make allowances. Comparisons were in the generals' minds. Six years later Meade said that his Army of the Potomac had suffered 60 per cent of the Union casualties of the whole war.

That night Sherman ordered his officers, "Be careful about your intervals and your tactics. I will give plenty of time to go to the Capitol and see everything afterward, but let them keep their eyes fifteen feet to the front and march by in the old customary way." Many men had new uniforms, but rags were still common. The *World* man noted many bare feet. Hazen was still making vain efforts to have the Fifteenth Corps cut its hair. Sherman was going to let the East see his army as it had lived, for better or for worse.

Through the night he moved in from Virginia, closer to the city, and at break of day bugles blew and the *World* reporter wrote:

> . . . directly all sorts of colors, over a wild monotony of columns, began to sway to and fro, up and down, and like the uncoiling of a tremendous python, the Army of Sherman winds into Washington.

The Fifteenth Corps led the way. For a little while it paused behind the Capitol, snickering to see Uncle Billy ride past, "dressed up after dingy carelessness for years." His horse wore wreaths on its neck. Young ladies were thrusting roses in lapels and down gun barrels, or bringing ice water from tubs on street corners. Springtime flirtations danced up and down the waiting lines. Sherman eyed his men anxiously. Had he any right to expect them, after all those reckless years and miles, to march like bandbox soldiers?

He would not ride alone. Howard would be seen at his side. In Carolina he had said that if he were killed Howard must take command and end the campaign. Now Howard, although transferred to the Freedmen's Bureau, was entitled to ride at the head of the Army of the Tennessee, but Sherman had asked him, out of respect for Logan's disappointment at Atlanta, to let the Illinois soldier have that honor.

The Capitol was blooming with flags. The morning was bright and soft. A cannon boomed. Nine o'clock! Sherman shook a spur; his horse stepped forward, drumsticks made the air flutter like flying canister or wild-geese wings. Bands blared into "The Star-spangled Banner." Around the corner of the Capitol the Westerners came.

Stage fright stuck in plowboys' throats. The roofs and trees were black with people. Pennsylvania Avenue stretched like a long, long river between human banks. White handkerchiefs waved like apple blossoms in an Indiana wind. Boys' eyes caught blurred sights of signs spanning the avenue—"Hail to the Western Heroes" . . . "Hail, Champions of Belmont, Donelson, Shiloh, Vicksburg, Chattanooga, Atlanta, Savannah, Bentonville —Pride of the Nation."

Cheers crashed against the blushing faces of the

marchers. Their lips twitched and their eyes fell in self-consciousness. Many of them wished they were back among the swamps of Carolina—even among the bullets of Vicksburg. J. W. Anderson, Company G, Nineteenth Illinois, heard people pray as his regiment swept by; he noted sobbing women hold up babies to see the soldiers. Mourning still hung on buildings—mourning for Lincoln. Crape draped all flags. Now and then curious cheers welled up from the marching men, wild cries arising from the excitement and from comprehending at last the tremendous miles behind them.

Sherman, riding ahead, his old slouch hat in hand—the sun on his red hair—was listening to the tread of his men. Sometimes in sudden hushes he could hear one footfall behind him. The hushes came when ambulances rolled by with bloodstained stretchers fastened on their sides. Gales of laughter followed hushes, as at the end of the corps came Negro refugees of both sexes and all ages, leading or riding mules, walking beside wagons filled with tents and kettles surmounted by turkeys and pet raccoons. Pigs grunted from end gates here and there. Gamecocks rode cannon, crowing. Ragamuffin Negroes bearing Revolutionary blunderbusses grinned at guffawing spectators.

Sherman hoped, as perhaps he had never hoped anything in his lifetime, that his men were marching well. They sounded all right, but he couldn't be sure in the roaring current of noise. They *must* show the East that they were not "an undisciplined mob." Sherman neared the White House, where the test would come. Ellen would be in the stand, with Tommy and Old Solitude; Willy's eyes would not be there to shine. Cold eyes of elegant society people would be leveled.

Sherman's horse walked up the avenue slope before the Treasury Building. In a minute it would swing to the right and come into view of the stand. Behind him he heard the tumult growing louder. Were his wild young fellows behaving? He dared not look back; he had ordered everybody to hold eyes front.

He was on the crest of the rise now. He could hold his nerves no longer. He spun in the saddle and looked. A blissful thrill ran to his finger tips. His legions were coming in line, every man locked in steady formation— formal for perhaps the first and the last time in their lives. "They have swung into it," said Sherman to himself. Long afterwards he said, "I believe it was the happiest and most satisfactory moment of my life."

He turned back to the front and led the way up the avenue before the Treasury and the White House. Some one called to him to look at a window. From it peered a face that Charles A. Dana described as "one of the most horrible spectacles that the human eye ever beheld"—the face of Secretary Seward recovering from a series of injuries: a jaw broken in a carriage runaway, a face and throat scarred by a would-be assassin on April 14. Bands of steel and rubber, clamps on top of his head and under his chin, made him hideous, but not to Sherman, who had been looking at wounded men across four years. Sherman waved his hat. Seward waved a wan hand. Sherman fixed his hat on his head, whipped out his sword, and rode past the stand, saluting the President. The *World* man wrote:

> . . . the acclamation given Sherman was without precedent . . . greater than the day before . . . the whole assemblage raised and waved and shouted as if he had been the personal friend of each and every one of them. . . . Sherman was the idol of the day.

Ellen, standing with Mrs. Grant, looked for Cump

past black silk hats that waved and white handkerchiefs that flew. It would be her first sight of him in eighteen months. There he was on a "shining bay"—his saber was flashing in front of his face . . . his beard was getting terribly grizzled . . . his hair was cut closer than usual, thank the Lord . . . he was very thin . . . he was gone.

The whole army was thin. Carl Schurz, in the stand, felt his heart leap as the Westerners wheeled into view —"nothing but bone and muscle and skin under their tattered battle-flags." Their flags were thin, too, from wind and bullets—many were nothing but shreds of faded red and white and blue. Cheers drowned the bands. The street in front of the stand was ankle-deep in flowers—worn heels, bare heels, kept step among the roses.

Cheers for Howard with the empty sleeve . . . for Logan with the black hair . . . For Hazen, very handsome . . . for Mother Bickerdyke riding an army horse side-saddle, a sunbonnet on her head, a calico dress on her capable body. The *New York Tribune* reporter saw officers of the Fifteenth Corps shout something unintelligible in the uproar, and the men

> without turning their heads, their eyes still front, relax their imperturbable faces and break into wild yells, tearing off their hats with free hands and waving them in air—their eyes still front.

They were cheering the President and Grant. Boys of the Twelfth Wisconsin said, "We couldn't look at the reviewing stand. If Lincoln had been there I'm afraid our line would have broken up."

Almost all the spectators, it seemed, noted that the Westerners took a more springy stride than had the Easterners the day before, a step guessed at from two •

to four inches longer—a proud, rolling, swinging step. One old man in the stand thrilled as he saw it; Tom Corwin, who at seventy-one had been remembering how, so long ago, he had sat beside the deathbed of Judge Sherman. Who would have thought then that the judge's boy Cump would march so far in history? Eloquence came from Corwin as the river of Westerners rolled by.

"They march like the lords of the world," he said.

Another Ohio pioneer sat glowing in the stand, the Methodist Episcopal Bishop Edward R. Ames, remorseless traveler of the wilderness, itinerant preacher, missionary to the Indians, criss-crosser of the continent, understanding, now, those "splendid legs." Beside him sat the German ambassador, who said as the Fifteenth Corps passed: "An army like that could whip all Europe." As the Twentieth Corps went by he said: "An army like that could whip the world"; and when the Fourteenth Corps had gone, ending the parade, he said to Ames, "An army like that could whip the devil."

It was commonly agreed that Sherman's men were taller, leaner, than Easterners; their beards were longer and more shaggy—more of them wore beards, more of the beards were yellow and red. It was also agreed that the Westerners were more obviously the symbol of democracy, the private soldiers apparently hailing from the same social strata as their officers. Spectators had difficulty distinguishing officers from the men, whereas such differences had been plain in the Army of the Potomac. Many observers noted how completely the Eastern regiments in Sherman's Twentieth Corps had taken on the characteristics of their Western comrades—"they walked like Westerners."

The East had shown better clothing, more paper collars, superior discipline; the West had marched far better. Western boys had older faces. The *New York World* man thought Sherman's soldiers "hardier, knottier, weirder." He concluded that the army of the East had been composed of "citizens, the West of pioneers." Charles A. Page of the *New York Tribune* declared the Westerners' "faces were more intelligent, self-reliant and determined."

To Washingtonians, Sherman's army had the variety and strangeness of a foreign caravan—blackamoors, mules, swaying wagons, signalmen carrying sixteen-foot staffs with small flags that looked to the *New York World* man like "talismanic banners, emblems of a grander Masonry than the world is worthy of." Excited onlookers spoke of the Crusaders—a word that no member of the army, so far as later research would reveal, had ever applied to themselves.

Once he had passed the reviewing stand, Sherman left the line of march and with his staff entered the White House grounds, where he dismounted and hurried to enter the tier of seats. He found Ellen, Tommy and the Salt-Boiler and embraced them, then hurried to shake hands with President Johnson. Grant was next, then Stanton.

The time had come to repay insult with insult. The Secretary of War held out his hand, but Sherman ignored it. Elbridge J. Copp, a telegrapher in the War Department, saw the incident plainly; "Sherman's face was scarlet and his red hair seemed to stand on end." A buzz of surprise eddied through the stand, whispers flew. Sherman sat down to watch his men go by.

Charles A. Dana, admirer of Sherman and assistant to Stanton, thought that the affair had been carefully plotted. He said that the Blairs, who had been working to persuade President Johnson to desert the Radicals and swing back to Lincolnian gentleness toward the

South, had been conniving to oust Stanton from office. Dana declared that for some days before the review Cump's brother Charles "had been very active in stirring up a quarrel" and, with the Blairs and other anti-Radical politicians, had gathered on the stand to humiliate Stanton publicly. In all likelihood General Sherman had not been acting in concert with any one. For a month he had planned to insult Stanton, and this had been his first opportunity.

As the last pickaninny-laden mule disappeared, the notables came down from the stand. Copp, the telegrapher, saw throngs pump Sherman's hand and shower bouquets upon him:

> At first he was affable, then he grew less cordial as the crowds crushed in. He pushed down the steps, step by step, and refused proffered hands, finally exclaiming, "Damn you, get out of the way, damn you!"

That night when serenaders called him out from John Sherman's house—next door to Stanton's—he said he wouldn't make a speech because he might get excited and say things better left unsaid. The *World* man heard him add:

> For when I speak, I speak to the point and when I act in earnest I act to the point. If a man minds his own business I let him alone, but if he crosses my path, he must get out of the way. I want peace and freedom for every man to go where he pleases, to California or to any other portion of our country without restriction.

From the crowd came a voice referring to gossip that the army was to help Mexico drive out Emperor Maximilian:

"How about going to Mexico, General?"

"You can go there if you like and you can go to hell if you want to!" barked Sherman, and he went indoors.

For days and nights he was busy with complaints that his Westerners were fighting with Eastern soldiers in saloons, stealing horses and buggies—the Eighty-fifth Illinois played such a prank upon Washington's chief of police—capturing horse cars, kicking off conductors, collecting fares, refusing to make change, and carrying passengers beyond their stops. He heard of one group who refused to alight at the end of the line. "End, hell!" they bellowed. "We paid to be hauled out to camp, five cents to be hauled out to camp, and we're not going to be swindled." And, said Sherman in later years, "Do you know, those boys seized the reins and drove that car right up on the road to camp a mile beyond the end of the track? Fortunately the road was smooth and hard and the poor horses were able to pull it."

Grant wrote him that General Augur, policing Washington, complained that Western and Eastern troops whenever they met "are sure to fight" and that Sherman's men exhibited "deep feeling, especially when in a little liquor, on account of the difficulties between yourself and Secretary Stanton." Augur described how Western officers jumped on bars, gave "three groans for Mr. Stanton, then get down and take another drink." Sherman rode the streets after midnight calming his men. Soon Dana was writing General Wilson that Grant had been forced to put the Potomac River between the Westerners and the Easterners, on account of the fist-fighting.

I have heard of one or two men who have been killed and one or two who have been seriously wounded. Sherman's men are pretty troublesome to the farmers and other quiet people where they are.

Hazen thought the Army of the Tennessee was ordered to Louisville for demobilization with unseemly haste. He admitted that the boys were still free with "reckless appropriation of other people's property" and that "an amount of investigation and police-court work was done daily which very soon made it necessary to send the Army of the Tennessee away, so that our expected long rest at Washington was reduced to a few days."

On May 30 Sherman wrote his farewell address to his men. As the soldiers read it, they were sad. They rejoiced, of course, at the prospect of seeing home folks, yet army comrades now seemed closer than relatives. They had prayed and sung about the happy day when "the cruel war is over." They had longed to be done with stinking death. But that had been in days when peace was far away. Now it was here, and it was not what they had expected. It was hard to say good-by to boys with whom they had walked, fought, bled, and stolen chickens.

All at once they knew that the sun would not rise on danger in Ohio, and that in the twilights of Indiana would come the boom of frogs—not Joe Johnston's cannon. There would be fireflies and not sharpshooters blazing in the long grass of Missouri. Soon they would be hunting work instead of hens. All too quickly now their iron legs would be following plows and harrows round and round a narrow field—their feet would be boxed in by inviolate fences or frame villages that never changed. Never again would they move with the equinoxes, sweating in the Southern sun. Life's supreme sweetness was ending, not beginning. "Our work is done," they read in Uncle Billy's farewell. Their eyes ran down the printed page regretfully. They caught sentences that recounted their triumphs—he was reminding them that success in the past was due to hard work and discipline and that the same work and discipline were equally important in the future:

> . . . our favored country is so grand, so expansive, so diversified in climate, soil and productions, that every man may find a home and occupation suited to his taste . . . none should yield to the natural impatience sure to result from our past life of excitement and adventure. You will be invited to seek new adventures abroad; do not yield to the temptation, for it will lead only to death and disappointment . . . farewell . . . you have been good soldiers . . . you will make good citizens. . . .

To the men the paper read like a lament, until near the end:

> If, unfortunately, new war should rise in our country, "Sherman's army" will be the first to buckle on its old armor, and come forth to defend and maintain the Government of our inheritance.

"New war?" Occasionally boys wondered vaguely about this as the railroad trains hauled them westward. War with whom? Certainly not with the South. The West need never go there again. With France over Mexico? Not likely.

No, if war came it would be with those damned Easterners in the paper collars!

THREE SPEECHES

BY OLIVER WENDELL HOLMES, JR.

*Here are printed three samples of oral prose by the younger Holmes,
the third being his own contribution to a birthday observance celebrated
by the radio while he was still serving as an Associate Justice of the
United States Supreme Court. The first Oliver Wendell Holmes is
represented earlier in these pages by "The Last Leaf," a poem of which
Poe always carried a copy in his pocket. Lincoln didn't have to. He
knew it by heart and used to recite it. Another father and son contribute
to this volume—the Whites of Emporia.*

I.

(From a lecture on "THE PROFESSION OF THE LAW"
delivered at Harvard in 1886.)

NO man has earned the right to intellectual ambition until he has learned to lay his course by a
star which he has never seen,—to dig by the divining
rod for springs which he may never reach. In saying
this, I point to that which will make your study heroic.
For I say to you in all sadness of conviction, that to
think great thoughts you must be heroes as well as
idealists. Only when you have worked alone,—when
you have felt around you a black gulf of solitude more
isolating than that which surrounds the dying man, and
in hope and in despair have trusted to your own unshaken will,—then only will you have achieved. Thus
only can you gain the secret isolated joy of the thinker,
who knows that, a hundred years after he is dead and

forgotten, men who never heard of him will be moving to the measure of his thought,—the subtle rapture of a postponed power, which the world knows not because it has no external trappings, but which to his prophetic vision is more real than that which commands an army. And if this joy should not be yours, still it is only thus that you can know that you have done what it lay in you to do,—can say that you have lived, and be ready for the end.

II.

(From an address on "THE SOLDIER'S FAITH," delivered at Harvard on Memorial Day, 1895.)

Three years ago died the old colonel of my regiment, the Twentieth Massachusetts. He gave our regiment its soul. No man could falter who heard his "Forward, Twentieth!" I went to his funeral. From a side door of the church a body of little choir-boys came in like a flight of careless doves. At the same time the doors opened at the front, and up the main aisle advanced his coffin, followed by the few gray heads who stood for the men of the Twentieth, the rank and file whom he had loved, and whom he led for the last time. The church was empty. No one remembered the old man whom we were burying, no one save those next to him, and us. And I said to myself, The Twentieth has shrunk to a skeleton, a ghost, a memory, a forgotten name which we other old men alone keep in our hearts. And then I thought: It is right. It is as the colonel would have had it. This also is part of the soldier's faith: Having known great things, to be content with silence. Just

then there fell into my hands a little song sung by a
warlike people on the Danube, which seemed to me fit
for a soldier's last word, another song of the sword, but
a song of the sword in its scabbard, a song of oblivion
and peace.

A soldier has been buried on the battle-field.

"And when the wind in the tree-tops roared,
   The soldier asked from the deep dark grave:
      'Did the banner flutter then?'
'Not so, my hero,' the wind replied,
'The fight is done, but the banner won,
Thy comrades of old have borne it hence,
   Have borne it in triumph hence.'
Then the soldier spake from the deep dark grave:
      'I am content.'

"Then he heareth the lovers laughing pass,
   And the soldier asks once more:
'Are these not the voices of them that love,
   That love—and remember me?'
'Not so, my hero,' the lovers say,
'We are those that remember not;
For the spring has come and the earth has smiled,
   And the dead must be forgot.'
Then the soldier spake from the deep dark grave:
      'I am content.'

III.

(A broadcast on his ninetieth birthday.)

In this symposium my part is only to sit in silence. To express one's feelings as the end draws near is too intimate a task.

But I may mention one thought that comes to me as a listener-in. The riders in a race do not stop short when they reach the goal. There is a little finishing canter before coming to a standstill. There is time to hear the kind voice of friends and to say to one's self: "The work is done."

But just as one says that, the answer comes: "The race is over, but the work never is done while the power to work remains."

The canter that brings you to a standstill need not be only coming to rest. It cannot be while you still live. For to live is to function. That is all there is in living.

And so I end with a line from a Latin poet who uttered the message more than fifteen hundred years ago:

> "Death plucks my ear and says, Live—
> I am coming."

THE TRAWNBEIGHS

BY CHARLES M. FLANDRAU

This account of an English family on their uppers in exile is a true story recorded by an appreciative resident of St. Paul, Minnesota. If it forms a chapter of Viva Mexico, it is only because Mr. Flandrau (who was a "good neighbor" in advance of his time) happened just then to be writing his beautiful book on his adventures in that country. Actually he had encountered the Trawnbeighs in Minneapolis. Any thoughtful student of that household when under pressure—the word "guts" has been defined as "grace under pressure"—will better understand why, after Dunkirk, the Nazis encountered something stronger than they were.

WHEN my first New Year's party dispersed, I walked back to the center of the town with a man who had lived for many years in Mexico, who had been everywhere and had done everything, and who seemed to know something funny or tragic or scandalous about everybody in the world. He loved to talk, to describe, to recall; and while we had some drinks together at a café under the sky-blue portales, he aroused my interest in people I never had heard of and never should see. He told me, among other things, about the Trawnbeighs.

This, as nearly as I can remember, is what he told me about the Trawnbeighs:

The Trawnbeighs, he said, were the sort of people who "dressed for dinner," even when, as sometimes happened, they had no dinner in the house to dress for. It is perhaps unnecessary to add that the Trawnbeighs were English. Indeed, on looking back, I often feel that to my first apparently flippant statement it is unneces-

560

sary to add *anything*. For to one who knew Mr. and Mrs. Trawnbeigh, Edwina, Violet, Maud, and Cyril, it was the first and last word on them; their alpha and omega, together with all that went between. Not that the statement *is* flippant—far from it. There is in it a seriousness, a profundity, an immense philosophic import. At times it has almost moved me to lift my hat, very much as one does for reasons of state, or religion, or death.

This, let me hasten to explain, is not at all the way I feel when I put on evening clothes myself, which I do at least twice out of my every three hundred and sixty-five opportunities. No born American could feel that way about his own dress coat. He sometimes thinks he does; he often—and isn't it boresome!—pretends he does, but he really doesn't. As a matter of unimportant fact, the born American may have "dressed" every evening of his grown-up life. But if he found himself on an isolated, played-out Mexican coffee and vanilla finca, with a wife, four children, a tiled roof that leaked whenever there was a "norther," an unsealed sala through the bamboo partitions of which a cold, wet wind howled sometimes for a week at a time, with no money, no capacity for making any, no "prospects," and no cook—under these depressing circumstances it is impossible to conceive of an American dressing for dinner every night at a quarter before seven in any spirit but one of ghastly humor.

With the Trawnbeighs' performance of this sacred rite, however, irony and humor had nothing to do. The Trawnbeighs had a robust sense of fun (so, I feel sure, have pumpkins and turnips and the larger varieties of the nutritious potato family); but humor, when they didn't recognize it, bewildered them, and it always struck them as just a trifle underbred when they did.

Trawnbeigh had come over to Mexico—"come out from England," he would have expressed it—as a kind of secretary to his cousin, Sir Somebody Something, who was building a harbor or a railway or a canal (I don't believe Trawnbeigh himself ever knew just what it was) for a British company down in the hot country. Mrs. Trawnbeigh, with her young, was to follow on the next steamer a month later; and as she was in mid-ocean when Sir Somebody suddenly died of yellow fever, she did not learn of this inopportune event until it was too late to turn back. Still I doubt whether she would have turned back if she could. For, as Trawnbeigh once explained to me at a time when they literally hadn't enough to eat (a hail storm had not only destroyed his coffee crop, but had frozen the roots of most of his trees, and the price of vanilla had fallen from ten cents a bean to three and a half), leaving England at all, he explained, had necessitated "burning their bridges behind them." He did not tell me the nature of their bridges, nor whether they had made much of a blaze. In fact, that one vague, inflammatory allusion was the nearest approach to a personal confidence Trawnbeigh was ever known to make in all his fifteen years of Mexican life.

The situation, when he met Mrs. Trawnbeigh and the children on the dock at Vera Cruz, was extremely dreary, and at the end of a month it had grown much worse, although the Trawnbeighs apparently didn't think so. They even spoke and wrote as if their affairs were "looking up a bit." For, after a few weeks of visiting among kindly compatriots at Vera Cruz and Rebozo, Mrs. Trawnbeigh became cook for some English engineers (there were seven of them) in a sizzling, mosquitoey, feverish mudhole on the Isthmus of Tehuantepec. The Trawnbeighs didn't call it "cook," neither did the seven engineers. I don't believe the engineers even thought of it as cook. (What Mrs. Trawnbeigh thought of it will never be known.) How *could* they when that lady, after feeding the four little Trawnbeighs (or rather the four young Trawnbeighs; they had never been little) a meal I think they called "the nursery tea," managed every afternoon, within the next two hours, first to create out of nothing a perfectly edible dinner for nine persons, and, secondly, to receive them all at seven forty-five in a red-striped, lemon satin ball gown (it looked like poisonous wall paper), eleven silver bangles, a cameo necklace, and an ostrich tip sprouting from the top of her head. Trawnbeigh, too, was in evening clothes. And they didn't call it cooking; they spoke of it as "looking after the mess" or "keeping an eye on the young chaps' livers." Nevertheless, Mrs. Trawnbeigh, daughter of the late the Honorable Cyril Cosby Godolphin Dundas and the late Clare Walpurga Emmeline Moate, cooked— and cooked hard—for almost a year; at the end of which time she was stricken with what she was pleased to refer to as "a bad go of fevah."

Fortunately, they were spared having to pass around the hat, although it would have amounted to that if Trawnbeigh hadn't, after the pleasant English fashion, come into some money. In the United States people know to a cent what they may expect to inherit, and then they sometimes don't get it; but in England there seems to be an endless succession of retired and un-married army officers who die every little while in Jermyn Street and leave two thousand pounds to a dis-tant relative they have never met. Something like this happened to Trawnbeigh, and on the prospect of his legacy he was able to pull out of the Tehuantepec mud-hole and restore his wife to her usual state of health in the pure and bracing air of Rebozo.

Various things can be done with two thousand pounds, but just what *shall* be done ought to depend very largely on whether they happen to be one's first two thousand or one's last. Trawnbeigh, however, invested his ("interred" would be a more accurate term) quite as if they never would be missed. The disposition to be a country gentleman was in Trawnbeigh's blood. Indeed, the first impression one received from the family was that everything they did was in their blood. It never seemed to me that Trawnbeigh had immediately sunk the whole of his little fortune in an old, small, and dilapidated coffee place so much because he was dazzled by the glittering financial future the shameless owner (another Englishman, by the way) predicted for him, as because to own an estate and live on it was, so to speak, his natural element. He had tried, while Mrs. Trawnbeigh was cooking on the Isthmus, to get "something to do." But there was really nothing in Mexico he *could* do. He was splendidly strong, and in the United States he very cheerfully, and with no loss of self-respect or point of view, would have temporarily shoveled wheat or coal, or driven a team, or worked on the street force, as many another Englishman of noble lineage has done before and since; but in the tropics an Anglo-Saxon cannot be a day laborer. He can't because he can't. And there was in Mexico no clerical position open to Trawnbeigh because he did not know Spanish. (It is significant that after fifteen consecutive years of residence in the country, *none* of the Trawnbeighs knew Spanish.) To be, somehow and somewhere, an English country gentleman of a well-known, slightly old-fashioned type, was as much Trawnbeigh's destiny as it is the destiny of, say, a polar bear to be a polar bear or a camel to be a camel. As soon as he got his two thousand pounds, he became one.

When I first met them all, he had been one for about ten years. I had recently settled in Trawnbeigh's neighborhood, which in Mexico means that my ranch was a hard day-and-a-half ride from his, over roads that are not roads, but merely ditches full of liquefied mud on the level stretches, and ditches full of assorted bowlders on the ascent. So, although we looked neighborly on a small map, I might not have had the joy of meeting the Trawnbeighs for years if my mule hadn't gone lame one day when I was making the interminable trip to Rebozo. Trawnbeigh's place was seven miles from the main road, and as I happened to be near the parting of the ways when the off hind leg of Catalina began to limp, I decided to leave her with my mozo at an Indian village until a pack train should pass by (there is always someone in a pack train who can remove a bad shoe), while I proceeded on the mozo's mule to the Trawnbeighs'. My usual stopping place for the night was five miles farther on, and the Indian village was—well, it was an Indian village. Time and again I had been told of Trawnbeigh's early adventures, and I felt sure he could "put me up" (as he would have said himself) for the night. He "put me up" not only that night, but as my mozo didn't appear until late the next afternoon, a second night as well. And when I at last rode away, it was with the feeling of having learned from the Trawnbeighs a great lesson.

In the first place they couldn't have expected me; they couldn't possibly have expected anyone. And it was a hot afternoon. But as it was the hour at which people at "home" dropped in for tea, Mrs. Trawnbeigh and her three plain, heavy-looking daughters were perfectly prepared to dispense hospitality to any number of mythical friends. They had on hideous but distinctly "dressy" dresses of amazingly stamped materials known, I be-

lieve, as "summer silks," and they were all four tightly
laced. Current fashion in Paris, London, and New York
by no means insisted on small, smooth, round waists,
but the Trawnbeigh women had them because (as it
gradually dawned on me) to have had any other kind
would have been a concession to anatomy and the
weather. To anything so compressible as one's anatomy,
or as vulgarly impartial as the weather, the Trawnbeighs simply did not concede. I never could get over
the feeling that they all secretly regarded weather in
general as a kind of popular institution, of vital importance only to the middle class. Cyril, an extremely
beautiful young person of twenty-two, who had been
playing tennis (by himself) on the asoleadero, was in
"flannels," and Trawnbeigh admirably looked the part
in gray, middle-aged riding things, although, as I discovered before leaving, their stable at the time consisted
of one senile burro with ingrowing hoofs.

From the first it all seemed too flawless to be true. I
had never visited in England, but I doubt if there is
another country whose literature gives one so definite
and lasting an impression of its "home life." Perhaps
this is because the life of families of the class to which
the Trawnbeighs belonged proceeds in England by such
a series of definite and traditional episodes. In a household like theirs, the unexpected must have a devil of a
time in finding a chance to happen. For, during my
visit, absolutely nothing happened that I hadn't long
since chuckled over in making the acquaintance of Jane
Austen, Thackeray, George Eliot, and Anthony Trollope;
not to mention Ouida (it was Cyril, of course, who
from time to time struck the Ouida note), and the more
laborious performances of Mrs. Humphrey Ward. They
all of them did at every tick of the clock precisely what
they ought to have done. They were a page, the least

bit crumpled, torn from *Half Hours with the Best Authors*, and cast, dear Heaven! upon a hillside in darkest Mexico.

Of course we had tea in the garden. There wasn't any garden, but we nevertheless had tea in it. The house would have been cooler, less glaring, and free from the venomous little rodadoras that stung the backs of my hands full of microscopic polka dots; but we all strolled out to a spot some fifty yards away where a bench, half a dozen shaky, homemade chairs, and a rustic table were most imperfectly shaded by three tattered banana trees.

"We love to drink tea in the dingle dangle," Mrs. Trawnbeigh explained. How the tea tray itself got to the "dingle dangle," I have only a general suspicion, for when we arrived it was already there, equipped with caddy, cozy, a plate of buttered toast, a pot of strawberry jam, and all the rest of it. But try as I might, I simply could not rid myself of the feeling that at least two footmen had arranged it all and then discreetly retired; a feeling that also sought to account for the tray's subsequent removal, which took place while Trawnbeigh, Cyril, Edwina, and I walked over to inspect the asoleadero and washing tanks. I wanted to look back; but something (the fear, perhaps, of being turned into a pillar of salt) restrained me.

With most English-speaking persons in that part of the world, conversation has to do with coffee, coffee, and—coffee. The Trawnbeighs, however, scarcely touched on the insistent topic. While we sat on the low wall of the dilapidated little asoleadero we discussed pheasant shooting and the "best places" for haberdashery and "Gladstone bags." Cyril, as if it were but a matter of inclination, said he thought he might go over for the shooting that year; a cousin had asked him "to make a seventh." I never found out what this meant and didn't have the nerve to ask.

"Bertie shoots the twelfth, doesn't he?" Edwina here inquired.

To which her brother replied, as if she had shown a distressing ignorance of some fundamental date in history, like 1066 or 1215, "Bertie *always* shoots the twelfth."

The best place for haberdashery in Mr. Trawnbeigh's opinion was "the Stores." But Cyril preferred a small shop in Bond Street, maintaining firmly, but with good humor, that it was not merely, as "the pater" insisted, because the fellow charged more, but because one didn't "run the risk of seeing some beastly bounder in a cravat uncommonly like one's own." Trawnbeigh, as a sedate parent bordering on middle age, felt obliged to stand up for the more economical "Stores," but it was evident that he really admired Cyril's exclusive principles and approved of them. Edwina cut short the argument with an abrupt question.

"I say," she inquired anxiously, "has the dressing bell gone yet?" The dressing bell hadn't gone, but it soon went. For Mr. Trawnbeigh, after looking at his watch, bustled off to the house and rang it himself. Then we withdrew to our respective apartments to dress for dinner.

"I've put you in the north wing, old man; there's always a breeze in the wing," my host declared as he ushered me into a bamboo shed they used apparently for storing corn and iron implements of an agricultural nature. But there was also in the room a recently made-up cot with real sheets, a tin bath tub, hot and cold water in two earthenware jars, and an empty packing case upholstered in oilcloth. When Trawnbeigh spoke of this last as a "wash-hand-stand," I knew I had indeed strayed from life into the realms of mid-Victorian romance.

The breeze Trawnbeigh had referred to developed in the violent Mexican way, while I was enjoying the bath tub, into an unmistakable norther. Water fell on the roof like so much lead and then sprang off (some of it did) in thick, round streams from the tin spouts; the wind screamed in and out of the tiles overhead, and through the "north wing's" blurred windows the writhing banana trees of the "dingle dangle" looked like strange things one sees in an aquarium. As soon as I could get into my clothes again—a bath was as far as I was able to live up to the Trawnbeigh ideal—I went into the sala where the dinner table was already set with a really heart-rending attempt at splendor. I have said that nothing happened with which I had not a sort of literary acquaintance; but I was wrong. While I was standing there wondering how the Trawnbeighs had been able all those years to keep it up, a window in the next room blew open with a bang. I ran in to shut it; but before I reached it, I stopped short and, as hastily and quietly as I could, tiptoed back to the "wing." For the next room was the kitchen and at one end of it Trawnbeigh, in a shabby but perfectly fitting dress-coat, his trousers rolled up halfway to his knees, was patiently holding an umbrella over his wife's sacred dinner gown, while she—bebangled, becameoed, beplumed, and stripped to the buff—masterfully cooked our dinner on the brasero.

To me it was all extremely wonderful, and the wonder of it did not lessen during the five years in which, on my way to and from Rebozo, I stopped over at the Trawnbeighs' several times a year. For, although I knew that they were often financially all but down and out, the endless red tape of their daily life never struck me as being merely a pathetic bluff. Their rising bells and dressing bells, their apparent dependence on all sorts of pleasant accessories that simply did not exist, their occupations (I mean those on which I did not have to turn a tactful back, such as "botanizing," "crewel work," painting horrible water colors, and composing long lists of British-sounding things to be "sent out from the Stores"), the informality with which we waited on ourselves at luncheon and the stately, punctilious manner in which we did precisely the same thing at dinner, the preordained hour at which Mrs. Trawnbeigh and the girls each took a candle and said good-night, leaving Trawnbeigh, Cyril, and me to smoke a pipe and "do a whisky peg" (Trawnbeigh had spent some years in India), the whole inflexibly insular scheme of their existence was more, infinitely more, than a bluff. It was a placid, tenacious clinging to the straw of their ideal in a great, deep sea of poverty, discomfort, and isolation. And it had its reward.

For after fourteen years of Mexican life, Cyril was almost exactly what he would have been had he never seen the place; and Cyril was the Trawnbeighs' one asset of immense value. He was most agreeable to look at, he was both related to and connected with many of the most historical-sounding ladies and gentlemen in England, and he had just the limited, selfish, amiable outlook on the world in general that was sure (granting the other things) to impress Miss Irene Slapp of Pittsburgh as the height of both breeding and distinction.

Irene Slapp had beauty and distinction of her own. Somehow, although they all "needed the money," I don't believe Cyril would have married her if she hadn't. Anyhow, one evening in the City of Mexico he took her in to dinner at the British Legation where he had been asked to dine as a matter of course, and before the second entrée, Miss Slapp was slightly in love with him and very deeply in love with the scheme of life, the standard, the ideal, or whatever you choose to call it, he had inherited and had been brought up, under staggering difficulties, to represent.

"The young beggar has made a pot of money in the States," Trawnbeigh gravely informed me after Cyril had spent seven weeks in Pittsburgh—whither he had been persuaded to journey on the Slapps' private train.

"And, you know I've decided to sell the old place," he casually remarked a month or so later. "Yes, yes," he went on, "the young people are beginning to leave us." (I hadn't noticed any signs of impending flight on the part of Edwina, Violet, and Maud.) "Mrs. Trawnbeigh and I want to end our days at home. Slapp believes there's gold on the place—or would it be petroleum? He's welcome to it. After all, I've never been fearfully keen on business."

And I rode away pondering, as I always did, on the great lesson of the Trawnbeighs.

THANKSGIVING
PROCLAMATION

STATE OF CONNECTICUT

By His Excellency WILBUR L. CROSS, Governor: a

PROCLAMATION

TIME out of mind at this turn of the seasons when the hardy oak leaves rustle in the wind and the frost gives a tang to the air and the dusk falls early and the friendly evenings lengthen under the heel of Orion, it has seemed good to our people to join together in praising the Creator and Preserver, who has brought us by a way that we did not know to the end of another year. In observance of this custom, I appoint Thursday, the twenty-sixth of November, as a day of

PUBLIC THANKSGIVING

for the blessings that have been our common lot and have placed our beloved State with the favored regions of earth—for all the creature comforts: the yield of the soil that has fed us and the richer yield from labor of every kind that has sustained our lives—and for all those things, as dear as breath to the body, that quicken man's faith in his manhood, that nourish and strengthen his spirit to do the great work still before him: for the brotherly word and act; for honor held above price; for steadfast courage and zeal in the long, long search after truth; for liberty and for justice freely granted by each to his fellow and so as freely enjoyed; and for the crowning glory and mercy of peace upon our land—that we may humbly take heart of these blessings as we gather once again with solemn and festive rites to keep our Harvest Home.

Given under my hand and seal of the State at the Capitol, in Hartford, this twelfth day of November, in the year of our Lord one thousand nine hundred and thirty-six and of the independence of the United States the one hundred and sixty-first.

(Seal)

(signed)   Wilbur L. Cross

By His Excellency's Command:

(signed)   C. John Satti
Secretary.

MARY WHITE

BY WILLIAM ALLEN WHITE

Here is the story of a short life which was lived to the hilt in Emporia, Kansas. That life came to an end on May 14, 1921, and this is the obituary notice which Mary White's father wrote for the May 17 issue of the Emporia Gazette, of which he was and is the editor. The brother Bill, whose Harvard classmates sent those roses to deck her coffin, is the now celebrated W. L. White who wrote They Were Expendable and is represented further along in this volume by another piece of hot-off-the-griddle war-time journalism called "The Norse Travel Again."

THE Associated Press reports carrying the news of Mary White's death declared that it came as the result of a fall from a horse. How she would have hooted at that! She never fell from a horse in her life. Horses have fallen on her and with her—"I'm always trying to hold 'em in my lap," she used to say. But she was proud of few things, and one was that she could ride anything that had four legs and hair. Her death resulted not from a fall, but from a blow on the head which fractured her skull, and the blow came from the limb of an overhanging tree on the parking.

The last hour of her life was typical of its happiness. She came home from a day's work at school, topped off by a hard grind with the copy on the High School Annual, and felt that a ride would refresh her. She climbed into her khakis, chattering to her mother about the work she was doing, and hurried to get her horse and be out on the dirt roads for the country air and the radiant green fields of the spring. As she rode through the town on an easy gallop, she kept waving at passers-by. She knew everyone in town. For a decade the little figure with the long pig-tail and the red hair-ribbon has been familiar on the streets of Emporia, and she got in the way of speaking to those who nodded at her. She passed the Kerrs—walking the horse—in front of the Normal Library, and waved at them; passed another friend a few hundred feet further on, and waved at her. The horse was walking and, as she turned into North Merchant Street, she took off her cowboy hat, and the horse swung into a lope. She passed the Tripletts and waved her cowboy hat at them, still moving gayly north on Merchant Street. A *Gazette* carrier passed—a High School boy friend—and she waved at him, but with her bridle hand; the horse veered quickly, plunged into the parking where the low-hanging limb faced her, and, while she still looked back waving, the blow came. But she did not fall from the horse; she slipped off, dazed a bit, staggered, and fell in a faint. She never quite recovered consciousness.

But she did not fall from the horse, neither was she riding fast. A year or so ago she used to go like the wind. But that habit was broken, and she used the horse to get into the open to get fresh, hard exercise and to work off a certain surplus energy that welled up in her and needed a physical outlet. That need has been in her heart for years. It was back of the impulse that kept the dauntless little brown-clad figure on the streets and country roads of this community and built into a strong, muscular body what had been a frail and sickly frame during the first years of her life. But the riding gave her more than a body. It released a gay and hardy soul. She was the happiest

thing in the world. And she was happy because she was
enlarging her horizon. She came to know all sorts and
conditions of men; Charley O'Brien, the traffic cop, was
one of her best friends. W. L. Holtz, the Latin teacher,
was another. Tom O'Connor, farmer-politician, and
Rev. J. H. J. Rice, preacher and police judge, and Frank
Beach, music master, were her special friends, and all
the girls, black and white, above the track and below
the track, in Pepville and Stringtown, were among
her acquaintances. And she brought home riotous
stories of her adventures. She loved to rollick; persi-
flage was her natural expression at home. Her humor
was a continual bubble of joy. She seemed to think in
hyperbole and metaphor. She was mischievous without
malice, as full of faults as an old shoe. No angel was
Mary White, but an easy girl to live with, for she
never nursed a grouch five minutes in her life.

With all her eagerness for the out-of-doors, she loved
books. On her table when she left her room were a
book by Conrad, one by Galsworthy, *Creative Chem-
istry*, by E. E. Slosson, and a Kipling book. She read
Mark Twain, Dickens, and Kipling before she was
ten—all of their writings. Wells and Arnold Bennett
particularly amused and diverted her. She was entered
as a student in Wellesley in 1922; was assistant editor
of the High School Annual this year, and in line for
election to the editorship of the Annual next year. She
was a member of the executive committee of the High
School Y.W.C.A.

Within the last two years she had begun to be moved
by an ambition to draw. She began as most children
do by scribbling in her school books, funny pictures.
She bought cartoon magazines and took a course—
rather casually, naturally, for she was, after all, a
child with no strong purposes—and this year she

tasted the first fruits of success by having her pictures accepted by the High School Annual. But the thrill of delight she got when Mr. Ecord, of the Normal Annual, asked her to do the cartooning for that book this spring was too beautiful for words. She fell to her work with all her enthusiastic heart. Her drawings were accepted, and her pride—always repressed by a lively sense of the ridiculousness of the figure she was cutting—was a really gorgeous thing to see. No successful artist ever drank a deeper draft of satisfaction than she took from the little fame her work was getting among her schoolfellows. In her glory she almost forgot her horse—but never her car.

For she used the car as a jitney bus. It was her social life. She never had a "party" in all her nearly seventeen years—wouldn't have one; but she never drove a block in the car in her life that she didn't begin to fill the car with pick-ups! Everybody rode with Mary White—white and black, old and young, rich and poor, men and women. She liked nothing better than to fill the car full of long-legged High School boys and an occasional girl, and parade the town. She never had a "date," nor went to a dance, except once with her brother Bill, and the "boy proposition" didn't interest her—yet. But young people—great spring-breaking, varnish-cracking, fender-bending, door-sagging carloads of "kids"—gave her great pleasure. Her zests were keen. But the most fun she ever had in her life was acting as chairman of the committee that got up the big turkey dinner for the poor folks at the county home; scores of pies, gallons of slaw, jam, cakes, preserves, oranges, and a wilderness of turkey were loaded in the car and taken to the county home. And, being of a practical turn of mind, she risked her own Christmas dinner by staying to see that the poor folks actually got it all. Not that she was a cynic; she just disliked to tempt folks. While there she found a blind colored uncle, very old, who could do nothing but make rag rugs, and she rustled up from her school friends rags enough to keep him busy for a season. The last engagement she tried to make was to take the guests at the county home out for a car ride. And the last endeavor of her life was to try to get a rest room for colored girls in the High School. She found one girl reading in the toilet, because there was no better place for a colored girl to loaf, and it inflamed her sense of injustice and she became a nagging harpy to those who, she thought, could remedy the evil. The poor she had always with her, and was glad of it. She hungered and thirsted for righteousness; and was the most impious creature in the world. She joined the Congregational Church without consulting her parents; not particularly for her soul's good. She never had a thrill of piety in her life, and would have hooted at "testimony." But even as a little child she felt the church was an agency for helping people to more of life's abundance, and she wanted to help. She never wanted help for herself. Clothes meant little to her. It was a fight to get a new rig on her; but eventually a harder fight to get it off. She never wore a jewel and had no ring but her High School class ring, and never asked for anything but a wrist watch. She refused to have her hair up, though she was nearly seventeen. "Mother," she protested, "you don't know how much I get by with, in my braided pigtails, that I could not with my hair up." Above every other passion of her life was her passion not to grow up, to be a child. The tomboy in her, which was big, seemed to loathe to be put away forever in skirts. She was a Peter Pan, who refused to grow up.

Her funeral yesterday at the Congregational Church was as she would have wished it; no singing, no flowers save the big bunch of red roses from her Brother Bill's Harvard classmen—Heavens, how proud that would have made her!—and the red roses from the *Gazette* force—in vases at her head and feet. A short prayer, Paul's beautiful essay on "Love" from the Thirteenth Chapter of First Corinthians, some remarks about her democratic spirit by her friend, John H. J. Rice, pastor and police judge, which she would have deprecated if she could, a prayer sent down for her by her friend, Carl Nau, and opening the service the slow, poignant movement from Beethoven's *Moonlight Sonata*, which she loved, and closing the service a cutting from the joyously melancholy first movement of Tschaikowski's *Pathetic Symphony*, which she liked to hear in certain moods on the phonograph; then the Lord's Prayer by her friends in the High School.

That was all.

For her pall-bearers only her friends were chosen: her Latin teacher, W. L. Holtz; her High School principal, Rice Brown; her doctor, Frank Foncannon; her friend, W. W. Finney; her pal at the *Gazette* office, Walter Hughes; and her brother Bill. It would have made her smile to know that her friend Charley O'Brien, the traffic cop, had been transferred from Sixth and Commercial to the corner near the church to direct her friends who came to bid her good-by.

A rift in the clouds in a gray day threw a shaft of sunlight upon her coffin as her nervous energetic little body sank to its last sleep. But the soul of her, the glowing, gorgeous, fervent soul of her, surely was flaming in eager joy upon some other dawn.

A WEDDING NOTICE FROM THE *FOUNTAIN INN TRIBUNE*

BY ROBERT QUILLEN

In writing this uncommonly candid social note, the editor of a small-town South Carolina newspaper employed fictitious names in order to guard against libel suits and simple assault, and was thereby enabled to realize the ambition of every day-dreaming reporter—to write just once an honest account of a local wedding.

MR. ROBERT CHETWAY and Miss Alice Broadkin were married at noon Monday at the home of the bride's parents, Mr. and Mrs. P. D. Broadkin, Rev. M. L. Gassoway officiating.

The groom is a popular young bum who hasn't done a lick of work since he got shipped in the middle of his junior year at college. He manages to dress well and keep a supply of spending money because his dad is a soft-hearted old fool who takes up his bad checks instead of letting him go to jail where he belongs.

The bride is a skinny, fast little idiot who has been kissed and handled by every boy in town since she was twelve years old. She paints like a Sioux Indian, sucks cigarettes in secret, and drinks mean corn liquor when she is out joy-riding in her dad's car at night. She doesn't know how to cook, sew or keep house.

The house was newly plastered for the wedding and the exterior newly painted, thus appropriately carrying out the decorative scheme, for the groom was newly plastered, also, and the bride newly painted.

The groom wore a rented dinner suit over athletic underwear of imitation silk. His pants were held up by pale green suspenders. His number eight patent leather shoes matched his state in tightness and harmonized nicely with the axle-grease polish of his hair. In addition to his jag he carried a pocket knife, a bunch of keys, a dun for the ring and his usual look of imbecility.

The bride wore some kind of white thing that left most of her legs sticking out at one end and the boney upper end sticking out at the other.

The young people will make their home with the bride's parents—which means they will sponge on the old man until he dies and then she will take in washing.

The happy pair anticipates a blessed event in about five months.

Postscript: This may be the last issue of THE TRIBUNE but my life ambition has been to write up one wedding and tell the unvarnished truth. Now that it is done, death can have no sting.

A LETTER FROM
NICOLA SACCO TO HIS SON

This letter was written by Nicola Sacco, an untutored workman in a shoe factory, who, along with a fish-peddler named Bartolomeo Vanzetti, was put to death nine days later by the Commonwealth of Massachusetts. They had been convicted of a murder committed by someone in the course of a payroll robbery. Clamorous doubts as to their guilt and misgivings as to the fairness of their trial delayed but did not prevent their execution. In the intervening years these doubts and misgivings have not lessened.

August 18, 1927, Charlestown State Prison

My Dear Son and Companion:

Since the day I saw you last I had always the idea to write you this letter, but the length of my hunger strike and the thought I might not be able to explain myself, made me put it off all this time.

The other day, I ended my hunger strike and just as soon as I did that I thought of you to write to you, but I find that I did not have enough strength and I cannot finish it at one time. However, I want to get it down in any way before they take us again to the death-house, because it is my conviction that just as soon as the court refuses a new trial to us they will take us there. And between Friday and Monday, if nothing happens, they will electrocute us right after midnight, on August 22nd. Therefore, here I am, right with you with love and with open heart as ever I was yesterday.

I never thought that our inseparable life could be separated, but the thought of seven dolorous years makes it seem it did come, but then it has not changed really the unrest and the heart-beat of affection. That has remained as it was. More. I say that our ineffable affection reciprocal, is today more than any other time, of course. That is not only a great deal but it is grand because you can see the real brotherly love, not only in joy but also and more in the struggle of suffering. Remember this, Dante. We have demonstrated this, and modesty apart, we are proud of it.

Much we have suffered during this long Calvary. We protest today as we protested yesterday. We protest always for our freedom.

If I stopped hunger strike the other day, it was because there was no more sign of life in me. Because I protested with my hunger strike yesterday as today I protest for life and not for death.

I sacrificed because I wanted to come back to the embrace of your dear little sister Ines and your mother and all the beloved friends and comrades of life and not death. So Son, today life begins to revive slow and calm, but yet without horizon and always with sadness and visions of death.

Well, my dear boy, after your mother had talked to me so much and I had dreamed of you day and night, how joyful it was to see you at last. To have talked with you like we used to in the days—in those days. Much I told you on that visit and more I wanted to say, but I saw that you will remain the same affectionate boy, faithful to your mother who loves you so much, and I did not want to hurt your sensibilities any longer, because I am sure that you will continue to be the same boy and remember what I have told you. I knew that and what here I am going to tell you will touch your sensibilities, but don't cry Dante, because many tears have been wasted, as your mother's have been wasted for seven years, and never did any good. So, Son, in-

stead of crying, be strong, so as to be able to comfort
your mother, and when you want to distract your
mother from the discouraging soulness, I will tell you
what I used to do. To take her for a long walk in the
quiet country, gathering wild flowers here and there,
resting under the shade of trees, between the harmony
of the vivid stream and the gentle tranquility of the
mothernature, and I am sure that she will enjoy this
very much, as you surely would be happy for it. But
remember always, Dante, in the play of happiness,
don't you use all for yourself only, but down yourself
just one step, at your side and help the weak ones that
cry for help, help the prosecuted and the victim, because that are your better friends; they are the comrades that fight and fall as your father and Bartolo
fought and fell yesterday for the conquest of the joy of
freedom for all and the poor workers. In this struggle
of life you will find more love and you will be loved.

I am sure that from what your mother told me about
what you said during these last terrible days when I
was lying in the iniquitous death-house—that description gave me happiness because it showed you will be
the beloved boy I had always dreamed.

Therefore whatever should happen tomorrow, nobody knows, but if they should kill us, you must not
forget to look at your friends and comrades with the
smiling gaze of gratitude as you look at your beloved
ones, because they love you as they love every one of
the fallen persecuted comrades. I tell you, your father
that is all the life to you, your father that loved you
and saw them, and knows their noble faith (that is
mine) their supreme sacrifice that they are still doing
for our freedom, for I have fought with them, and they
are the ones that still hold the last of our hope that
today they can still save us from electrocution, it is the

struggle and fight between the rich and the poor for safety and freedom, Son, which you will understand in the future of your years to come, of this unrest and struggle of life's death.

Much I thought of you when I was lying in the death-house—the singing, the kind tender voices of the children from the playground, where there was all the life and the joy of liberty—just one step from the wall which contains the buried agony of three buried souls. It would remind me so often of you and your sister Ines, and I wish I could see you every moment. But I feel better that you did not come to the death-house so that you could not see the horrible picture of three lying in agony waiting to be electrocuted, because I do not know what effect it would have on your young age. But then, in another way if you were not so sensitive it would be very useful to you tomorrow when you could use this horrible memory to hold up to the world the shame of the country in this cruel persecution and unjust death. Yes, Dante, they can crucify our bodies today as they are doing, but they cannot destroy our ideas, that will remain for the youth of the future to come.

Dante, when I said three human lives buried, I meant to say that with us there is another young man by the name of Celestino Maderios that is to be electrocuted at the same time with us. He has been twice before in that horrible death-house, that should be destroyed with the hammers of real progress—that horrible house that will shame forever the future of the citizens of Massachusetts. They should destroy that house and put up a factory or school, to teach many of the hundreds of the poor orphan boys of the world.

Dante, I say once more to love and be nearest to your mother and the beloved ones in these sad days, and

I am sure that with your brave heart and kind goodness they will feel less discomfort. And you will also not forget to love me a little for I do—O Sonny! thinking so much and so often of you.

Best fraternal greetings to all the beloved ones, love and kisses to your little Ines and mother. Most hearty affectionate embrace.

Your Father And Companion

P.S. Bartolo send you the most effectionate greetings. I hope that your mother will help you to understand this letter because I could have written much better and more simple, if I was feeling good. But I am so weak.

MON PAYS

BY EDNA ST. VINCENT MILLAY

This is part of the foreword which Miss Millay wrote for Flowers of Evil *which she and George Dillon had translated from the French of Baudelaire. Three of Miss Millay's own poems will be found elsewhere in this book.*

THE French have no word which means "home." They are so well aware of the lack of this word in their language that they are gradually taking over the English word. It is to be found in their standard dictionary, the Larousse, and is given as follows: *home, mot anglais signifiant maison, employé pour désigner le chez-soi, la famille, la vie intime.* It is even found in the abridged form of this dictionary. And more and more one sees the word—always looking rather forlorn and reproachful and extremely funny, like a dog in ruffles—above the doorways of hotels and boarding-houses in France: *Le Home; Le Home Sans Souci; Le Home Maréchal Foch.*

French people, a few generations from now, will very likely use the word "home" as naturally as they use any other word in their vocabulary, unaware that there was ever a time when their language was without it. But today they are still conscious when they use it that it is a foreign word. And the French translator detailed by his employer to translate "Home, Sweet Home" into French, will be pardoned if he does a little gesticulating.

There are, on the other hand, words in French, which the English language cannot approximate. How, for instance, am I to translate the Frenchman's expression

587

"mon pays"? I cannot translate it as "my country"; when I say "my country", I mean "my country, 'tis of thee"; I mean the United States of America. But the Frenchman, when he says *"mon pays"*, is not thinking of France; France is *"la patrie."* He is thinking of a part of Normandie, a part of Provence, bounded by no lines visible on any map, bounded only by the horizon of his early associations, made significant for him by the simple and marvellous events of his childhood and adolescence; it is the part of the world he "comes from". To *"La France"* he gives his loyalty, his patriotism; if necessary, his life. But what he really loves is *"son pays."*

How can I render this into English? I cannot say "my state", "my county". I was born in the state of Maine; but the state of Maine is very big; I have not picked mayflowers on every hillside of its many rocky hillsides; I have not steamed clams in seaweed on every spruce-wooded island off its coast; no, it is not quite that. But sometimes, when motoring up along the shore of Maine, after we have passed Wiscasset, when we are coming to Waldoboro and Thomaston, when I know that only a few miles further on are Rockland, Rockport, Union, Camden, I say to my companion—in French, because there is no way of saying it in English—*"C'est mon pays."*

COON HUNT

BY E. B. WHITE

THIS week in our county the two leading topics are deerslaying and civilian defense. Our best defenders are off in the woods, sharpening their aim and laying up protein reserves. The rest of us attend the meetings and listen to the speakers; in our minds we rebuild, with the volunteer bricklayers, the still unruined cities. On the way home we pass the cars of the hunters and note that they are wearing antlers. If Hitler had ever spent a fall in a New England village, watching the bucks go by on the running boards, he never would have dared reoccupy the Rhineland.

Everyone is excited about the local defense program, and there is a pleasing confusion in all quarters—the sort of confusion which makes a democracy so lovable and so frightening. The absence of the tangible foe, the unlikelihood of his soon appearing in military guise, these give the whole thing a certain incredibility without lessening its intensity. In a day or two a registrar will be around to find out whether I want to join a demolition squad or learn tap dancing to amuse the draftees. In scope, the co-ordinating program is quite amazing—a curious blend of rather elusive vitamins for school-children and protection against even more elusive poison gas for adults. At the moment its advantage to the cause, I suspect, is glandular: it will release, in many people including myself, a pent-up desire to serve their country in this fight. Its disadvantage is that sheer activity often creates the illusion of accomplishment;

people's gaze will be diverted from the theater of war to the theater of defense, and a sense of invincibility not in accord with the facts will be developed. In a military way America is about as invincible as anyone could wish, but in other ways I believe she is in immediate peril.

A few days before the defense meeting, where the civilians gathered to raise their barricades against the invader, the enemy slipped into town and out again, and I think there were hardly a dozen people who caught a glimpse of his coat tails. The populace was watching for planes in the sky—but when the enemy came he came in the curious shape of certain old boxes and hencoops and logs and odds and ends of rubbish that the town boys piled up, on Halloween, against the door of the Jewish merchant, the unpopular storekeeper who had been too grasping. It was a passing visit. The next day the hencoops were rolled away. The dummy which dangled in a noose from the elm tree, with the legend "This is what happens to you if you trade at ——'s," was cut down. Bystanders laughed to see such fun, a few of the elders complimented the boys on the job, and the town settled into its stride. People got ready to attend the defense meeting where they could volunteer to serve democracy by organizing a motor corps and preparing surgical dressings. The enemy had disappeared, virtually unnoticed, and all that remained were the fame of his European successes and the shadow of distant wings. Only a few people had felt his hot breath in the branches of the elm.

There would never be a moment, in war or in peace, when I wouldn't trade all the patriots in the county for one tolerant man. Or when I wouldn't swap the vitamins in a child's lunchbox for a jelly glass of magnanimity.

There were two dogs with us the night we went coon hunting. One was an old hound, veteran of a thousand campaigns, who knew what we were up to and who wasted no time in idle diversions. The other was a puppy, brought along to observe and learn; to him the star-sprinkled sky and the deep dark woods and the myriad scents and the lateness of the hour and the frosty ground were intoxicating. The excitement of our departure was too much for his bowels. Tied in the truck, he was purged all the way over to Winkumpaw Brook and was hollow as a rotten log before the night was well under way. This may have had something to do with what happened.

It was great hunting that night, perfect for man and beast, a fateful night for coon. The stars leaned close, and some lost their hold and fell. I was amazed at how quickly and easily the men moved through the woods in strange country, guided by hunches and a bit of lantern gleam. The woods hit back at you if you let your guard down.

We were an odd lot. A couple of the men were in coveralls—those bunny suits garage mechanics wear. One old fellow had been all stove to pieces in a car accident; another was down with a hard cold and a racking cough; another had broken two ribs the day before and had been strapped up that afternoon by a doctor. He had killed the pain with a few shots of whiskey and the spirits had evidently reminded him of coon hunting. This fellow had a terrible thirst for water all during the night and he had a way of straying off from the main party and hugging the water courses where he could kneel and drink when the need was great. We could sometimes follow the progress of his thirst in the winking of his buglight, in some faraway valley. After a bit he would rejoin us. "I'm drier'n a covered bridge," he would say disconsolately.

I felt a strong affinity for the puppy because he and I were the new ones to this strange game, and somehow it seemed to me we were sharing the same excitement and mystery of a night in the woods. I had begun to feel the excitement back in the kitchen of the farmhouse, where the hunters had gathered, dropping in and standing about against the walls of the room. The talk began right away, all the cooning lore, the tales of being lost from three in the morning until six, and the tricks a coon would play on a dog. There was a woman in the room, wife of the owner of the old dog, and she was the only one for whom the night held no special allure. She sat knitting a huge mitten. Mostly, the hunters paid no attention to her. Only one remark went her way. One of the men, observing the mitten, asked:

"Gettin' that man o' yours ready for winter?"

She nodded.

"I should kill him before winter if he was mine—he's no good for anything else," the fellow continued, pleasantly.

The woman raised a grudging smile to this sure-fire witticism. She plied the needles without interruption. This obviously was not the first time she had been left at home while men and dogs went about their business, and it wasn't going to be the last time either. For her it was just one night in a long succession of nights. This was the fall and in the fall the men hunted coon. They left after sundown and returned before sunup. That was all there was to that.

The best coon country is always far away. Men are roamers, and getting a long way from home is part of the sport. Our motorcade consisted of two vehicles, a truck for the dogs and owners, and a sedan for the hangers-on, lantern-bearers, and advisory committee. The old dog jumped into place the minute he was let out of the barn; the puppy was hoisted in and tied. The two of them sat on a pile of straw just behind the cab. The man with the broken ribs got into the sedan. Nobody seemed to think it was in the least odd that he was going coon hunting, to walk twelve or fifteen miles in rough country. He said the adhesive tape held everything O.K. and anyway, he said, the only time his chest hurt was when he breathed.

We advanced without stealth, the truck leading. The headlights of our car shone directly in the faces of the dogs. The old dog leaned back craftily against the sideboards, to steady himself against the motion. He half closed his eyes and was as quiet on the journey as a middle-aged drummer on a way train. The pup crouched uneasily and was frequently thrown. He would rare up and sniff, then crouch again, then a curve would throw him and he would lose his balance and go down. He found a hole in the sideboards and occasionally would press his nose through to sniff the air. Then the excitement would attack his bowels and he would let go all over everything—with some difficulty because of the violent motion of the truck. The old dog observed this untidiness with profound contempt.

We got away from the highway after a while and followed a rough back road up into some country I had never been into. At last we got out and let the old hound go. He went to work instantly, dropping downhill out of sight. We could hear his little bell tinkling as he ranged about in the dim valley between us and a night-struck lake. When he picked up a scent, suddenly his full round tones went through you, and the night was a gong that had been struck. The old dog knew his business. The men, waiting around, would discuss in great detail his hunting and would describe what he was doing off there, and what the coon was doing; but I doubted that they knew, and they just kept making things up the way children do. As soon as the hound barked tree, which is a slightly different sound than the sound of the running, we followed his voice and shot the coon.

Once the dog led us to an old apple tree in an almost impenetrable thicket, and when the flashlights were shined up into the topmost branches no coon was there. The owner was puzzled and embarrassed. Nothing like this had ever happened before, he said. There was a long period of consultation and speculation, all sorts of theories were advanced. The most popular was that the coon had climbed the apple tree, then crossed, squirrel-like, into the branches of a nearby hackmatack, then descended, fooling the hound. Either this was the case or the dog had made an error. Upward of an hour was spent trying every angle of this delicious contretemps.

The puppy was held in leash most of the time, but when the first coon was treed he was allowed to watch the kill. Lights from half a dozen flashlights swept the tree top and converged to make a halo, with the coon's bright little sharp face in the center of the luminous ring. Our host lethargically drew his pistol, prolonging the climax with a legitimate sense of the theater. No one spoke while he drew a bead. The shot seemed to puncture first the night, then the coon. The coon lost his grip and landed with a thud, still alive and fighting. The old hound rushed in savagely, to grab him by the throat and finish him off. It was a big bull coon; he died bravely and swiftly, and the hound worked with silent fury. Then the puppy, in leash, was allowed to advance and sniff. He was trembling in every muscle, and was all eyes and ears and nose—like a child being allowed to see something meant only for grownups. (I felt a little that way myself.) As he stretched his nose forward timidly to inhale the heady smell of warm coon the old hound, jealous, snarled and leaped. The owner jerked back. The puppy yelped in terror. Everyone laughed. It was a youngster, getting burned by life—that sort of sight. Made you laugh.

After midnight we moved into easier country about ten miles away. Here the going was better—old fields and orchards, where the little wild apples lay in thick clusters under the trees. Old stone walls ran into the woods, and now and then there would be an empty barn as a ghostly landmark. The night grew frosty and the ground underfoot was slippery with rime. The bare birches wore the stars on their fingers, and the world rolled seductively, a dark symphony of brooding groves and plains. Things had gone well, and everyone was content just to be out in the small hours, following the musical directions of a wise and busy dog.

The puppy's owner had slipped the leash and allowed his charge to range about a bit. Nobody was paying much attention to him. The pup stayed with the party mostly, and although he was aware of the long-range operations of the older dog, he seemed to know that this was out of his class; he seemed timid of the woods and tended to stay close, contenting himself with sniffing about and occasionally jumping up to kiss someone's face. We were stepping along through the woods, the old hound near at hand, when the thing happened. Suddenly the puppy (who had not made a sound up to this point) let out a loud whoop and went charging off on a tangent. Everybody stopped dead in surprise.

"What goes on here anyway?" said somebody quietly.

The old hound was as mystified as the rest of us. This was a show-off stunt apparently, this puppy trying to bark coon. Nobody could make it out. Obviously there was no coon scent or the old dog would have picked it up instantly and been at his work.

"What in *the* devil?" asked somebody.

The puppy was howling unmercifully as though possessed. He charged here and there and came back along his own track passing us at a crazy mad pace, and diving into the woods on the other side of the trail. The yelps sounded hysterical now. Again the puppy charged back. This time as he passed we could see that he had a queer look in his eye and that his movements were erratic. He would dive one way at a terrible clip, then stop and back off as though ducking an enemy, half cringing; but he kept putting up this terrible holler and commotion. Once he came straight at me. I stepped aside and he went by screaming.

"Runnin' fit," said his owner. "That's the trouble. I can tell now by the way he acts. He's took with cramps in his bowwils and he don't know anythin to do 'cept run and holler. C'mon, Dusty, c'mon, boy!"

He kept calling him softly. But Dusty was in another world and the shapes were after him. It was an eerie business, this crazy dog tearing around in the dark woods, half coming at you, half running from you. Even the old dog seemed disturbed and worried, as though to say: "You see—you *will* bring a child along, after his bedtime."

The men were patient, sympathetic now.

"That's all it is, he's took with a fit."

Dusty charged into the midst of us, scattering us. He stopped, bristling, his eyes too bright, a trace of froth at his mouth. He seemed half angry, half scared and wanting comfort. "Nothing much you can do, he'll run it off," they said.

And Dusty ran it off, in the deep dark woods, big

with imaginary coons and enormous jealous old hounds, alive with the beautiful smells of the wild. His evening had been too much for him; for the time being he was as crazy as a loon. Someone suggested we go home.

We started moving up toward the cars, which were two or three fields away over where you could see the elms black against the sky. The thought of home wasn't popular. A counter suggestion was made to prolong the hunting, and we separated off into two parties, one to return to the cars, the other to cut across country with the old dog and intercept the main body where a certain woods road met the highway. I walked several more miles, and for the first time began to feel cold. It was another hour before I saw Dusty again. He was all right. All he needed was to be held in somebody's arms. He was very, very sleepy. He and I were both sleepy. I think we will both remember the first night we ever went coon hunting.

A VISIT TO LONDON

BY FRANK SULLIVAN

WE arrived in London in a fog. The great sprawling metropolis was completely enveloped in a pea-soup mist which, we were told, had descended a month and a half previously. We didn't mind, because somehow it seemed right that we should have our first sight of the great sprawling metropolis in a fog. Nell's only regret was that on account of the fog we could only get a dim view of the famous old Waterloo Station which we heard had been built on the cricket fields of Eton.

Nell wanted to put up at one of the fashionable caravansaries in Tooting Bec, but I vetoed that. I told her as long as we were in London we ought to try to get the flavour of the great sprawling metropolis (which I shall refer to from now on as London) by stopping at one of those cosy old inns replete with historical interest and devoid of modern plumbing. Nell then suggested we go to the Cheshire Cheese, but I demurred again. I wanted to stop at the famous old inn frequented by Dr. Johnson and those other noted Regency bucks, but for the life of me I couldn't think of the name of the place, so to the Cheshire Cheese we went.

It proved utterly charming, exactly as we had pictured an old English inn—mullioned windows, mullioned waiters, ceilings with broad beams, barmaids with broader beams, et cetera. There was a room where Queen Elizabeth hid from Essex and his army, and another room where she hid with Essex and his army, and a third room where Essex and his army later hid from her.

There was a room where Shakespeare had been arrested for poaching and a room where Charles I hid from the Parliament while the Parliament was hiding from him in the room next door, which was the same room where Titus Oates hatched his plot. It was called the Plot Hatching Room on account of the fact that Guy Fawkes had also hatched his plot there.

Off the kitchen was a room where King Alfred let the cakes burn. And the tapster looked exactly like Sam Weller. Nell and I were delighted at our good fortune in finding such a really mellow old place.

We hired the Plot Hatching Room and proceeded to make ourselves comfortable. Both Nell and I had been looking forward with considerable interest to tasting British food, and we were not disappointed, for we dined excellently; a typical English meal of clotted Devonshire cream, roast beef, port wine, and plum pudding. Afterward we took a tram (short for terambulator) to His Majesty's Theatre in Ludgate Circus and there saw a play by Noel Coward.

Next morning we were awakened bright and early by the cries of the hawksters, tipsters, drapers, mercers, et cetera, vending their wares in the streets below. (London newsboys are not permitted to shout their headlines. They come up and whisper the news in your ear. This often tickles your ear, particularly if the whispered headline contains a lot of sibilants, such as "Lady Susan Sursingham Shoots Sire, Sir Seth Sursingham.")

There was a dense fog out. It was much denser than the pea-soap fog that had greeted our arrival. It was more the consistency of creamed cauliflower soup. You could scarcely see Windsor Castle.

A rosy-cheeked serving-wench who reminded Nell

of Sam Weller came in and laid a fire of sea coals and we breakfasted cosily by it. Typical English breakfast of clotted Devonshire cream, kedgeree, roast beef, Yorkshire pudding, mulled ale, crumpets, sack, and port. The girl was curious about America and wanted to know if the Indians still used bows and arrows in attacking Manhattan. Then she asked if we would give her an Indian yell, so Nell and I obliged with the old Ojibway war cry:

"Cornell I yell yell yell Cornell!"

"Team Team Team! ! !"

She was quite impressed, even a bit terrified.

We spent that day sightseeing and went in the evening to Their Majesties' Theatre to see a play. It was by Noel Coward.

What a fog next morning! I thought it was like *potage à la reine*, but Nell said it reminded her more of *borsch*. And those fascinating London noises, coming at you out of the mysterious fog. Nell and I are greatly interested in the noises characteristic of the various cities we visit. In Paris her favourite sound was the scrunch of the French burying the family sock, full of gold, in the back-yard. Mine was the low hum of models posing for artists in the nude. Her favourite London noise was the click of pearl buttons dropping from costers' weskits, but I preferred the throaty drawl of duchesses snubbing persons in trade.

Nothing daunted by the fog, we sallied forth on our sightseeing, first taking the precaution of donning our raincoats, or waterproofs, as the English call them.

The English have the most peculiar words for things. Our subway, for instance, is their tube. I believe they have no word for our tube. They call baggage luggage; a cracker a lift, and an elevator a biscuit. Their meat is our poison and our drink is theirs. They call a spade a spade. In telephoning they say, "Are you there?" where we say, "Hello. Hello. Hello. Operator. Operator. Yes, they do answer. There's always somebody there. Ring them again."

The English are a great people for clipping their words, for making one syllable do the work of two or three. For instance, if an American were dining with a British lady of quality and he wanted the Worcestershire sauce he would say, "Lady Ursula, could I trouble you for the Worcestershire sauce?" but an Englishman would say, "Lady Ursula, pass the Woosh."

On the other hand, they sometimes go to the other extreme. When they wish to express scepticism or incredulity they say, "Oh, I say now, not really, you know, what?" when we achieve the same effect by saying, "Nuts!" A London society woman says, "too perfectly divayne," where a New York society woman says, "too poifectly divine." And when the British want to express disapproval of conduct they consider unsportsmanlike or unethical they say, "That's not cricket," where we say, "That's probably wrestling."

One soon gets used to these little strangenesses. By the time we had been in London a week, nobody would have dreamed we were Americans had it not been for our tortoise-shell glasses, Nell's habit of chewing tobacco and saying, "Waal now, I reckon," and of course the large American flags she and I always carried.

The following day was Thursday and there was a really superb fog, like lobster bisque with toast Melba, I thought, but Nell said she saw it as cream of asparagus. She read in "The Old Lady of Threadneedle Street," as the British call the London *Times,* that a debate on the Boston Tea Party was the order of the day in the House of Lords, so we gulped a typical English breakfast of fish and chips, jugged hare, and gin and bitters, and hurried over to the Houses of Parliament. But the debate was not very exciting and there was such a dense fog in the House of Lords that we couldn't see anything anyhow, so we went over to the Commons in the hope of hearing Lady Astor, the American-born peeress, in action.

They were debating the oakum situation in Woking (or it may have been the woking situation in Oakum) and the Prime Minister was being interrogated by the Opposition, Mr. Winston Churchill.

Next morning there was a glorious fog, just like oyster gumbo. I wanted to go over to Rotten Row to see the regatta, but Nell had her heart set on going down to Trafalgar Square to see the famous statue of Lord Nelson. This is the statue which according to the old story (see any high-school textbook in English history) tips its hat every time a virgin passes. We no sooner reached the Square than Lord Nelson tipped his hat to Nell. Not only tipped his hat to her but told her in a low but quite audible whisper that she reminded him of Sam Weller. Nell was furious, on both counts, and strode off muttering, "It's a fake. It's a fake."

Nell went shopping the next day but flopped badly. The shopkeepers wouldn't sell her anything because she had never been formally introduced to them. British shopkeepers are very strict about this. Nell came home angry and desperate.

"I need a new tooth-brush," she wailed, "and I don't know a single druggist in London socially. What am I going to do?"

"Well, for one thing, don't say druggist," I warned her. In England a druggist is a chemist. A public school is a private school. The left side of the road is the right side, and gasoline is petrol. And *My Country 'tis of Thee* is *God Save the King*.

That night we thought we'd go to Soho, the Italian or Bohemian quarter of London, as we had heard there were some very good Italian restaurants there. We found a very good one and dined magnificently for two and thruppence hapenny on clotted Devonshire cream, roast beef, bubble and squeak, ale and ravioli.

Passing through Upper Tooting on the way home, I was interested in seeing the offices of the famous humorous weekly, *Punch*, or "The Thunderer," as the English affectionately call it. Once a week the staff of *Punch* lunch together and then, over the port, decide on the cover for the next week.

Nell and I liked the London cops or bobbies very much. They are a highly efficient body of men who wear chin straps and never allow a murderer to escape. Murder is rare in England and an unsolved murder is rarer. The low rate of homicide is due to the fact that the British never get well enough acquainted to kill each other. Once in a while a foreigner kills an Englishman for being too reticent, but if you see an Englishman murdering another Englishman you can be pretty sure the victim is either a blood relative or a friend of long standing.

The suicides in London are mainly foreigners driven to despair by attempts to understand the difference between the city with a small c and the City with a capital C. It seems that the City is part of the city, but the City is not all of the city. You can be in the city and not be in the City, but you cannot be in the City without being in the city. Nell spent two days trying to figure this out and then I had to take her to a nursing home where she spent a week in a dense fog.

Our stay in London ended rather unexpectedly. After she returned from the nursing home Nell did not seem her usual self. Irritable and upset. One morning when I passed her the clotted Devonshire cream she glared at me and hissed, "I don't want any clotted Devonshire cream. See?"

And a moment later she added.

"Nor any clotted Yorkshire pudding either. See?"

I thought this rather odd. Nell generally has a good appetite and cleans her plate.

I looked out of the window after we finished breakfast.

"My, there's a magnificent fog out, Nell," I said, to make conversation. "Just like mulligatawny soup."

"It's not like mulligatawny soup at all," she snapped. "It's like clam chowder."

For some time past she had been growing more and more unreasonable on the subject of the fogs. It seemed to me she had an uncanny faculty for picking the wrong soup to fit a fog, and while much of the happiness of our life together has been based on mutual respect for each other's opinions, I considered this a plain question of fact on which it was my duty to set Nell right. The fog was certainly mulligatawny, not clam chowder. I told her so.

"The other day, I added, "when it really was clam chowder you said it was like Philadelphia pepper pot."

She flew into a rage, told me that it was I who had been quoting the wrong soups all along; that she was sick of it, sick of the fogs, and sick of me. With that she packed her bag and left for Cannes.

I dined alone at a pub that night and later went to a play. But somehow I could not enjoy it. Something was missing. Suddenly I realized what it was. The play was not by Noel Coward. I went home, restless and uneasy.

Another day went by and then, feeling very blue indeed, I was on the point of sending Nell a wire telling her she could name her own fogs if she would only come back, when a message arrived from her. It read as follows:

"Sorry I dusted off in such a huff. Lovely cream of tomato soup down here. Do come on down before it's all gone. Love. Nell."

I took the next train for Cannes.

THE TURTLE

BY OGDEN NASH

The turtle lives 'twixt plated decks
Which practically conceal its sex.
I think it clever of the turtle
In such a fix to be so fertile.

THE NORSE TRAVEL AGAIN

BY W. L. WHITE

"I THINK we should not tell you our names," says the boy. The three of them, in blue pilot's uniforms, are sitting on the ground facing me, under the wing of a Curtiss P-36 fighter standing on the Toronto airdrome. You did not need to look at the word "Norway" embroidered on their tunic shoulders to know they were from the north.

"It is better not," says the second boy. "Then no one of our families will be shot by the Germans."

The three were of high-school age, all had blue eyes and creamy pink-and-white skins; the hair of each, showing under their jaunty air-force caps, was almost equally blond.

"It is best that you know only that I am called Erik, and that I was a student, and that this other is called Rolf, who is a fisher living on an island off the mouth of a certain fjord, and that the third, who is called Johan, is working on his father's farm, which is far to the north of Oslo, but the name of its parish we should not say."

The other two nodded.

"But before you can really know why we are stealing a boat to come out and make a resistance against the Germans," continued Erik, "you must understand how our hearts have changed since the Germans are first coming in. That first day I am Oslo attending high school. At noon, when the Germans are marching through the street, it is like I have been hit on the head and cannot think; only stand staring at these ranks of round helmets.

"We hear only that everyone is a traitor and our forts did not shoot. Only later do we learn that the Germans are spreading such lies. On the third day I hear our government has escaped to the north, where armies are forming. I have a friend who owns a car, and we decide to go north for the fighting. At Hamar they give us uniforms and guns, and I am put in a ski patrol. Our company is to hold one narrow pass through which the Germans must come, while the English are landing at Andalsnes to help us. We were told we should sweep the column until all had scattered from the road.

"Yet on that first day I argued with our officer that, from our hiding place, we should first fire a machine-gun burst over the heads of the Germans, because it would not be fair to shoot directly at men who do not even know we are there. But he said that wars are won not by the side which is fairest, but by that which is most clever, and I could see this was right. Yet, when the first of the Germans came, I could not at once make my finger pull on the trigger which would start the firing. In those first days we all felt like this whenever it was necessary to pull a trigger. But it did not last long, and we pulled gladly many triggers before that day when the British evacuated and we had to surrender. For two weeks I was a prisoner, but then I was released and went home."

"But I must sleep with my brother, because a German officer is in my room. A German major has come a few days after the occupation, and when he knocks, he asks if it is not my father's house. Then he says, in good Norwegian, 'Do you not know me?'

Then he tells my mother that more than twenty years before, during the other war, he has lived with them when he was a little boy sent from Berlin to Norway for its butter and cream, when these things could not be had for children in Germany. My mother looks, and it is indeed the same one whom they have made fat and pink when he was only twelve. At last she says, 'You can take my house as you have taken my country, but we are moving out,' and closes the door.

"For a while the Germans try to make much of us, and smile, but soon this is dropped when they see it is no good, and many of the German soldiers, those who are young and good-looking and think greatly of themselves, are angry because none of our girls will speak with them. But the only girls who will speak with them are those of the water front. Yet soon the Germans are tired of these girls, and want very much the girls with bright hair in the good part of town who will not look at them."

"On our island they admire toward our girls too," said Rolf, the fisherman, "but we tell them our meaning toward them—that we do not like them, that we do not want them on our island or in our country."

"There is something I would ask," said Johan, the farmer. "In our parish there are two boys who are of the *Hird*—the young Quislings—what is officially of the *Ungherden*. But I have heard that in the cities there are many, and they march in uniform. Is this true?"

"Our city is a great one," said Erik, "with many scores of thousands of people. Yet from all these, only twenty-three are of the *Hird* in uniforms. These twenty-three sometimes march in broad day, but only when the German soldiers are near to shelter them.

The Germans do not like them much. They think little of traitors in their own land, and not much more of traitors in ours, even if these help them.

"The *Hird* in my city were boys of the street, or ones who had been in trouble with the police before the invasion, and hope now in the *Hird* they can make their names better and to make money from the Germans. But now their friends do not see them when they meet, and this makes them very angry. Yet Quisling says over the Oslo radio they are the best youth of Norway!

"The good Norwegians hate the *Hird* even more than the Germans, and try to stop their marchings. Whenever those of the new government come down from Oslo to speak to our people, the *Hird* is there to surround the new government, and the German soldiers come to shelter the *Hird*. Many people come into the market square, where the new-government man is always speaking from the steps of the town hall with the *Hird* around him. But from the steps of a building opposite, a man would come out of the crowd to make another kind of talk, and the people would turn toward him, and away from the man of the new government from Oslo, and afterward sing the King's Song. Then, after the meeting, we would try to find the *Hird* to make fights with them, but the Germans always shelter them. When the people whistle at the *Hird*, the Germans charge and break them up with kicks and bayonets. One night I have seen a friend of mine knocked down by the Germans, who then kick him in the mouth, knocking out his teeth. When this boy's brother goes to pick him up, the Germans knock him down, and when he calls them, 'Swine!' he is taken to prison. It was on this night I decided to go to England for more fighting."

"I have heard of this even back in my parish," said Johan.

"The two things which make Norway most angry are this *Hird* and the Gestapo tortures and in addition the food, which is worse and worse," said Rolf. "We left Norway in August, but before that, I had not eaten meat since the Easter feast. And then it is whale. During the first year the Germans come, we had much whale meat, for our ships tow in carcasses which formerly they had stripped of oil and left to sink. It tastes as beef, only coarser, and there was some for all at a low price. But the Germans also find it is good to eat. So they take the whale for themselves, so we get only dried fish once a day."

"They also take our good Australian corn," said Johan. "The old government had stored enough for three years, as well as sugar and coffee. But the Germans take it. Milk they also take to Germany, so that now a child in Norway can have but one pint a day."

"When the Germans secretly ship our coffee and sugar away, we learn from the broadcasts of the Freedom Sender the next day exactly how much they take and where they send it," said Rolf.

"Many nights I cannot get the Freedom Sender on my radio," said Johan. "Do you know what town it is in?"

"If I did, I should not say, even here in America," said Erik. "But I can tell you where it is not. One day the Quisling newspaper has an attack on it, saying it is all lies made up by the British and broadcast from England, only pretending to come from here in Norway. So that very night the Freedom Sender comes on the air in its regular channel at twenty-nine point eight meters, and the announcer tells us just what the weather is here in Norway as he talks, how the clouds are, what is the temperature and from where is the wind, which no one could know who is not in Norway."

"The Freedom Sender began a month after the invasion, and soon all were talking of it. It has saved many lives. This summer there was a lawyer who went whispering about among the young men, asking which of them planned to travel, telling them he could arrange for them to go without cost to England to continue the resistance. Many listened, believing that the money for the boats and gasoline must come from our government abroad, and quickly several hundred have said that they wanted to travel. But one night we get a sending over the air from the Freedom station, giving this man's name and his town, and telling all good Norwegians to beware. Because he arranges for a boat, but when, in the night, those who want to travel climb in it, he also arranges for a German destroyer to come alongside just as it leaves the fjord, and none are ever seen again, for he is with the Gestapo. One morning this lawyer is found dead in his bed with knives in him, and I think this is done by the brothers of some whom he has betrayed to their death."

"In my parish," said Johan, "we have heard much of the secret work that is being done in the towns, but we really know very little. If you are helping in these things, you seek to know nothing except your own part. I get an unsigned letter from someone which tells me on the next midnight I will find pamphlets hidden in a special place. I do not know who of my friends send this letter; sometimes I see it in his eyes when he greets me, but I never speak of it or seek to know for sure."

Erik nodded. "So it is always in these things. Little

talking, and each wants to know no more than what he should do. It was last spring I have decided to escape to England for the fighting," Erik continued, "and I can tell you the day and hour. It was when I see the front teeth of my friend kicked out by the German soldiers as he lay in the street. Then it is in my mind to travel as soon as I can.

"Following the custom of all who travel, I decide I will say nothing to my family. Then, when they are questioned afterward, they can truly say to the Germans that they knew nothing of it, and so cannot be trapped into a lie and sent to prison. Also, if they are knowing that you go, for the first two days they are very fearful, imagining that even in this hour a German patrol plane with machine guns may be diving on your boat. All in the streets may read this fear or grief upon their faces, and questions may be asked.

"I remember a friend of mine who is leaving a note for his mother, which she finds an hour after he goes, and is telephoning the Norwegian police, asking that he be stopped. Through the police, the Germans are learning of it, and a German patrol ship is coming on their boat when it is hardly out of the fjord. So all are taken, and are still in a German prison. This woman was not for the Germans; she was only a frightened fool who did not stop to think what will happen if she talks. So those who plan to travel keep their mouths tight, and say nothing to their best friends or their girls or their parents that they have decided to go."

"First I am saying to some who I think are helping in these things that I would like to travel. They say nothing to this. When a week goes by and they do not telephone me to be ready, I see I must find the means for myself. First I am looking at school for friends who are to be trusted, and who are of my mind to travel. After much talking softly, there are five of us. Our gasoline we get from a man who owns a truck and is hauling for the Germans—paying him one dollar a gallon for forty gallons. Then food—we are saving our ration cards until we have seventeen breads, with meat and fish balls and other things in tins which could last three weeks, if we miss Scotland or the islands and are blown out toward Iceland or beyond—as many are.

"Then we are looking along the water front for a fisher's boat we may steal. Finally we see a good one with both a motor and sail. Then each puts what money he has in an envelope, and there is enough to pay the fisher for his boat, only he will get it in the mail and with no names, after we are gone. We have asked and find that he is a good Norwegian, so we know he will not report that his boat is stolen for some time, giving us a chance to get far out to sea. On a Saturday all is ready and I pack my bag, telling my family I go for a holiday in the mountains, so we will not be missed until school is beginning again on Monday.

"We take our boat down the fjord, past the fort where are the German soldiers. We do not look at them nor they at us, since from our oilskins we might be fishers. At the mouth of the fjord we turn south around the point, and go into a place of which I know, where few people come. Here we eat and sleep, although it is yet day, for we wish to start in the night.

"But just before the sun is setting we are wakened by the noise of another boat, which comes around the point, so we make believe we are working on the motor, for we cannot know if they are Germans or only fishers. When they see us, they turn toward us. Then their motor is stopping and they are drifting along-side. 'You have a good boat,' one of them calls to us.

"'We think it is,' I answer, but I go on working, hoping to make as little talk as I can. But the fishers do not start their motor.

"'Such a boat might go to England,' says one of them.

"'It is too small,' I say. 'It is good only for pleasure trips such as we make today.'

"'A larger boat like ours would be better for travel-ing,' said another of the fishers. 'One could get to England more quickly and surely. We might trade.'

"'If one wanted to go,' I answer. 'But for pleasure, a little boat like this is good enough.'

"'Then you should have much pleasure,' he says. 'For I see you have many cans of gasoline—perhaps enough for three days.' All of the fishers laugh at this. Then they start their motor and go past us, com-ing very close. One stands up and calls, 'Here is some-thing to help in your pleasure,' and throws into our boat what seems to be only a rolled-up paper. But when we open it, there is a costly sea captain's chart of all these northern waters and their islands, with shoals and soundings large and plain, showing the Shetlands and Orkneys and even the Faeroes, and on it, marked in pencil, is the best passage from where we are to Scotland. And now they are waving to us as they go around the point, and we wave back, for we know they are good Northmen, wishing us God-speed.

"An hour after sundown we start, heading south and somewhat west, following the fisher's chart. But at two in the morning the motor stops, and none of us can get it started, although we work until the battery in our torch is exhausted. Then there is nothing but to wait until dawn for light. We try to sleep, but the boat rolls much in the troughs of the waves, and we argue how much we are drifting, so we can set a course. But even with the light we cannot repair the motor, although we are still in sight of land, which lies blue in the east under the rising sun. We work until noon, and then decide we can do nothing but raise the sail and go back to land, hoping that we will meet, not Germans on the shore but fishers who will fix our motor. But the wind is against us and it is almost sunset when we are near enough to see a village on a headland at the mouth of a fjord.

"But now we all hold council. Because if we are stopped by Germans, they surely will see the many tins of petrol in our boat, by which they will know we are hoping to travel to England, and we will be shot. So we decide there is nothing to do but empty the gasoline and sink the tins.

"We are sad when we throw the tins into the sea, until all is gone except the little in the tank. For, when the motor is fixed, and even if then we had money to buy more and could find one who would sell to us, this could not be done until tomorrow, and it is already Sunday night. By tomorrow morning we will be missed from school, and if it is guessed we are traveling to England, the German patrol plane would have been told to look for us.

"Yet the worst of all is that half an hour after we have thrown away the gasoline, suddenly we succeed in starting the motor! But now there remains to us so little gas that there can be no thought of England, and we can only go on in to land, and hope we can get back to school before we are missed.

"But because trains are so few, it is Wednesday before I am back. But at school I have not been missed. To my family I am telling that I must wait back in the mountains with a comrade who is taken with a fever on a trail. They say nothing, nor do they ask what mountains I was in, yet I think then that they are believing me.

"But it is not until August that I again try to travel. One day on the telephone comes a voice I do not know asking if I would go to a certain place back in the hills which rise above the fjord. Here I find four hiding until they can travel to England, and I am bringing them food. One of these is Johan, and this four will leave in a few days with six others from our town in a large boat. But since the four are not of our town and have no papers for the police, they must hide. Hidden with them among the pines are many tins of gasoline, which they are stealing from a German airdrome by night. Day by day we are bringing back into this hiding place breads and tinned food which would do us for three weeks. It is on one of these days that my uncle calls me for a talking. My uncle has a shop for men's clothing, and has many who work for him, and is sometimes doing business with the Germans. My uncle asks me if I have it in my heart to go to England. I tell him if such a thing is in my heart, it should not be spoken of. Then my uncle says if it is in my heart, I should put it away, because he has learned from the Gestapo that the families of those who travel will be punished. That might mean the Germans would take from my uncle his business and blacken our family name.

"Then I am angry. I say to my uncle that the name of our family can be no blacker than he has already made it among all good Norwegians by having business with the Germans. And if it would be in my heart to travel, my risk would be much greater than his and

I would do it, not for my own gain but for all our people, so that they will one day be free. So my uncle is much ashamed. He is truly not a bad Norwegian, but only rich, and therefore fearful of his money. So he says if such a thing is deeply in my heart, he will even help me if he can.

"So I think, and tell him I know some who are hoping to travel, and that they are greatly needing brandy to warm them against the cold seas. The Germans are letting the Norwegians have but one bottle a month, while they themselves have much, which they are taking from the French.

"Now, only that day there has been in my uncle's shop a German of the Gestapo, who is admiring greatly to have a suit made of good English woolens that are remaining of my uncle since before the invasion. So the next day my uncle calls me to his house, and is giving me six bottles of old French brandy he has of this one of the Gestapo because he is agreeing to sell him a suit of English wools at a low price, and without need of giving up clothing coupons, although this is against their German law.

"On the morning of the day we are to leave, I take this brandy where Johan and the other three wait. Just as I leave, my mother is coming into my room and seeing my suitcase open on the bed, so I am telling her I go for a holiday in the forest with friends. She stands there a minute, but there is nothing in her face. Then she goes quickly out with no word of good-by. I am thinking that she has not seen I have on my thickest clothes, although the month is August. And I am thinking how much better this is that she knows nothing, and that no farewells are said. But the first morning we are at sea I open my suitcase, and in it is a paper written by a hand which is shaky, but which I know well, and it tells: 'Oh, my son, I know what it is in your heart to do, and what you do is good, and you go with my love.' And this paper I still keep with me, although the ink is washed of sea water and it cannot now be read.

"I start for the water front, where the six should be busy making ready the boat. But on the way I meet two of these six running and very frightened, telling me it is all over, because the Germans have found our boat and arrested four of those who are working on it; one of them admits that we are trying to travel, and perhaps is giving even the names. So then we start back to my own house, so that I shall not be caught by the Germans with a suitcase. But when we are still a thousand meters away, I see two German soldiers outside my house, so I now know they have my name.

"So then I tell the two that we will be safe for a time back in the hills where the gasoline is hidden and the other four wait. We are seven, we have plenty of foods and gasoline, but we must have a boat quickly.

"And then I remember Rolf, the fisher, who lives out on the island, where few come. When I was a boy and go there for holidays, he was my good comrade. I have not seen him since the invasion, but I am sure he is a true Northman. So the six wait and are opening some of the canned foods to eat, while I climb down to the water where is a village, and find a fisher who will row me to the island."

"He comes knocking at my house after dark," says Rolf. "And I know by the voice it is Erik, although I am not seeing him for two years. When I find it concerns some who would travel to England and that they have plenty of gas, I am glad, and say we can have our pick of many boats to steal on this island,

and that I will go with them, for this has been my meaning for many weeks. So now it is only a question of whose boat we take. And I think of a very good one, the machine of which I know very well, because it is belonging to a friend. When we of the island are saying among ourselves that we want to travel to England, this one with the good boat is listening, but is never saying that it is also his meaning, because he is timid. So I tell Erik it is this boat we will take, for a joke on this friend who is ever timid.

"We go to the boat of my timid friend, and with a stone I am breaking the lock, and soon we are across the water to the place where the six wait with the gasoline and foods. These are quickly in the boat, but now we must paint it, and this takes an hour— smearing it with gray and green, the color of our summer seas, the top and even the sail, so it is not easily seen by German planes. I am also bringing my compass and charts, which we will throw in the sea if Germans approach, and am telling the others that it will be safest first to go north and then west. Because while it is closer to Scotland, it is also most dangerous, because we fishers, looking up from our boats, can see the German scouting planes patrolling many times a day. But to the north these planes are fewer, and then, turning west, I can bring them either to the Shetlands or the islands of the Faeroes, which are small and few and far to the north, in the direction of Iceland. These would take the most days, but it is the safest of all. And because of this, the others say I am captain and the boat goes as I say. Also I am oldest—twenty years.

"Then we start, keeping north along the coast in the darkness. I do not tell the others how dangerous are these waters, and because they are not fishers, they do not know. Some of them even sleep. But when dawn light coming from over the land begins to make our waters light, one of them sees a black shape rolling in the waves, and asks what it is. To show them, I turn the boat toward it. When we are less than fifty feet away, they know it for one of the great German horned mines which are strewn in these waters, so that the British may not make a landing. Then one of them says perhaps we were near a great many such in the night without seeing them.

"That morning I am sleeping a few hours. But at noon I waken, because the sound of the machine changes, and I know it is not going well. It is very hot, and I guess that something has stopped up the water pipe which cools the machine, and I make a test of this and it is true. And I tell the others that we should turn toward shore to get help for it, for such a pipe cannot be fixed at sea, but some fear we may be taken by the Germans.

"Then Erik tells them there is little danger. The Germans have already taken the first boat, and since in August there is no school from which we would be missed, no one can yet know we have left and there will be no hunt for us. So we turn toward the land. In the afternoon we are seeing a town, so we turn toward this, and come up to the quay. But when those on the dock guess that we travel to England they are fearful to help us, saying in whispers that many Germans are about this water front. Then they walk away, and none will talk with us. So, lying there by the dock, we try to fix it ourselves, but we can do nothing, as we lack the wrenches. While we work there are German soldiers who walk along the dock and come close to us, but do not notice, because since they are newly come do not see that our faces are strange in this town, and think we are only fishers.

"While we wait, there above passes a German flying patrol boat, moving up and down the coast as though making a search. Then two of us tell Erik what they should have said before—that the search is probably for us. For these two say they were but last week released from concentration camp, and must report each day to the Gestapo, and when they did not report this noon, it was guessed they were traveling to England. The German flying patrol comes near, but our boat seems to them no different from those of other fishers tied near by.

"When it is dark, the ones who were so timid by day are coming to help us, bringing wrenches and working by flashlight under cover of a canvas which we spread, so that their light is not seen. As soon as we leave, I am placing the compass. If we are hailed by German patrol boats, I can throw this into the water while we are yet far from them. Then we will put our nets out and maybe they will not guess we are making a long voyage.

"The first part of the night all is well. There are stars to steer by and there is no other sound in the darkness but the even running of the machine and the steady voice of the water through which we slide. But at two o'clock I notice that a straight line of thick high clouds is rising up from the southern horizon, covering the stars. I know there is much wind in such a cloud. Calling Erik to the tiller, I make sure that the ropes which lash our water casks are fast, and then that the canvas is fast over our food and over the spark plugs of our machine. The air is so still Erik will not at first believe, but just as the clouds are hooding the stars at the top of the sky, comes the first gust of breeze with the first raindrops, and I tell him to shake two of the sleepers, that they may test the pump, for I think we will be needing it soon. In half an hour that great wind is driving the drops almost level over the sea, and they come into our boat mixed with salt spray torn from the wave tops. I can hardly see the prow of our boat, and the great seas almost lift us up to touch the clouds, which are driving low over us, as we can see by the lightning. By dawn light we find half the breads soaked with water, but none can eat, for all those of the land have emptied their bellies hours ago from the great swinging of the boat, and now lean over the sides to retch, but nothing comes."

"You, too, have emptied yours," says Erik.

"But not from the swinging of the boat," insists Rolf; "it was another thing. The gasoline reservoir above the motor holds but a few liters—enough for five hours. Then it must be refilled through a small hole from one of our gasoline cans. There is no funnel, so I am finding a short length of hose and am making a siphon of this—sucking through it with my mouth of the gasoline in the can, then pinching the hose and lowering the tip into the reservoir. But it is gasoline stolen from the German airdrome, not honest gasoline, but that which they make in their factories, and with so foul a stink of those who made it that, after I have sucked, I must empty my guts over the boat's side like the rest.

"All day it blows, and most of the day it rains from those low clouds, which drift over, and I cannot steer straight west for the Shetlands, for this would put us into the troughs of the waves, where the great ones, spilling into the boat, would fill us faster than we could pump, or perhaps capsize us, and I know none could cling long in such a sea, with the water so cold.

"So I steer southwesterly, knowing this great wind with its current is pushing us always into the north, none can guess how fast or far, and yet I am hoping we will not miss the Shetlands, whose headlands we should raise by tomorrow afternoon. Those of the land do not think on this, but only of the pumps and how often they must retch over the side, but nothing comes.

"Yet I cheer them by saying that all danger from Germans will be past, for no German plane is flying in such weather, nor could a patrol boat see us from far in such thick air. This is true, and yet the greater danger is that we shall miss the Shetlands and, passing them, perhaps miss as well the Faeroes, moving between them out into the Atlantic, where our gas is giving out; and then, since because of the war there is no shipping in these northern waters, we must drift until we die, having no oars, which took our ancestors without fear all over these waters, to Iceland and Greenland and even to Vinland, as we know from our old poems.

"But if those of the land know enough to fear this, they do not speak of it. They are stout of heart and work long at the pumps. Just before darkness we eat, of that part of the breads which are not wetted, and of goat's cheese, and of fish balls, which we get by opening tins, and with the work we are so hungry that it stays on our stomachs.

"The dawn comes, with much wind and very cold, but with a clear sky. I am glad, for this afternoon I am hoping we are near the Shetlands, which is a great headland rising from the sea, and on so clear a day hardly to be missed. So, toward noon, as each great green sea lifts us into the sky, sparkling in the sun and with much froth blowing from its tops, I am standing up in the boat to look along the horizon for the Shetlands.

"But we see nothing. After lunch is eaten, those of the land spy black shapes down into the water which are following our boat, and when I explain it is only sharks, they are still afraid. I see it is a kind of shark which loves the coldest waters, and is seen by fishers off Northern Norway and Greenland, but seldom comes south. So I fear the storm has pushed us farther into the north than I had guessed—north of the Shetlands and maybe even north of the Faeroes—yet there is nothing to do but go on and hope that we will not miss them. So all afternoon we look each time the seas lift us, and little else happens, except we are stopped for an hour by some trouble with the boat, and then—"

"He means that of the rudder!" said Johan. "And that must be told, because it was the best thing of all."

"So they of the land think, because they have never before seen it," said Rolf, laughing a little scornfully; "all things are new to them, and they know not which to fear. It was only that in the afternoon one of the great seas is ripping loose our rudder, and of course this must be mended. So I am taking off my clothes and going over the side."

"When first he goes in, his body against the bright green and blue of those seas is white as a linen sheet," says Erik.

"When I am under the boat I am seeing what is wrong, and am pulling with all my strength on the rudder shaft and on the socket into which it is fitting, which is bent by the smashing of those seas. But the strength of any man in water is not what it is on land, and his arms feel feeble. Also the great cold of this water is sucking the heat from my body as a thirsty man sucks beer on a hot summer's day. So each time I can pull only a little, feeble as a baby, and then come up for air, holding onto the boat's side, before I go down again."

"And taking care every minute that the great seas do not smash the boat against his head while he is under water, cracking it like an egg," said Erik.

"So imagine they of the land," said Rolf. "But finally I see my strength under water is so little that I must have a tool, so I get back into the boat to search for what there may be."

"And as we pull him in," said Erik, "his body, which was white, is pink like a boiled lobster, and we are putting his clothes against the motor, so that the heat is drying them."

"In the boat I search until I find a steel bar for prying, and with this I jump into the sea again. But still it is not easy, for the metal slips and, even with the bar, there is no strength left in my hands, which are weaker in that cold than a baby's. But at last, after coming up many times for air, with one great pull on the bar I am hearing the shaft click into its socket, but I am so weak that the prying bar is slipping from my fingers and going down through the waters. And because I know if the seas again smash the rudder we are helpless without this bar, I am trying to swim down after, clutching at it as it turns over and over, glinting in the long sun rays which flicker down into that green water. But further and further it goes beyond my fingers. Then everything is turning black, and I know I must get up to air quickly."

"We are grabbing him by his long yellow hair," laughs Erik, "and then under the arms, and in the boat he is coughing out salt water from his throat, and that body, which was white and then pink, is now purple like his own eyes. And we are taking off our wool sweaters and wrapping him in these. Then one of us is getting out a bottle of that French brandy my uncle has had from the Gestapo. We have no opener, so we are knocking off its head against the motor, and pouring into a tin cup, almost full, which we give to Rolf. It is strong, but Rolf drinks this fire without once choking or stopping for a breath, which only a sailor could do."

"It is because it warms me," said Rolf. "I am so cold it tastes like a cup of milk still hot from the cow."

"Then he would stir and get up, but we make him lie there. And we say we can steer the course he has set, which is straight into the setting sun, if he will sleep. Then the splintered bottle moves from hand to hand, as each of us has a long draught for warming. Then we would break open another of the five bottles which remain, but Rolf hears and forbids, saying he knows not how many days we will be in this boat. Then he is sleeping, very hard and sound, until midnight, when he wakes and is saying all his weakness is gone, and is dressing in his clothes, which have been drying by the motor and which are now stiff of salt, but warm, and eating much from the canned foods, and then taking the tiller."

"After midnight, the sea is going down and there comes a mist, so that we see only those stars which are just above," says Rolf. "And with the dawn there is still much mist, which I do not like and hope will soon be gone, for although we should not sight the Faeroes until afternoon, they are tiny and I fear we will be losing them in the fog, and passing on out to sea.

"So, in the dawn light I look at my charts and give the tiller to Erik, telling him to steer straight into the west, as this should bring us onto the Faeroes. Then I lie down and sleep again, not needing to waken until afternoon, when we should begin looking for land. But at midday I am wakened by a roar of motors from above. Then we see, through the mist, a plane. Suddenly it is turning, and we guess that they see us, and are very much afraid at first, for it is coming down, and maybe it is a German bomber out to attack British shipping beyond Ireland, and is machine-gunning us. But when it is close, we see there are no black crosses on its wings but red, white and blue circles of the British. So we wave and signal, hoping they will guess we are lost, and perhaps they can send help. They come very low and pass over with a thundering so close we can see them looking out, and then going on into the southwest, where they are lost in the mist. Then we hear the plane again, and once more it is thundering over us and away into the southwest. They do not come again, and there is only the little popping sound of our machine.

"As we eat, I watch the mist which is moving about the horizon, yet ahead is nothing but the open sea when the mist there is lifting for a few minutes. At three o'clock I see birds, and when they come close, I see they are those of the land, which cannot be far. At four I see floating sea grasses of a kind which grow only in shallow waters beyond beaches, and then I am sure. So I keep looking into the west and also into the northwest for the Faeroes, and decide that when the sun is down, we shall stop our motor, for I fear that otherwise we will pass them in the darkness.

"Those of the land have no idea of our course, so they look in all directions for a shore, even to south-

ward, and at five they spy a shape in that direction
which they think is land, but which I say can only
be a low cloud, as land must be to the west or northwest. But they will not believe, and continue to look
at this thing, and at last borrow my telescope. Then
there is a great shout of laughter, and they say, 'Rolf,
you are a great sailor, and you know every wave and
island and cloud in the sea, but now we can show
even you a marvel—a cloud which has two radio
masts on its top.'

"So I take the glass, and it is true—that shape to
the southwest is really the Faeroes, and I wonder
greatly how mighty was the storm and the current
which carried us so far into the north. And also I
wonder at how closely we escaped this last danger, for
if those of the land had not spied this shape through
an opening in the mist, I would be taking them past
it, and ever farther west and north, searching for
the Faeroes until all our gasoline is gone.

"Then I turn our boat's head toward the islands,
and we all laugh and break the head from another
bottle, and pass it around. They swear I am a mightier
captain than they dreamed, one who would take them
not merely to England but beyond to Greenland or
Vinland, like those of a thousand years ago, when there
were many sea kings in the fjords of Norway who
led their people all over the world in wooden boats
not much greater than ours.

"As we near land we see a boat ahead and are
hoisting our Norwegian flag. It is a fisher from the
islands, and they call to us in their speech, which is
the old speech of the Northmen, only ours in Norway is so much changed now that it is hard for us
to understand them. They say that many boats from

Norway have come before us in these months, and
that we should not enter the harbor alone, for fear
of many mines which the British have planted to
protect it, but should wait at a bell buoy which we
will find a mile from the shore, where a patrol boat
will be coming out to show us a safe channel through
the mine fields.

"This boat we follow in, but at the dock we must
again wait until the British port officer is coming to
talk with us. Yet many people are gathered along the
quay, calling out to make us welcome, and throwing
us cigarettes or chocolates.

"Some call to us in Norwegian, and they say they
are two who have come all the way in a canoe, arriving only last week after eight days alone on the water,
until they were a little crazy and, on coming ashore,
could not stop talking, even at night, when there was
none to listen, but now they are well again. When the
British officer is bringing us ashore we see others who
have traveled from Norway."

"But now our own Norwegian consul is coming," says
Erik, "who tells us that the British will intern us for a
few days. Then they are bringing us to a most pleasant
jail, which is the biggest hotel in the town, and for
dinner they are giving us roasted beef, which we have
not tasted for many months, and also milk in a great
pitcher, and a plate high with yellow butter, and a
great bowl of sugar, and many other things we had
almost forgotten.

"After this, a British intelligence officer is asking
us many questions far into the night, and then they are
opening all the cans of fish balls and food we have
brought from Norway. They say that they must, because among the many who are traveling out of the

occupied countries to make a resistance have been a few Gestapo, talking the native language, sent by the Germans to spy.

"They tell us that only the week before one of these is hiding a small radio sealed in a tin can which is labeled 'fish balls.' So all must be opened. They search our clothes and even our shoes, and at last, saying they are very sorry, they even squeeze the shaving cream from my tube and cut into bits the soap which Rolf has brought, thinking maybe there might be writings hidden in it.

"But when it is over and they see we are true Northmen, we bring out the four bottles of good French brandy which remain, and offer of it to the British intelligence officer, who laughs greatly when he hears we have tricked it from the Gestapo. So we all drink to our king and to his.

"Then he tells what great numbers of men are coming out from Norway in boats and canoes. And he tells us the plane we have seen at midday was out to watch for such as we, and when it flew twice over us and each time off into the southwest, this was to show us the direction of land.

"Next day comes a British trawler on its regular weekly trip among these islands to collect the Norwegians, and we go to Scotland, and then to London, where is our own king and government, and more questions are asked. We find that through these questions our government knows all that happens in Norway each week, what the Germans are doing, and which ones are with them.

"Then they ask us where we will serve, and some choose the army, which trains in England for the day when we are landing again in Norway, and some the navy, which guards our Norwegian ships that are bringing supplies to the British from all the seven seas. But we three choose the Norwegian air force.

"So this is why we have traveled to make a resistance, and there is only one other little thing. My mother has a sister who lives at Minneapolis, and to this one she writes that to my family has come a great sorrow. For in August her son Erik has gone to sea, and since then there has been no word of him. Yet it is bitter to give up all hope, so my mother is writing to ask my aunt if by any chance there is word, even in America, of her son Erik.

"In writing, my mother takes a great risk, with all letters passing through the Germans. So my aunt at Minneapolis answers as though she had not received it. She writes that if my mother could only see her own son Harold—my mother knowing well her sister has no son—who is twenty years old last August nineteenth—which is exactly my age—and how brave is this Harold, who is now training to be a flier, and how proud my mother would be for our family if she could only see this boy, and how healthy he looks, and much other silliness about how quiet and modest are Harold's manners, and yet he is so handsome that in Toronto the girls are even melting on the streets as he passes in his new uniform. Yet I do not mind the silliness, for I know it will please my mother."

This is the story as it was told to me when I journeyed to "Little Norway," in the forests north of Toronto. There ever-increasing numbers of these young Norse who travel again appear at the gateway to offer themselves as combat and bomber pilots for Britain, so that Hitler may be defeated and their homeland freed of its Nazi fetters. Some of them come, still wearing the clothes in which they embarked in fisher boats from their saddened home shores. Many come because they are inspired to serve under the Norwegian who commands the camp in Canada, Ole Reistad, a man who was described to me as a "combination Red Grange, Babe Ruth and Billy Mitchell of Norway"— a famous Olympic-games athlete who became his country's best beloved air hero. All of them come with a will to win.

FIRST FIG

BY EDNA ST. VINCENT MILLAY

My candle burns at both ends;
    It will not last the night;
But ah, my foes, and oh, my friends—
    It gives a lovely light.

A TALK TO YOUNG MEN

BY ROBERT C. BENCHLEY

Graduation Address on the Decline of Sex

TO you young men who only recently were gradu-
ated from our various institutions of learning (laughter), I would bring a message, a message of warning and yet, at the same time, a message of good
cheer. Having been out in the world a whole month,
it is high time that you learned something about the
Facts of Life, something about how wonderfully Nature takes care of the thousand and one things which
go to make up what some people jokingly call our
"sex" life. I hardly know how to begin. Perhaps "Dear
Harry" would be as good a way as any.

The next time you are at your grocer's buying gin,
take a look at his eggs. They really are some hen's
eggs, but they belong to the grocer now, as he has
bought them and is entitled to sell them. So they
really *are* his eggs, funny as it may sound to anyone
who doesn't know. If you will look at these eggs, you
will see that each one is *almost* round, but not *quite*.
They are more of an "egg-shape." This may strike
you as odd at first, until you learn that this is Nature's
way of distinguishing eggs from large golf balls. You
see, Mother Nature takes no chances. She used to, but
she learned her lesson. And that is a lesson that all
of you must learn as well. It is called Old Mother
Nature's Lesson, and begins on page 145.

Now, these eggs have not always been like this.

That stands to reason. They once had something to do with a hen or they wouldn't be called hens' eggs. If they are called ducks' eggs, that means that they had something to do with a duck. Who can tell me what it means if they are called "ostrichs' eggs"? . . . That's right.

But the egg is not the only thing that had something to do with a hen. Who knows what else there was? . . . That's right.

Now the rooster is an entirely different sort of a bird from the hen. It is very proud and has a red crest on the top of his head. This red crest is put there by Nature so that the hen can see the rooster coming in a crowd and can hop into a taxi or make a previous engagement if she wants to. A favorite dodge of a lot of hens when they see the red crest of the rooster making in their direction across the barnyard is to work up a sick headache. One of the happiest and most contented roosters I ever saw was one who had had his red crest chewed off in a fight with a dog. He also wore sneakers.

But before we take up this phase of the question (for it is a question), let us go back to the fish kingdom. Fish are probably the worst example that you can find; in the first place, because they work under water, and in the second, because they don't know anything. You won't find one fish in a million that has enough sense to come in when it rains. They are just stupid, that's all, and nowhere is their stupidity more evident than in their sex life.

Take, for example, the carp. The carp is one of the least promising of all the fish. He has practically no forehead and brings nothing at all to a conversation. Now the mother carp is swimming around some fine spring day when suddenly she decides that it would be nice to have some children. So she makes out a deposit slip and deposits a couple million eggs on a rock (all this goes on *under* water, mind you, of all places). This done, she adjusts her hat, powders her nose, and swims away—a woman with a past.

It is not until all this is over and done with that papa enters the picture, and then only in an official capacity. Papa's job is very casual. He swims over the couple of million eggs and takes a chance that by sheer force of personality he can induce half a dozen of them to hatch out. The remainder either go to waste or are blacked up to represent caviar.

So you will see that the sex life of a fish is nothing much to brag about. It never would present a problem in a fish community as it does in ours. No committees ever have to be formed to regulate it, and about the only way in which a fish can go wrong is through drink or stealing. This makes a fish's life highly unattractive, you will agree, for, after a time, one would get very tired of drinking and stealing.

We have now covered the various agencies of Nature for populating the earth with the lesser forms of life. We have purposely omitted any reference to the reproduction of those unicellular organisms which reproduce by dividing themselves up into two, four, eight, etc., parts without any outside assistance at all. This method is too silly even to discuss.

All of which brings us to the point of wondering if it *all* isn't a gigantic hoax. If the specialists fall down on trap-shooting, they are going to begin to doubt the whole structure which they have erected, and before long there is going to be a reaction which will take the form of an absolute negation of sex. An Austrian scientist has already come out with the announcement that there is no such thing as a hundred-per-cent male or a hundred-per-cent female. If this is true, it is really a big step forward. It is going to throw a lot of people out of work, but think of the money that will be saved!

And so, young men, my message to you is this: Think the thing over very carefully and examine the evidence with fair-minded detachment. And if you decide that, within the next ten years, sex is going out of style, make your plans accordingly. Why not be pioneers in the new movement?

P. S. HE GOT THE JOB

Excerpt from a letter written to the editor of this book by a shattered buck private in the Air Corps stationed at Miami.

I DON'T know whether you are familiar with the board system whereby enlisted men who wish to attend a school for Officer Candidates are examined, cross-questioned, and interviewed as to their possible qualifications to be officers. If they pass the board, they are eligible for one of the numerous schools for officers in the various branches of the service—Artillery, Engineers, Anti-aircraft, Ordnance, etc. At any rate, to tell this story, the above information is necessary. Here, in the Air Corps, the board has the reputation of being very tough, but it actually isn't tough enough to justify the stories that spread around about it. It consists, generally, of a Major, a Captain, and a Lieutenant; and although a very large number of men *are* rejected, a large number also pass.

The procedure is that a man, after he has been in the army for three months, applies for OCS papers. He fills these out—a process which takes weeks and involves knowing where your father was born, where your wife's father was born (and trying to get the little woman to write a letter stating any facts about her old man was a career in itself), and the goddamndest information in general that I've ever attempted to assemble. At any rate, after that is done, you hand in your papers and expect to be called before the board in about a week, if all goes well. During the intervening time, you get a nice short haircut, have one uniform clean and pressed and ready in the closet, get polish for your belt buckle, and read any math books or magazines or newspapers available, as a large part of the examination is supposed to consist of questions on math and current events. Then you talk to everybody you know, meet, or can pick up, who has ever been before the board.

The conversation generally runs something like this:

Q: "What happens first?"

A: "Oh, all the candidates for that day are put in a room and you sit there until your name is called."

Q: "Then what do you do?"

A: "You go into the room, march in front of the board and say, 'Private Allen reporting to Major Jones as ordered, sir.'"

Q: "And then what?"

A: "Then they generally ask you to sit down."

Q: "Do you sit at ease or attention?"

A: "You sit at attention—and for Christ's sake don't cross your legs. Why, one guy in our squadron just started to cross his legs and they kicked him out then and there."

Q: "What sort of questions do they ask you?"

A: "Anything in the world. All kinds of current events. All kinds of math questions—why, they asked one guy to tell them what 73¼% of 876.535 was *in his head*. Why do you want to be an officer (and you'd better have a good answer ready for that one). How far is it to Wake Island? Where is Murmansk? Is Eisenhower a Lt. or a Major General? Name all the Aleutian Islands."

Q: "Gee, that sounds pretty tough."

A: "Tough! It's damned near impossible. I tell you

that board doesn't want anybody to be officers except themselves."

So anyway, I put in my papers for OCS and the next morning while I was drilling busily they called out my name and I went over to the Sergeant who said, "Allen, you're to report to the OCS board at 12:15."

It was then eleven and the drill field is two miles from the OCS board and both the drill field and the OCS board are three miles from my hotel. And I was in a filthy uniform and I needed a haircut so badly that I looked like a shepherd and I hadn't read *Time* that week and my good shoes were at the shoemaker's. Besides, I was scared to death.

Well, I was nearest to a barbershop so I bought a copy of *Time* and a newspaper and raced in. There an elderly of the 1864 draft swathed me in a filthy cloth while I roared at him that I was in a hurry because I was going up before the OCS board at 12:15. He set to work while I tried to read *Time* without my glasses, and twenty minutes later when I again urged him to be quick, he said, "Now don't you worry. I'm going to give you a nice olive-oil shampoo after I get done with this." So then I thought I'd better quit, so I jumped out of the chair with one side of my hair off (the effect was rather like Albert Carroll playing Brenda Frazier on one side and Arthur Guy Empey on the other) and dashed for a bus which was just passing outside. I made it and then discovered that I didn't have any money. So I got off, still reading *Time*, and saw a restaurant where I occasionally bought a hot-dog. I went in, gave them my watch to hold, and took twenty cents. Then on the next bus and so home. All the while saying to myself, "Morocco—Algiers—Tunisia. M A T. Remember it that way. Eisenhower is a Lieutenant General. The Solomons are north east of Australia. Private Allen reporting to Major Smith as ordered, sir. Well, he could through Turkey, or down through Italy, or possibly by way of Gibraltar. Murmansk is a port—"

And then I was at the hotel. And I opened the closet and my uniforms were still at the laundry, which I should have remembered all the time. So over to the laundry where I changed into my clean uniform, then to the shoemaker's where I put on my good shoes and had them shined by a colored boy (and if he's the same one who writes Irving Berlin's music, I don't know how Irving *ever* has a hit). And then on a bus again and so to the OCS board at 12:14. Oh, I forgot. While at the hotel I took a sodium amytal because by this time I was trembling so I couldn't comb my hair.

And then I waited from 12:14 until four o'clock; and nothing happened at all, except that all the other candidates went in one after one, looking incredibly competent and intelligent. And they all came out haggard, white-faced creatures, incapable of speech except to murmur: "Jesus! That Lieutenant." Or "Christ! That Captain is a son of a bitch."

Meanwhile the sodium amytal was taking its effect. (I had thought, of course, to wait at the most a half-hour, go in calm and collected, then be out in time for lunch with lots of coffee; and instead of being calm and collected I was acting like something in *The Moonstone*.) Finally, to fight it off, I stood up and walked the floor. This had, unfortunately, the effect of creating in me an irresistible desire to pee. So instead of pacing, I began hopping. And finally, when the last man but me went in and I knew I was next, I could stand it no longer. I had to go to a men's room, quick. So I asked where one was and they said there wasn't any on that floor. Oh, yes. There was one, but it was reserved solely for officers. But I took a chance—I had to—and went in.

Then with trembling fingers I proceeded to— Well, the trembling fingers did it. All down the front of my trousers. I looked as if I'd been holding Baby. So then I thought, well, all right, what the hell do you want to be an officer for, anyway. Besides you're going to be court-martialed for using this lavatory, anyway, if anyone catches you, and just then the door opened and a Captain came in. He looked sharply at me and I cringed. And then he said, "Aren't you Campbell Allen?" And I said yes, and as I said it I recognized him. We'd gone to VMI together. And he said, "Campbell, how the hell are you?" And I said, "Fine, for Christ's sake, lend me your pants."

And then while the Captain waited in his shorts in the can, I raced down the hall, and the other guy had just come out and they were calling my name. And I slowed down to a walk, entered, saluted and said, "Major Allen reporting to Private Smith as ordered, sir."

THE NEW COLOSSUS

BY EMMA LAZARUS

Give me your tired, your poor,
Your huddled masses, yearning to be free.
The wretched refuse of your teeming shore.
Send these; the homeless, tempest-tossed to me.
I lift the lamp beside the golden door.

Inscription
on the Statue of Liberty
in New York Harbor

HERE RESTS IN HONORED GLORY AN
AMERICAN SOLDIER KNOWN BUT TO GOD.

Inscription
on the Tomb
of the Unknown Soldier

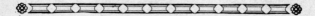

INDEX OF AUTHORS
INDEX OF TITLES
ACKNOWLEDGMENTS

INDEX OF AUTHORS

INDEX OF TITLES

ACKNOWLEDGMENTS

D. Appleton-Century Company: "The Trawnbeighs" from *Viva Mexico* by Charles Macomb Flandrau, copyright 1908 by D. Appleton and Company, 1935 by Charles Macomb Flandrau; "Song in Exile" from *Wings in the Night* by Alice Duer Miller, copyright 1918 by The Century Company.

Benchley, Robert: "A Talk to Young Men."

The Bobbs-Merrill Company: "The Old Man and Jim" from the Biographical Edition of the Complete Works of James Whitcomb Riley, copyright 1913, 1941. Used by special permission of the publishers.

Brandt & Brandt, Agents: "My Sweet Old Etcetera" from *Collected Poems*, published by Harcourt Brace & Company, copyright 1923, 1925, 1931, 1935, 1938 by E. E. Cummings; "Rupe Collins," "The Imitator," "Coloured Troops in Action," from *Penrod, His Complete Story* published by Doubleday, Doran & Company, copyright 1914 by Booth Tarkington; "Lament" from *Second April* published by Harper & Brothers, copyright 1921 by Edna St. Vincent Millay; "First Fig" from *A Few Figs from Thistles*, published by Harper & Brothers, copyright 1918, 1919, 1922 by Edna St. Vincent Millay; "Afternoon on a Hill," from *Renascence*, published by Harper & Brothers, copyright 1917 by Edna St. Vincent Millay; "Mon Pays" from the preface to *Flowers of Evil*, published by Harper & Brothers, copyright 1936 by George Dillon and Edna St. Vincent Millay; "Nancy Hanks" by Rosemary Benèt from *A Book of Americans* by Rosemary and Stephen Vincent Benèt, copyright 1933 by Rosemary Benèt; "The Devil and Daniel Webster" from *Thirteen O'clock*, copyright 1936 by Stephen Vincent Benèt; "The Norse Travel Again" by W. L. White, copyright 1941 by The Curtis Publishing Company.

Dodd, Mead & Company: *Tom Whipple*, by Walter D. Edmonds, copyright 1942; "Scum o' the Earth" from *New and Selected Poems* by Robert Haven Schauffler, copyright 1942.

Doubleday, Doran and Company, Inc.: "One Arrowhead Day" from *Ma Pettingill*, by Harry Leon Wilson, copyright 1919 by Doubleday, Doran and Company, Inc.; "The Skylight Room" from *The Four Million* by O. Henry, copyright 1905, 1933 by Doubleday, Doran and Company, Inc.

E. P. Dutton & Co., Inc.: From *Death and General Putnam* by Arthur Guiterman, copyright 1935 by E. P. Dutton & Co., Inc.

Focht, Mildred: "Aged Four" from *Four Trees*, copyright by Mildred Focht, published by G. P. Putnam's Sons.

655

Gordon, Ruth: "Our New Telephone" copyright 1942 by *The Atlantic Monthly*.

Harcourt, Brace and Company: "The First G. A. R. Parade" from *Sherman: Fighting Prophet* by Lloyd Lewis, copyright 1932 by Harcourt, Brace and Company, Inc.; "The Death of John Quincy Adams" from *Abraham Lincoln: The Prairie Years* by Carl Sandburg, copyright 1926 by Harcourt, Brace and Company, Inc.

Harper & Brothers: "Coon Hunt" from *One Man's Meat* by E. B. White, copyright 1941 by E. B. White; "The Duke and the Dauphin Come Aboard," from *The Adventures of Huckleberry Finn* by Mark Twain; "Shenandoah Road" from *The Lady Is Cold* by E. B. White, copyright 1929 by E. B. White.

The Estate of Joel Chandler Harris: "The Wonderful Tar Baby" and "How Mr. Rabbit was Too Sharp for Mr. Fox" from *Uncle Remus* by Joel Chandler Harris.

Henry Holt and Company, Inc.: "The Death of the Hired Man" from *North of Boston* by Robert Frost, copyright 1915 by Henry Holt and Company, Inc.; "Mending Wall" and "Stopping by Woods on a Snowy Evening" from *Selected Poems* by Robert Frost, copyright 1928 by Henry Holt and Company, Inc.; "Early Moon" and "Grass" from *Cornhuskers* by Carl Sandburg, copyright 1918 by Henry Holt and Company, Inc.

Houghton Mifflin Company: "The Outcasts of Poker Flat" and "Plain Talk from Truthful James" by Bret Harte; "The Mystery of Gilgal" from *Pike County Ballads* by John Hay; "Paul Revere's Ride" by Henry Wadsworth Longfellow; "The Last Leaf" by Oliver Wendell Holmes; "Battle Hymn of the Republic" by Julia Ward Howe; "Where I Lived and What I Lived For" from *Walden* by Henry David Thoreau; "The Concord Hymn" by Ralph Waldo Emerson; "The New Colossus" from *Poems of Emma Lazarus*.

Alfred A. Knopf, Inc.: "Missionary Journeys" from *Death Comes for the Archbishop*, copyright 1926, 1927, 1929 by Willa Cather.

Lampman, Ben Hur: "At the End of the Car Line" from *"The End of the Car Line"* originally published in *The Oregonian*, copyright 1942 by Binfords & Mort, Publishers, Portland, Oregon.

Little, Brown & Company: "To Fight Aloud is Very Brave" from *The Poems of Emily Dickinson* edited by Martha Dickinson Bianchi and Alfred Leete Hampson; "The Turtle" and "The Japanese" from *The Face Is Familiar* by Ogden Nash; Three Speeches from *Speeches of Oliver Wendell Holmes*: "The Hunting Camp" from *The Oregon Trail* by Francis Parkman.

The Macmillan Company: "John L. Sullivan: Strong Boy of Boston" and "Abraham Lincoln Walks at Midnight" from *Collected Poems* by Vachel Lindsay; "Mr. Flood's Party" from *Collected Poems* by Edwin Arlington Robinson.

Miller, Maude Barnes: "The Only One," copyright 1937 by Curtis Publishing Company.

The New Yorker: "Farewell, My Friends" by Clarence Day.

Quillen, Robert: "A Wedding Notice" from the *Fountain Inn Tribune.*

Robinson, Kenneth Allan: "American Laughter"

Charles Scribner's Sons: "Fifty Grand" from *The Fifth Column and Other Stories* by Ernest Hemingway, copyright 1938 by Ernest Hemingway; "I Have a Rendezvous with Death" from *Poems* by Alan Seeger, copyright 1916 by Charles Scribner's Sons; "Little Boy Blue" by Eugene Field; "Miniver Cheevy" from *Children of the Night* by Edwin Arlington Robinson, copyright 1914 by Charles Scribner's Sons; "Some Like Them Cold" from *How to Write Short Stories* by Ring Lardner, copyright 1924 by Charles Scribner's Sons; "A Preacher Goes to War," and "The Confederate Army" from the introduction to *Lone Star Preacher* by John W. Thomason, Jr., copyright 1941.

Simon and Schuster, Inc.: "You Mean Common" from *Thunder Over the Bronx* by Arthur Kober, copyright 1935; "Address Unknown" by Kressmann Taylor, copyright 1939 by Kressmann Taylor.

Sullivan, Frank: "A Visit to London."

The Viking Press, Inc.: "The Waltz" from *Here Lies* by Dorothy Parker, copyright 1933 and 1939 by Dorothy Parker; "Two-Volume Novel" and "The Maid Servant at the Inn" from *Not so Deep as a Well* by Dorothy Parker, copyright 1926, 1928, 1931 and 1936; "My City" from *Saint Peter Relates an Incident* by James Weldon Johnson, copyright 1917, 1921 and 1935 by James Weldon Johnson; Sacco's Letter to His Son from *Letters of Sacco and Vanzetti*, edited by Marion Denman Frankfurter and Gardner Jackson, copyright 1928 by The Viking Press, Inc.

Yale University Press—"Thanksgiving Proclamation" by Wilbur L. Cross.

William Allen White—"Mary White" copyright 1921 by the *Emporia Gazette.*